Preface

Like the three previous editions, which were published in the Chronica Botanica's "A New Series of Plant Science Books," this one summarises and correlates current knowledge on the behaviour and properties of plant viruses gained from many and widely differing kinds of work. During the fourteen years since the third edition was published, the study of viruses and virus diseases has been so productive, and ideas have changed so radically, that in effect it is a new book rather than simply a revision.

Notable advances have been made in all of the many branches of the subject and the detailed information about the structure and composition of some viruses far exceeds what could reasonably have been anticipated, but outstanding is the discovery that virus nucleic acids can initiate infection when free from their proteins. This has not only profoundly changed ideas about virus multiplication but has opened new lines of research that have already yielded a rich harvest of results.

There is still much to discover and the subject is certain to attract increasing numbers of workers, less because it may help to prevent the economically important diseases that viruses cause than because it promises to elucidate some of the problems basic to all biological systems. How nucleic acid replicates; the kinds of change in nucleic acids responsible for mutations; the relation between the structure of nucleic acid and the protein it induces; the conditions in which nucleic acids induce protein synthesis—these are only some of the problems for whose study viruses currently provide the most convenient subjects. If sequence of nucleotides in nucleic acids represent a code translatable into sequence of aminoacids in proteins, this is perhaps more likely to be demonstrated by work with virus strains than with any other systems. Thus, important as viruses are in pathology, this has long ceased to be the sole reason for their study, which increasingly proves significant for many other subjects.

I am greatly indebted to my colleagues working with viruses at Rothamsted for countless stimulating discussions, much excellent instruction, and many constructive criticisms. I thank those who have been so generous in giving me permission to reproduce illustrations, the sources of which are acknowledged in the text, and the Editors of "Annals of Applied Biology" for the loan of some blocks. I also gratefully acknowledge the invaluable help I have received from Miss Mildred E. Ashford while writing the text and compiling the references.

F. C. BAWDEN

Harpenden, Herts.
January, 1963

PLANT VIRUSES
AND
VIRUS DISEASES

F. C. BAWDEN

Rothamsted Experimental Station, England

FOURTH EDITION

THE RONALD PRESS COMPANY • NEW YORK

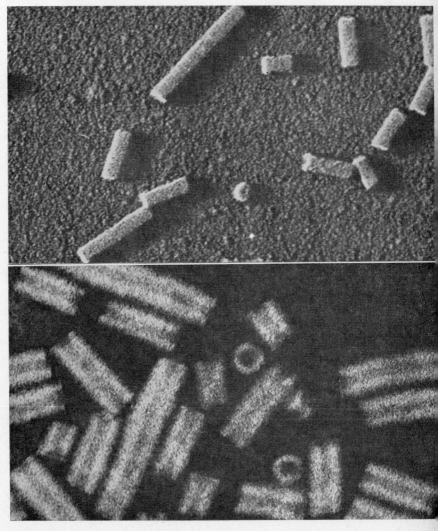

Electron micrographs of purified preparations of tobacco rattle virus. *Top:* specimen shadowed with platinum-iridium alloy, showing seemingly smooth rods, although a small fragment seen end-on has a hole in the centre, × 182,000. *Bottom:* stained in phosphotungstate, showing the particles to be hollow tubes with grooved surfaces, × 455,000. (Photographs provided by Mr. H. L. Nixon).

F. C. Bawden, Director of Rothamsted Experimental Station, England, since 1958, is widely known for his work on viruses and virus diseases. He is a graduate of Cambridge University and was elected a Fellow of the Royal Society in 1949. Mr. Bawden was research assistant at the Potato Virus Research Station, Cambridge, before being appointed Virus Physiologist in 1936 at Rothamsted, where he was Head of the Plant Pathology Department from 1940 to 1958.

JULIUS

Contents

v

PLANT VIRUSES
AND
VIRUS DISEASES

Introduction

Definition of subject. The study of viruses and virus diseases originated in pathology, but has now grown into a subject in its own right, increasingly referred to by the hybrid name virology, which is also the title of an international journal specifically devoted to it. Nevertheless, there is still no agreed definition for the entities that virologists in ever increasing numbers study by an ever increasing number of techniques. In earlier editions of this book, the definition attempted stressed the three features that largely determine the methods whereby viruses were studied, one of which, pathogenicity, is positive, and the other two, invisibility and inability to multiply saprophytically, are essentially negative. Other definitions have since been proposed.

Luria (1953), who also based his definition on methodology rather than taxonomy, omitted pathogenicity and defined viruses as "sub-microscopic entities, capable of being introduced into specific living cells and of reproducing inside such cells only." The ability to infect is undoubtedly a more fundamental property than pathogenicity and it has long been known (Nishamura, 1918) that not all plant viruses cause obvious diseases in all the hosts they can infect. Infections by and the multiplication of viruses in hosts that show no signs of disease can readily be detected by modern techniques, so that we no longer depend as much as previously on pathogenicity to recognise the fact of infection. However, not only is pathogenicity implicit in the history of the subject, but it is the ability of viruses to cause diseases that makes them economically important and that usually draws attention to their occurrence. Also, although there may be viruses that are harmless to all the cells they can infect,

1

as far as I know none has yet been described. Pathogenicity is obviously incidental to rather than an essential feature of infection and virus multiplication, but it is behaviour always potential in the process and is likely often to become actual because the difficulties that beset a host in accommodating virus multiplication without disturbing its normal functioning must be considerable.

Lwoff's (1957) short definition of viruses as "strictly intracellular and potentially pathogenic entities with an infectious phase" recognises these facts. Size does not appear in this definition, which however Lwoff extends by four clauses stating that viruses (1) possess only one type of nucleic acid, (2) multiply in the form of their genetic material (nucleic acid), (3) do not grow or undergo binary fission and (4) contain no "Lippman system," the enzyme system that converts "the potential energy of foodstuffs into the high energy bonds which are needed for biological syntheses." From what is known about the plant viruses that have so far been studied in detail, they probably fulfil the clauses of this definition, but we cannot adopt it because to do so would mean excluding from this book many of the pathogens that are now called plant viruses. These pathogens do not necessarily have any properties that conflict with those specified, but they would be excluded because the definition is exclusive and demands more knowledge than there is about the constitution and behaviour of most plant viruses. Those whose gross constitution and behaviour are known consist largely of nucleic acid and protein, and they all behave as specified. No doubt many of the others, perhaps all, resemble them, but this is a postulate and some of the pathogens now called viruses may prove to be of different types. Hence our definition must be broader, inclusive rather than exclusive, so that if need be it can extend to entities of different composition. In place of the four defining clauses of Lwoff's definition, which may all reflect small size, we can perhaps reintroduce invisibility as a criterion and proceed to define viruses as *sub-microscopic, infective entities that multiply only intracellularly and are potentially pathogenic.*

General as it is, this definition still takes us far from the original meaning of the Latin word virus, which was poison or toxin. However, pathologists seem rarely to have used virus in this sense and, in an attempt to understand current use, it is worth considering how its meaning has changed. Until the germ theory of infectious diseases was established in the second half of the nineteenth century, even though the knowledge that some diseases were contagious was age-old, virus was applied indiscriminately to the causes of all kinds of diseases. After Pasteur convincingly demonstrated the pathogenic role of microbes, usage seems to have changed abruptly and virus became synonymous with microbe or germ. Since then its meaning in pathology has become increasingly restricted, though politicians often widen it when they describe as viruses creeds opposed to their own, but this abuse need not concern us.

Bullough (1938) states that the term virus disease was used in France around 1880 for diseases such as small pox which confer a lasting immunity on those who have once suffered an attack, but it seems unlikely that this restriction became generally accepted. Had it done so, it is difficult to see how plant diseases could have come into the category, and Pasteur was clearly using it more broadly when in 1889 he wrote ". . . virulent affections are caused by small microscopic beings which are called microbes. The anthrax of cattle is produced by a microbe. . . . The microbe of rabies has not been isolated as yet, but judging by analogy, we must believe in its existence. To resume: every virus is a microbe. Although these beings are of infinite smallness, the conditions of their life and propagation are subject to the same general laws which regulate the birth and multiplication of the higher animal and vegetable beings." We have, therefore, the authority of Pasteur to show that, in 1889, virus was a generic term applied to recognised micro-organisms and to pathogens of unknown identity. This use continued for several more years, indeed for some time after the first significant distinction was made between bacteria and the pathogens we now call viruses. This distinction came with the discoveries by Iwanowski with tobacco mosaic in 1892 and by Loeffler and Frosch with foot-and-mouth disease of cattle in 1898 that the causes of these diseases pass through bacteria-proof filters. In other words, it came from the failure of an accepted bacteriological technique to give its expected result, a product both sterile and pathogen-free. At first few workers attached any significance to these discoveries, but Beijerinck as early as 1898 and Baur in 1904 were calling the causes of tobacco mosaic and *Abutilon* variegation viruses as a contrast to, rather than in Pasteur's meaning, of a synonym for, micro-organism. To point the contrast, it was the custom for some years to describe such pathogens as "filterable viruses," but as the ones that were retained by bacteria-proof filters were increasingly identified and placed in specific taxonomic categories, such as the bacteria or fungi, the word virus fell into disuse for them. Consequently in time it became the specific name for those whose taxonomy was unestablished, so the epithet filterable became superfluous and was abandoned.

This brief semantic excursion shows that the only constant use of the word virus has been to label the unknown. When all diseases had unknown causes, virus covered the lot, and as causes were established for some, virus remained a convenient label for the others. Even now this is true in part. Disease can be defined as any appreciable departure from the normal appearance or behaviour of an organism, and abnormalities have very many different causes. However, they divide sharply into two main groups, infectious and not infectious, depending on whether or not the causes can be transmitted to healthy organisms and the abnormal condition reproduced in them. Infectious diseases in their turn also divide conveniently for our purpose into two, depending on whether the cause is an obvious organism, either macroscopic or microscopic, or whether there is no visible cause. The second group comprises those currently called virus diseases; much is now known about the causes of some virus diseases and it is clear that these do not fit into any previously described major taxonomic group. Possibly the time will soon be reached when the name virus will itself have unequivocal taxonomic significance, perhaps as already stated by Lwoff, but that time is not yet, because it still covers entities of unknown morphology and constitution. Inevitably this book is concerned largely with viruses about which much is known, but there are many others and the only characters all can be said certainly to share are pathogenicity, invisibility and ability to multiply only intracellularly. Many of these others almost certainly resemble those which could now be grouped taxonomically as infective particles containing protein and nucleic acid, but it is not a safe assumption that all do.

The development of ideas on the nature of viruses. The discovery that seemingly sterile fluids could be infective came only a few years after the germ theory of disease had become firmly established, at a time when most pathologists were confident that, for each infectious disease, there would be found a micro-organism identifiable under the microscope and able to be cultivated on nutrient medium. The failure to see or grow any causes for such disease as tobacco mosaic or foot-and-mouth of cattle was disconcerting but not enough to change concepts radically. Several undoubted organisms, some fungi and a few bacteria, had also failed to grow on nutrient media and some organisms that did grow saprophytically were only just large enough to be clearly resolved by microscopes. Hence most pathologists saw no impelling reason to abandon their new and fruitful creed that infectious diseases were caused by one kind of organism preying on another. Any objections to the idea that viruses were extremely minute organisms could be more than countered by pointing out obvious similarities between the behaviour of viruses and bacteria, of which the most significant biologically were the unquestioned ability of viruses to multiply in infected organisms and, while doing so, occasionally to vary and produce offspring differing in some way from their parents. This variability was evident in Pasteur's work with rabies, but the ability of plant viruses to vary was not clearly established until the work of Carsner (1925), Johnson (1926) and McKinney (1926).

However, not all workers accepted the organismal view of viruses and the nature of viruses has not only been a subject of much speculation but also of much dispute. This was not surprising in the early days when the nature of viruses was wholly obscure, for nothing gives freer rein to speculation and dogmatic assertions than ignorance. Nevertheless, it is odd that the disputes should have continued so long and that eminent virologists (Andrewes, 1952; Stanley, 1952) could be debating whether viruses were organisms or molecules years after it should have been obvious that they did not fit easily into either category.

The stage for the disputes was set by almost the first papers. Iwanowski (1892) is rightly given the credit for being the first to show that the cause of tobacco mosaic passes through a bacteria-proof filter, but whether it is right also to credit him with the discovery of viruses is less certain, for he appears to have been unimpressed with the significance of his discovery and remained convinced he was dealing with a bacterial disease. Beijerinck (1898), who confirmed Iwanowski's results, drew different conclusions. He considered tobacco mosaic virus to differ fundamentally from a bacterium and attempted to express his ideas by calling it a *"contagium vivum fluidum."* He also suggested that the virus was not corpuscular, by which he presumably meant that it forms stable solutions or suspensions, but this suggestion also had its repercussions, for whether or not viruses were particulate was solemnly debated, without apparently anyone asking what they could be if they were not particles of some size or other. Woods (1899, 1900), too, thought that tobacco mosaic was not caused by a bacterium, and attributed it to an excess of oxidising enzymes. Hunger (1905) and Freiberg (1917) also came down on the side of enzymes or toxins, but for long most people accepted Allard's (1916) conclusion that an organism was the cause.

The organismal theory was influenced by the occurrence of unusual inclusion bodies in the cells of some virus-infected organisms. These were described as a feature of some animal diseases long before the existence of viruses was appreciated, but their connection with viruses seems to have been first indicated by Iwanowski (1903), who described two kinds in tobacco plants suffering from mosaic. One (Fig. 1-1) was a vacuolate and amoeba-like body, often found near to the nucleus, and the other (Fig. 1-2) crystalline. Analogous bodies were later described in many kinds of plants infected with many different viruses, but their etiological significance was a matter of disagreement. Iwanowski, who concluded they could not be the organisms responsible for the disease because they were too large to pass through bacteria-proof filters, suggested they were either abnormal products of nuclear division or reaction products of the cells to the disease. Although he could not isolate bacteria, he saw short rods resembling bacteria and thought these were the cause of the disease. In this he may have been right, for although not bacteria they may perhaps have been visible precipitates of virus particles. The crystals are now known to consist largely and perhaps exclusively of virus particles regularly arrayed, but for years all subsequent workers agreed with Iwanowski that the crystals were plant reaction products and, unfortunately, the crystals got scant attention compared with the amoeba-like bodies, which were treated as more significant, with some workers concluding that they also were cell reaction products but others considering them to be stages in the life cycle of a causative organism. In addition to the inclusion bodies, various other "organisms" have been described from time to time as causing plant virus diseases, but as no such claim was substantiated, they need not be discussed here.

For the first 30 or so years after viruses were discovered, their study was almost the exclusive preserve of pathologists, for whatever the doubts about the biological status of viruses, there was none about their ability to cause diseases. This period was rich in practical results; it disclosed a wide range of virus diseases, unravelled the ways in which many spread, and produced control measures against some. That it produced no positive information about the nature of viruses is not surprising, because few techniques are less appropriate than microscopy and the cultural methods of traditional microbiology for studying invisible entities that will not grow on nutrient media.

Other approaches to the problem were needed and these began to be made during the 1920's, when it was found that tobacco mosaic virus could be precipitated by protein precipitants and resuspended without losing its infectivity (Mulvania, 1926). Vinson and Petre (1929, 1931) obtained reasonably active, colourless preparations of tobacco mosaic virus and concluded that it was a nitrogen-containing substance. There was also a claim to have isolated it as a nitrogen-free crystalline product (Barton-Wright and McBain, 1933), but this was disproved (Caldwell, 1934). These early at-

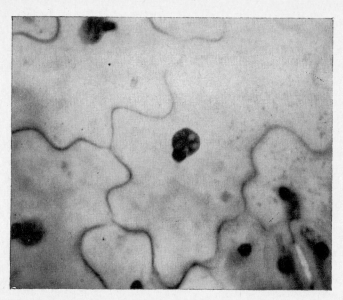

Fig. 1–1. Epidermal strip from *Solanum nodiflorum* infected with tomato aucuba mosaic virus, a strain of tobacco mosaic virus. The vacuolate inclusion is in contact with the nucleus, which has stained deeply with Feulgen's reagent. × 480. (J. Henderson Smith, 1930, Ann. appl. Biol. 17: 213).

Fig. 1–2. Hair cell of *Nicotiana tabacum* infected with tobacco mosaic virus. Two plate-like crystals are seen, one being almost a perfect hexagon. × 450. (F. C. Bawden and F. M. L. Sheffield, 1939, Ann. appl. Biol. 26: 102).

tempts to isolate the virus by chemical methods failed for various reasons. The methods of precipitation were inappropriate, the workers did not attempt to concentrate the virus enough, and reasonable methods for assaying preparations were only just beginning to be developed, after Holmes (1928, 1929) had pointed out that the necrotic local lesions produced in *Nicotiana glutinosa* could be used to compare the relative infectivity of inocula. It is something that the attempts were even made, for in the light of existing knowledge the chances of success seemed small. Robbins (1934), for example,

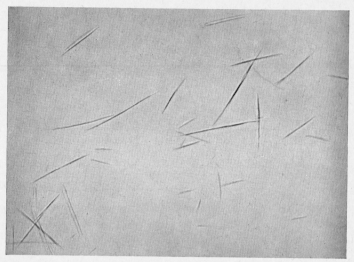

Fig. 1–3. Needle-shaped paracrystals of tobacco mosaic virus produced by precipitation with acid and ammonium sulphate. × 675. (W. M. Stanley, 1937, Amer. J. Bot. 24: 59).

came to the depressing conclusion that more than 600,000,000 litres of sap from infected leaves might be needed to provide 1 mg of tobacco mosaic virus, a conclusion reasonable on the current assumptions about the size of virus particles and that inocula containing one virus particle would be infective. However, by this time serological techniques, which were first applied to virus-infected plants by Dvorak (1927) but whose significance was shown only by the pioneer work of Purdy Beale (1928, 1929, 1931), had given a more reliable basis for estimating the virus content of sap, and using these Chester (1935) reached the more hopeful and accurate conclusion that infective sap might contain from 0.1 to 1 mg of tobacco mosaic virus per ml. He seems to have been the first to suggest that inocula may need to contain several millions of virus particles per ml to produce a single infection, and his suggestion was soon confirmed.

Stanley (1935, 1936) fractionated large volumes of infective sap by the methods used to isolate proteolytic enzymes and obtained substantial amounts of what he called "a crystalline protein possessing the properties of tobacco mosaic virus." His original description of this product makes it difficult to decide exactly what he did isolate, for many of the properties he ascribed to it are not those of tobacco mosaic virus. That the product contained much virus seems established from the characteristic needle-like precipitates (Fig. 1–3) that formed when the preparations were treated with ammonium sulphate or acidified, but the statements that the protein was a globulin, containing 20 per cent of nitrogen, with no phosphorus or carbohydrate, and partially digestible with pepsin, suggest that the preparations were either highly contaminated or consisted largely of inactivated virus. That plants infected with strains of tobacco mosaic virus contain large amounts of anomalous proteins was soon confirmed (Bawden, Pirie, Bernal and Fankuchen, 1936; Bawden and Pirie, 1937a, b), but Bawden and Pirie described their products as liquid crystalline nucleoproteins, containing a nucleic acid of the ribose type. The proteins from plants infected with different strains had similar general properties but differed in slight details. Concentrated solutions separated into two liquid layers, the lower of which was liquid crystalline (Fig. 1–4), whereas solutions too dilute to be birefringent spontaneously became so temporarily when shaken. This showed that the particles were grossly anisometric, confirming a suggestion by Takahashi and Rawlins (1932) when they observed the phenomenon of anisotropy of flow in clarified sap from infected plants. X-ray analyses of these proteins showed them to be about 15 mμ wide and that they were at least 10 times as long as they were wide (Bernal and Fankuchen, 1937). They also showed that the individual particles were composed from sub-units of a uniform size arranged with a perfect three-dimensional regularity.

Since the first work with strains of tobacco mosaic virus, plants infected with other viruses have also been found to contain specific nucleoproteins. The next to be isolated resembled those from plants with tobacco mosaic virus in forming liquid crystals (Bawden and Pirie, 1938a, 1939), although they gave amorphous and not paracrystalline precipitates when brought out of solution with acid or salt. The first virus with isometric particles to be isolated was tomato bushy stunt, and when salted out this crystallised in the form of rhombic dodecahedra (Fig. 1–5) (Bawden and Pirie, 1938b). This also contained a nucleic acid of the ribose type, amounting to about 15 per cent of its dry weight instead of the 5 per cent of the anisometric particles.

At the time these purified virus preparations were first made, it was their ability to crystallise that attracted most attention, but this was not the fact that was biologically significant. It is true that the uniformity of particle size needed to fit into a crystalline lattice seemed incompatible with multiplication by binary fission, which necessarily entails an increase in size followed by separation into

Fig. 1–4. Photograph, in polarised light, of a 2% solution of purified tobacco mosaic virus which has settled into layers, showing the spontaneous birefringence of the lower layer. (F. C. Bawden and N. W. Pirie, 1937, Proc. R. Soc. B. 123: 274).

halves, but much more important in distinguishing the viruses from organisms were their chemical simplicity and their regular internal structure. These, too, have proved constant features of all the viruses since purified, whereas not all have formed crystals or liquid crystals. In striking contrast to the wide range of materials contained in even the smallest organism and to the continually changing internal structure of cells, the virus particles contain only two major components, protein and nucleic acid, and are built of uniform sized sub-units arranged in a fixed and regular manner.

All viruses yet isolated from flowering plants resemble tobacco mosaic virus in containing nucleic acid of the ribose type, but viruses (bacteriophages) that attack bacteria and some of those that attack animals contain deoxynucleic acid. No other major difference in composition has yet been found, although the viruses examined differ greatly from one another in their host ranges, particle shapes and sizes, stabilities, methods of transmission, and many other properties. In composition and structure, virus particles resemble in-

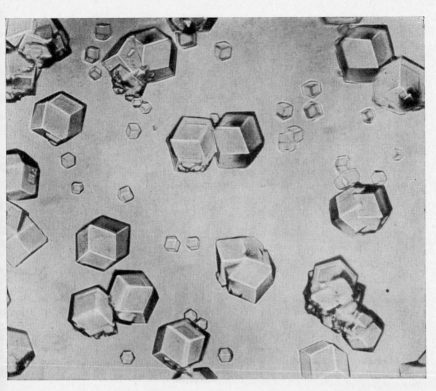

Fig. 1–5. Dodecahedral crystals of tomato bushy stunt virus produced by slow precipitation with ammonium sulphate in the cold. The crystals were photographed on the wall of a vessel in which the same preparation was twice crystallised. The larger crystals were produced by the first crystallisation and the smaller by the second. × 250. (F. C. Bawden and N. W. Pirie, 1938, Brit. J. exp. Path. 19: 251).

dividual components of cells rather than whole cells. Their intracellular habit, long recognised, took on an added significance with this new knowledge, and the time had arrived to abandon old concepts of virus diseases as equivalent to the effects of one organism preying on another.

Although many pathologists, and particularly those working with animal viruses, were reluctant to admit it, virus diseases were most appropriately and profitably regarded as aberrations in the nucleo-

protein metabolism of the hosts, with virus multiplication a part of
the general synthetic activities of infected cells. The failure to
appreciate that viruses lack the metabolic capabilities of bacteria
and depend on their hosts not simply for sustenance, but also for the
mechanisms that synthesise their substance, both delayed progress
in the subject and had expensive results; for example, it meant that
much time and effort was expended fruitlessly seeking therapeutic
treatments for diseases of animals, tests of antibiotics and drugs that
were almost bound to fail because success demanded specific activities of viruses that there was no reason to assume they possessed.
Only substances that interfere with nucleic acid or protein synthesis
were *a priori* likely to affect virus multiplication, and this expectation has been fulfilled by the failure with most other things and the
partial success with some analogues of purines and pyrimidines.

The reluctance of pathologists to change their concepts about
viruses was stiffened almost into stubbornness by their justifiable
irritation at the claims of some chemists and physicists, who, over-
impressed by the success of physico-chemical techniques in isolating
viruses and by the apparent homogeneity of purified virus preparations, unhesitatingly called viruses "molecules" and thereby also
placed them in a wrong category. The apparently irreconcilable
differences between those who called viruses organisms and those
who called them molecules have now disappeared, for happily both
parties to the dispute have abandoned these names. Neither name
should ever have been applied, for each prejudged what should have
been an open question. The word organism demands a wealth of
independent metabolic activities there was never any reason to assume viruses possess, and the word molecule implies a precise knowledge of chemical composition impossible to get with particles as
large as viruses, and demands an unchangeable structure that conflicts strikingly with the great mutability of viruses. Both parties
to the dispute apparently overlooked the fact that there were other
categories into which viruses fitted more easily. Cells contain many
components with complex particles, some of which behave super-
ficially like viruses in seeming to reproduce and vary; if analogies
for viruses were to be sought, they were more likely to be found
among these complex and biologically active particles than among
the bacteria or the simple molecules of traditional chemistry.

There are various reasons for the dispute now ending. First,
the structure of some bacteriophages as revealed by modern electron
microscopy (Brenner *et al*, 1959) is so sophisticated that even to
call them particles seems almost insulting. A hexagonal head, consisting of a protein envelope surrounding the nucleic acid, carries a

cylindrical tail, which is itself of a complexity entailing many different kinds of molecules, with an inner, hollow core, surrounded by a contractile sheath, and ending in a hexagonal sheath, to which are attached six fibres (Fig. 1–6). Secondly, even the relatively simple particles of plant viruses are not built from uniform units of nucleoprotein, but consist of a protein structure with nucleic acid embedded in it. Thirdly, although for 20 years the nucleoprotein particles seemed to be replicating entities and the minimum infective units, this is now known not to be true. After Hershey and Chase (1952) showed that most of the protein of T2 bacteriophage never enters infected bacteria and so cannot be directly involved in replicating the particles, the bulk of the protein of several other viruses has also been shown to be inessential to their multiplication. As with so many other discoveries, this one also came first from work with tobacco mosaic virus, when particles disrupted by either a detergent (Fraenkel-Conrat, 1956) or phenol (Gierer and Schramm, 1956) were shown still to be infective. The infectivity, as with fragments of other viruses since disrupted by phenol, is ephemeral, and is rapidly destroyed by nucleases that do not inactivate intact virus particles. These facts provide the reason for the clause in Lwoff's definition of viruses stating that viruses multiply in the form of their genetic material. Viruses, then, are now generally accepted both as too complex to be called molecules, and unacceptable as organisms, because their method of multiplication clearly precludes multiplication by growth and fission.

If the proposition is accepted that tobacco mosaic virus contains two major components, protein and nucleic acid, and no precise chemical definition of nucleic acid is attempted, infectivity is obviously a property of the nucleic acid and not of the protein. The concept of virus diseases that follows from this is the current one that they are primarily disturbances in the host's metabolism of nucleic acid, with secondary consequences to the protein metabolism. If there is a moiety of the virus particle that directly replicates, it seems to be only the nucleic acid, which when established in susceptible cells not only engineers more of itself but also organises the synthesis of the appropriate protein or proteins to accompany it. However, ideas about the minimal infective unit have often changed, and always to something smaller. Perhaps in the thread of naked nucleic acid, the ultimate has been reached, but past experience should warn against being too sure of this. Before too much weight is placed on inactivation by nucleases and on the fact that infectivity seems to be lost when the nucleic acid thread is broken, it is well to remember that the apparent correlation be-

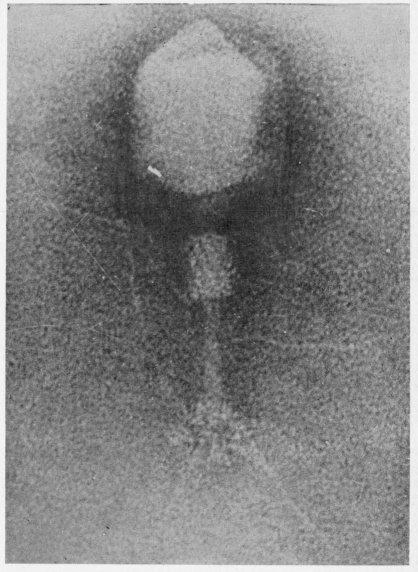

Fig 1–6. Electron micrograph of T2 bacteriophage treated with H_2O_2 and mounted in phosphotungstate, showing the hexagonal head, core of tail and contracted sheath, the tail plate and tail fibres. (Photograph provided by Dr. R. W. Horne).

tween protein denaturation and loss of infectivity was for long also regarded as good evidence that the virus protein was essential for infection and virus multiplication. Although small compared with the size of intact virus particles, the nucleic acid from tobacco mosaic virus has a weight equal to a molecular weight of over 2,000,000, amply big to be hiding many components, active groups and the like, which although quantitatively minor compared with the four nucleotides that make up its bulk, may still be immensely important biologically.

History and economic importance. The existence of viruses was recognised only in 1892 and for many years afterwards they received little attention compared with bacteria and fungi, but so many virus diseases have been described during the last 30 years that their economic importance is difficult to exaggerate. Despite the great frequency with which "new" viruses are reported and the fact that many workers consider virus diseases to be increasing in prevalence, there is no reason to assume they are afflictions peculiar to recent times. The modern world-wide traffic in plants and the increasing speed of travel have undoubtedly helped to spread over long distances many plant viruses that would otherwise have remained localised, and changing conditions of agriculture have also encouraged the spread of others. The increased use of clonal varieties, the growth of the same kinds of plants over ever increasing areas, the introduction of new crops into countries, all these are potentially apt to increase the prevalence of virus diseases, and no doubt have often done so.

The outbreak of a new virus disease, however, does not mean that a new virus has come into being; it usually means only that an old virus has been presented with a new host, or with a new environment in which it spreads more rapidly, or produces more obvious signs of its presence, than previously. For instance, swollen shoot of cocoa, which has been responsible for killing millions of cocoa trees in West Africa during recent years, could not have done so 100 years ago because cocoa was not then growing there. The disease is modern, but there is no reason to think that the causative virus (or viruses) is. Some plant species indigenous to West Africa are hosts and there is every reason to think the virus was in these before cocoa was introduced, but only when this susceptible crop was established over a wide area could the virus spread unrestrictedly and demonstrate its potentialities as a pathogen.

That virus diseases are not new afflictions of man, and some idea of their direct importance to him, will be clear simply by listing a

few names, such as small pox, yellow fever, mumps, poliomyelitis, in-
fluenza and the common cold. Similarly, rabies, distemper, equine
encephalomyelitis, swine fever, psittacosis, fowl pest and the polyhedral diseases of insects, are names enough to show that many kinds
of animals suffer virus infections and that the resulting diseases are
among the most troublesome.

This book is concerned primarily with the viruses that infect
flowering plants (Angiosperms). How many such viruses there
are it is impossible to say. This is partly because there are undoubtedly many still to be discovered, but partly because it is uncertain how many of those that have been discovered deserve the
distinguishing names their discoverers gave them. Synonymity is
rife, and the same virus has often been "discovered" many times.
The second edition of Smith's *Textbook of Plant Virus Diseases* published in 1957 lists 300 viruses that he then thought to be distinct
from one another, but already it is evident that some of his names
are either synonyms or refer to related strains of a virus rather than
to unrelated viruses. However, his figure of 300 is likely to be an
under rather than an over estimate, because since 1957 there have
possibly been more viruses newly described that seem distinct from
any others than names that could be removed from his list as demon-
strably synonyms.

The problems of deciding whether a virus found causing previously undescribed symptoms in a crop plant is similar or related
to one already known can be difficult. Not only do most viruses
exist in a range of strains differing in virulence and host range, but
many have very extensive host ranges and their properties and behaviour may differ in different hosts. When a virus is found causing
a mosaic disease in, say, peach, in which it can be transmitted only
by grafting, it seems wholly reasonable to assume that it is distinct
from one that causes ringspot symptoms in, say, tomato, and is also
readily transmitted by the mechanical inoculation of sap, but the
assumption is not always valid. Many viruses, which when first
found seemed to have a narrow host range and to be transmissible
only by grafting, have later been shown to have wide host ranges
and to be transmissible mechanically to and from some of their hosts.
The extension of their study to other hosts has often shown relationships with other viruses that previously could not have been suspected. As methods of transmitting viruses mechanically improve,
more and more viruses will be able to be tested for properties of
greater taxonomic significance than symptom production, and the
present doubts about synonymity will become fewer.

Although the total number of plant viruses is unknown, there is no doubt that crop plants are susceptible to a great many and that some virus diseases are enormously important. All kinds of plants, whether annuals, biennials, perennials, or trees, become infected but there are some features of virus diseases that make them particularly troublesome in perennials. For instance, most viruses are not transmitted from parent to offspring through sexually produced seed, so most crops raised annually from true seed start life virus-free and any viruses they contract must be introduced from outside sources. To do great damage in an annual crop, therefore, a virus must not only have an efficient method of spread but must also become widely disseminated through the crop early enough in the season to affect yield. There are plenty of viruses that can do this, of which we need bring as witness only five, sugar beet curly top and yellows, barley yellow dwarf, cauliflower mosaic and tomato mosaic, each of which sometimes infects all the plants in a given crop. However, although they may ruin crops, or greatly decrease yields, the effects of such viruses are transient, restricted to the one year, and the next year's crop will again start virus-free. In perennial plants, or those propagated vegetatively, things are otherwise, and infection means not simply a loss of yield in the year when infection happens, but a continuing loss. This is because plants do not recover from virus infections (they lack the mechanisms for making antibodies whereby animals can overcome their viruses and having once suffered an attack are usually left with a lasting immunity against another); once infected, a plant usually remains so for as long as it remains alive, and when any vegetative part of it is used for propagation, the progeny will also be infected in perpetuity. This persistence of viruses means that perennial (or vegetatively propagated) plants are continually infected with all the viruses they have ever contracted, and there is nothing unusual in finding an old potato variety, or a long established fruit tree, infected with several different viruses. If the effects of each virus were simply additive, vigour would be much decreased, but effects are often more than additive; as first demonstrated by Vanterpool (1926) with "glasshouse streak" of tomatoes and since found with many other diseases, simultaneous infection with two viruses, each of which alone may do little harm, can be devastating. Even though viruses spread between perennial plants at only a small fraction the rate they need to spread if they are to be important in annual crops, they can nevertheless be highly destructive. It would be idle even to guess at the losses viruses cause in plantation and orchard crops, and it must serve our purpose simply to say that there are serious virus diseases of all such crops, whether grown for fruit, a main food, a beverage or fibre, and that often virus diseases have threatened the growth of such crops in some areas.

Few of the many virus diseases now recognised attracted attention before the twentieth century and only tobacco mosaic in a crop raised annually from seed. The oldest records are of tulip mosaic in which the striking permanent change in the appearance of the flowers (breaking) could hardly have been overlooked. Broken blooms feature in many paintings by old Dutch masters and references to variegated flowers appear in botanical literature in 1576 (McKay and Warner, 1933). van Slogteren and Ouboter (1941) state that some Dutch bulb growers knew as early as 1637 that self-coloured tulips could be made to break by grafting them to bulbs of variegated plants and Blagrave in 1675 gave details for grafting halves of bulbs. Despite this early knowledge, breaking was generally considered to be a sign of maturity, which many people considered could be hastened by planting bulbs in impoverished soil or some other unfavourable conditions, and only in 1928 when Cayley demonstrated transmission unequivocally was it generally accepted as the result of virus infection. With this knowledge, the demand for variegated tulips, which in the past had often fetched high prices as new varieties, waned, and in today's bulb fields any variegated intruder is regarded as a danger to its self-coloured neighbours and is destroyed.

Our next oldest records of virus diseases are in the potato crop, which was so severely attacked in some parts of Europe by 1775 that many farmers abandoned its cultivation. In Britain prizes were offered to anyone who could find the cause of and remedy for this serious trouble in so useful a crop. Of the many papers published around this time, most stress the degenerate state of affected plants, and the condition became widely known as "degeneration," "running-out," or "senility." It was early noticed that new varieties, i.e. seedlings, were more vigorous than old ones, which led to the general belief that the condition was an inevitable consequence of continued propagation by "unnatural" asexual methods (Fig. 1–7). Although no experimental work was done, Anderson (1792) in an essay written in 1778 suggested many things modern work has confirmed. He noticed that tubers from degenerate parents always gave degenerate plants and that potato stocks grown in the south of Britain were usually worse than those in the north. He suggested that the condition was infectious, likening it to small pox, and that it might be controlled by destroying all infected plants as soon as they were noticed. Virus diseases of potatoes may have been new to Europe at this time, because most writers were agreed that the degeneration was unknown before 1770. Potato viruses prevalent at that time are still prevalent in many parts of the world. In Britain now they are rare, but this does not mean they are unimportant; they are rare only because they are controlled, at a cost to the English potato growers of about £10,000,000 a year.

Fig. 1–7. King Edward potato plants: *left,* healthy; *centre,* leaf roll; *right,* rugose (severe) mosaic, caused by potato virus Y.

Peach yellows, of which there have been several great outbreaks in north-east America, destroying many thousands of trees and making peach growing impossible over large areas, has a history almost as long as potato degeneration. It was described in 1791 and was probably doing damage as early as 1750 (Smith 1894). Around 1870 the variegated *Abutilon* was popular as an ornamental plant in Europe and it seems to have been known that green plants would become variegated when grafted with scions from variegated ones. However, the first experimental work on transmission of diseases now recognised to be virus diseases was by Mayer (1886), who named tobacco mosaic and showed that it could be produced by injecting healthy plants with juice from diseased ones, and by Smith (1891, 1894), who transmitted peach yellows by grafting scions from diseased trees onto healthy ones. These transmissions can legitimately be regarded as the starting point for experimental work on plant viruses and soon afterwards Iwanowski (1892) and Beijerinck (1898) showed that tobacco mosaic virus passes through bacteria-proof filters. One other happening in the nineteenth century was the first description of a virus disease of the vine by Pierce in 1892, but that virus diseases had existed in Europe long before this is shown by old illustrations of this plant.

The rest of this book deals with work done during the twentieth century, and it is impossible in this introductory chapter to give a historical review of all the discoveries. Progress at first was sur-prisingly slow, and the implications of new discoveries took a long time to be appreciated. Thus, although the role of insects in trans-mitting viruses was indicated as early as 1900, when the mosquito vector of yellow fever was discovered, and 1901, when the first leaf-hopper vector of a plant virus, rice stunt, was discovered by Takami, it was not until 1923 that aphids were shown to transmit potato viruses (Schultz and Folsom, 1923; Murphy, 1923) and several more years passed before tulip break, a condition known for more than 300 years, was also shown to be aphid-transmitted (Hughes, 1930). The first report that spraying with insecticides checked the spread of aphid-borne viruses came in 1937, when Watson found that weekly spraying with nicotine checked virus diseases in *Hyoscyamus niger*. The possibilities of curing plants from virus diseases by various heat treatments were also oddly neglected. Kobus as early as 1889 ob-served that the growth of sugar-cane cuttings suffering from sereh disease was improved by immersing them in hot water, but it was not until 1935 that virus diseases of any other plant were shown to be amenable to heat therapy (Kunkel, 1935), the wide applications of which were not demonstrated until almost another 20 years (Kassanis, 1954).

In striking contrast to the flowering plants, of which all kinds, whether monocotyledons or dicotyledons, forest trees or bushes, fruit trees or shrubs, herbaceous perennials or annuals, crops or weeds, have been reported to be susceptible to viruses, most other groups of plants remain without any known viruses that attack them. To match the wealth of viruses known in flowering plants, it is nec-essary to descend as far as the Shizomycetes, of which, as with Angiosperms, almost every species studied has been found to be susceptible to one or more viruses (bacteriophage). It is true that leaf mottlings, resembling the symptoms caused in Angiosperms by some viruses, have been reported occasionally in Gymnosperms and Pteridophytes, but only one of these conditions, a chlorosis of spruce trees (*Picea excelsa*), seems to have been confirmed as a virus dis-ease by electron microscopy and appropriate transmission tests

(Cech, Kralik and Blattny, 1961). Similarly, there is only one report about a disease of fungi, die-back of mushroom, in which there is good evidence for a virus being responsible (Gandy and Hollings, 1962). Whether this apparent preference of viruses for the flowering plants as habitats is also real, and therefore of considerable evolutionary interest, or whether it simply reflects lack of knowledge and there are many viruses of Gymnosperms and Cryptogams waiting discovery, only time will tell.

The naming of viruses. As the study of viruses grew out of pathology, so the names given to viruses have largely been derived from the diseases they cause. At the beginning of the twentieth century, it was reasonable to consider that viruses were host specific and that one found causing a disease in one species would be distinct from one causing a different disease in another species. The custom, which began with tobacco mosaic virus, of calling a virus after the host in which it was discovered, and the main symptom it causes in that host, became general; hence aster yellows virus, cucumber mosaic virus, potato leaf roll virus, tobacco ringspot virus, and the like.

The main purpose of a name is to act as a label for unequivocal reference, and any kind of name can serve this purpose provided it is kept specific. There was nothing basically wrong in naming viruses by this method, which indeed provided more than a mere label because the names carry a little information, and some were quaint enough to be unforgettable. However, the assumption that viruses were host specific was unwarranted, and with no agreed tests for identifying viruses, the same virus (or strains of the same virus) was inevitably reported as "new" by different workers and given several different names, whereas different viruses were often given the same or similar names. That virus nomenclature was, and to a large extent still is, in a state near chaos, is undeniable, but it is idle to blame the disease names for this. The chaos was achieved not because the names were unsuitable, but because workers named uncritically. The resulting plague of synonymity would have been the same whatever kind of name had been used; it followed automatically from naming viruses without adequate tests to ensure that a previously undescribed syndrome was caused by a previously unnamed virus. It is odd that there should have been no agreed method of identifying viruses, at least for those transmitted mechanically, because Johnson (1929) early pointed out that tests of stability *in vitro* were often of more use than symptomatology as criteria for identification. Also, from the middle 1930s serological relationship and tests of mutual antagonism in plants, which followed the discovery by Thung (1931) and Salaman (1933) that infection by one strain of a virus protects plants against other strains of that virus, were obviously of great value in virus identification, yet they singularly failed to impress the many who continued to name new viruses on symptomatology alone.

Those who were bothered about the growing chaos in nomenclature diagnosed the trouble wrongly and suggestions to overcome it were largely that types of names should be used that distinguished the viruses from the diseases they cause. It cannot be said that any of the suggestions met with great success, and their main result has been to increase the number of synonyms. The first, from Johnson in 1927, was that descriptive names should be restricted to diseases and that viruses should be referred to by the common name of the host in which they were discovered, followed by a distinguishing number. In his scheme, the causes of tobacco mosaic and cucumber mosaic became, respectively, tobacco virus 1 and cucumber virus 1. The International Botanical Conference in 1930 set up an International Committee on Virus Nomenclature under the chairmanship of Professor James Johnson, which reported to the Botanical Conference in 1935 and proposed an elaboration of Johnson's original scheme, designed to cover virus strains as well as distinct viruses. In it, common cucumber mosaic virus became cucumber virus 1, the strain that produces a yellow mottle 1B, and sub-strains derived from this 1Ba, 1Bb, and so on. However, this scheme was never formally published. In the first edition of his *Textbook of Plant Virus Diseases* (1937), Smith modified the scheme by using the Latin generic name of the host instead of the common name, so that tobacco mosaic virus now became Nicotiana virus 1. Before this Smith (1931) had introduced the alphabet into virus nomenclature by labelling two viruses potato virus X and Y, a practice extended by Salaman who also used letters as indices to distinguish strains, for example, X^s for a strain that produces ringspot symptoms in tobacco and X^g for one that produces only a faint mottling. The limited use of numbers or letters worked reasonably well, but the extension of such a system to all viruses had many disadvantages. A number or letter tells nothing about the virus, and the difficulties of remembering precisely which virus is meant by such a name as tobacco virus 18 or Solanum virus 17 are considerable. Perhaps the most telling comment to be made on the system is that Smith abandoned numbers in favour of disease names in the second edition of his *Textbook* (1957).

Holmes (1939) introduced a Latin binomial nomenclature, similar to the one used for organisms, with a trinomial to indicate strains. Ordinary tobacco mosaic virus then became *Marmor tabaci,* var. *vulgare,* and the strain that causes tomato aucuba mosaic became *Marmor tabaci* var. *Aucuba,* and Salaman's X^s became *Marmor dubium* var. *annulus.* Both Smith and Holmes did a useful service in showing that many names previously in use were synonyms, but that this did not need a new system of nomenclature was demonstrated in a list of common names published by the Imperial Mycological Institute (1946) to show under what names viruses would be indexed in the Review of Applied Mycology. In 1948 Holmes extended his system to all viruses and it was published as a supplement to the sixth edition of *Bergey's Manual of Determinative Bacteriology.* Some people were willing to accept Latin binomial names, but few were willing to accept the names put forward by Holmes, so many of which suggested false relationships. Hence, new names were put forward and before long alternatives for *Marmor tabaci* (tobacco mosaic virus) were *Musivum tabaci* and *Baculus tabaci.* Various other forms of Latinised names differing from the binomials used in the Linnean naming of organisms were also put forward. Bennett (1939) stressed the advantages of names over numbers and proposed a temporary scheme in which tobacco mosaic virus would be *Nicotiana virus altathermus;* should it ultimately be decided that viruses could be classified into genera and species, this name could readily be turned into a binomial such as *Paracrystalis altathermus.* However, should it be decided that viruses are better fitted by a nomenclature of the type used by chemists than by that used by biologists, then the temporary specific name could be given an appropriate suffix. As the suffix "ase" denotes enzymes, so Bennett suggested the suffix "vir" could denote virus, and tobacco mosaic virus could become "altathermovir."

The International Microbiological Congress in 1947 decided to include viruses under its code of nomenclature and after various meetings the Virus Subcommittee recommended at the Rome Congress in 1953 that the starting date for valid Linnean nomenclature for viruses should not yet be determined and until this was done names for viruses already proposed should have no standing. They recommended that Latin names of the type *Poxvirus variolae* (small pox virus) should be used for animal viruses and set up study groups to propose suitable names. They further recommended that no other names than those proposed by the study groups and accepted by the subcommittee should have any official status. No such names have yet been accepted by the subcommittee for plant viruses, but a *Commission de Nomenclature des Virus* of the International Botanical and Microbiological Congresses has been busy renaming on a system whereby tobacco mosaic virus may become *Nicotianavirus vulgare utrans*, potato virus X *Solanumvirus X-nomine*, and aster yellows virus *Callistephusvirus flavescens*. But if they do, it is difficult to see who will benefit. Supporters of Latin names often speak eloquently of the virtues or need of names to be in an international language, although fewer people now understand Latin than understand any modern language. The argument would be cogent if the description of viruses were also to be given in Latin, but if virus workers adopt Latin names they will presumably follow the bacteriologists and, while demanding Latin names, will accept descriptions in other languages as valid. This reduces the argument to nonsense, for an individual who cannot be expected to understand a name in English, French, Spanish or Chinese, is apparently expected to be able to reach his identification from details recorded in such languages. Meanwhile, as Latin names have no status, I shall rest content with common names and, as far as possible, use those in the revised list published by the Commonwealth Bureau of Mycology in 1957.

REFERENCES

ALLARD, H. A. 1961. J. agric. Res. 7: 481.

ANDERSON, J. 1792. Bath Soc. Papers 4:92.

ANDREWES, C. H. 1952. Proc. 2nd int. Poliomyelitis Conf. 3.

BARTON-WRIGHT, E., and A. M. McBAIN. 1933. Nature, Lond. 132: 1003.

BAUR, E. 1904. Ber. Dtsch. bot. Ges. 22: 453.

BAWDEN, F. C., and N. W. PIRIE. 1937a. Proc. roy. Soc. 123: 274.

———, and ———. 1937b. Brit. J. exp. Path. 18: 275.

———, and ———. 1938a. *Ibid.* 19: 66.

———, and ———. 1938b. *Ibid.* 19: 251.

———, and ———. 1939. *Ibid.* 20: 322.

———, ———, J. D. BERNAL, and I. FANKUCHEN. 1936. Nature, Lond. 138: 1051.

BEALE, H. PURDY. 1928. Proc. Soc. exp. Biol., N.Y. 25: 702.

———. 1929. J. exp. Med. 49: 919.

———. 1931. *Ibid.* 54: 463.

BEIJERINCK, M. W. 1898. Verh. Akad. Wet. Amst. 6: 1.

BENNETT, C. W. 1939. Phytopathology 29: 422.

BERNAL, J. D., and I. FANKUCHEN. 1937. Nature, Lond. 139: 923.

BRENNER, S., G. STREISINGER, R. W. HORNE, S. P. CHAMPE, L. BARNETT, S. BENZER, and M. W. REES. 1959. J. mol. Biol. 1: 281.

BULLOUGH, W. 1938. The History of Bacteriology. Oxford University Press, London.

CALDWELL, J. 1934. Nature, Lond. 133: 177.

CARSNER, E. 1925. Phytopathology 15: 745.

CAYLEY, D. M. 1928. Ann. appl. Biol. 15: 429.

CECH, M., O. KRALIK, and C. BLATTNY. 1961. Phytopathology 51: 183.

CHESTER, K. S. 1935. Science 82: 17.
DVORAK, M. 1927. J. infect. Dis. 41: 215.
FRAENKEL-CONRAT, H. 1956. J. Amer. chem. Soc. 78: 882.
FREIBERG, G. W. 1917. Ann. Missouri bot. Gard. 4: 175.
GANDY, D. G., and M. HOLLINGS. 1962. Rep. Glasshouse Res. Inst. 1961, p. 103.
GIERER, A., and G. SCHRAMM. 1956. Nature, Lond. 177: 702.
HERSHEY, A. D., and M. CHASE. 1952. J. gen. Physiol. 36: 39.
HOLMES, F. O. 1928. Bot. Gaz. 86: 66.
———. 1929. Ibid. 87: 56.
———. 1939. Handbook of Phytopathogenic viruses. Burgess, Minneapolis.
———. 1948. In Bergey's Manual of Determinative Bacteriology, 6th edition. Bailliere, Tindall and Cox, London.
HUGHES, A. W. McKENNY. 1930. Ann. appl. Biol. 17: 36.
HUNGER, F. W. T. 1905. Ber. Dtsch. bot. Ges. 23: 415.
IWANOWSKI, D. 1892. Bull. Acad. Sci. St. Petersb. 35: 67.
———. 1903. Zeit. PflKrankh. 13: 1.
JOHNSON, J. 1926. Science 64: 210.
———. 1927. Wis. agric. Exp. Sta. Res Bull. 76.
———. 1929. Ibid. 87.
KASSANIS, B. 1954. Ann. appl. Biol. 41: 470.
KOBUS, J. D. 1889. Meded. Proefst. Oost-Java 24: 230.
KUNKEL, L. O. 1935. Phytopathology 25: 24.
LOEFFLER, F., and P. FROSCH. 1898. Zbl. Bakt. 23: 371.
LURIA, S. E. 1953. General Virology. John Wiley and Sons, Inc., New York.
LWOFF, A. 1957. J. gen. Microbiol. 17: 239.
McKAY, M. B., and M. F. WARNER. 1933. Nat. hort. Mag.
McKINNEY, H. H. 1926. Phytopathology 16: 893.
MAYER, A. E. 1886. Landw. Versuchsw. 32: 450.
MULVANIA, M. 1926. Ibid. 16: 853.
MURPHY, P. A. 1923. Sci. Proc. R. Dublin Soc. 18: 169.
NISHAMURA, M. 1918. Bull. Torrey bot. Cl. 45: 219.
PIERCE, N. B. 1892. Bull. U.S. Div. Veg. Physiol. Path. 2.
ROBBINS, W. J. 1934. Science 80: 275.
SALAMAN, R. N. 1933. Nature, Lond. 131: 468.
SCHULTZ, E. S., and D. FOLSOM. 1923. J. agric. Res. 25: 2.
SLOGTEREN, E. VAN, and M. P. OUBOTER. 1941. Meded. LandbHoogesch., Wageningen 45.
SMITH, E. F. 1891. Bull. U.S. Div. Veg. Physiol. Path. 1.
———. 1894. Fmr's. Bull. U.S. Dep. Agric. 17.
SMITH, K. M. 1931. Proc. roy. Soc. B. 109: 251.
———. 1957. Textbook of Plant Virus Diseases. Churchill, London.
STANLEY, W. M. 1935. Science 81: 644.
———. 1936. Phytopathology 26: 395.
———. 1952. Proc. 2nd int. Poliomyelitis Conf. 6.
TAKAHASHI, W. N., and T. E. RAWLINS. 1932. Proc. Soc. exp. Biol., N.Y. 30: 155.
TAKAMI, N. 1901. J. Agric., Japan 241: 22.
THUNG, T. H. 1931. Hand. 6th med. ind. Naturw. Congr., p. 450.
VANTERPOOL, T. C. 1926. Phytopathology 16: 311.
VINSON, C. G., and A. W. PETRE. 1929. Bot. Gaz. 87: 14.
———, and ———. 1931. Contr. Boyce Thompson Inst. 3: 131.
WATSON, M. A. 1937. Ann. appl. Biol. 24: 557.
WOODS, A. F. 1899. Zbl. Bakt. 5: 745.
———. 1900. Science 11: 17.

Symptomatology: Changes in the Appearance of Plants

As new techniques of testing for the presence of viruses are developed, the role of symptomatology in the study of viruses becomes less dominating than it was, but even so its importance is difficult to exaggerate. It is true that a few of the many known viruses were discovered from serological tests before any host was known in which they caused overt symptoms, but these are rare happenings and most viruses have first attracted attention because some plant looked abnormal. Also, although symptoms and host range are unreliable for specific diagnoses, they often provide invaluable clues to the identity of viruses and suggest relationships that can be checked by tests of more specific characters. Obviously, too, as viruses are economically important because they change the growth of plants in ways that decrease the yield or quality of crops, however many other methods may be developed of studying or assaying them, infecting plants and noting the consequences must always remain an essential part of virus research. Having said this, however, it is to be hoped that symptomatology will develop beyond the practice of simply recording the visible effects of infection; the subject should be more than descriptive and it is high time that attempts were made to get explanations in biochemical terms for the many and varied changes viruses cause in plants.

It is not the aim of this chapter to attempt diagnostic descriptions of viruses diseases. Dr. Kenneth M. Smith's *Textbook of Plant*

Virus Diseases does this systematically and contains many excellent photographs illustrating a great range of symptoms. Here all that is attempted is to outline the ways plants react to infection and to show how the reactions can change with time or with changing environments.

Types of symptoms. Probably the commonest effect of virus infection is to decrease the rate at which plants grow and so make them smaller than they otherwise would be (Fig. 1–7). In a few diseases, for example, sugar-cane stunt, this may be the only obvious effect, but usually the decreased growth is accompanied by other changes in individual tissues. Any parts, roots, stems, leaves, flowers or fruits, may be changed but the leaves most often provide both the most evident and the first signs of infection. Colour changes are the commonest; instead of being uniformly green, the leaves show spots, blotches, streaks or rings of light-green, yellow, white, brown or black, or they may become almost wholly yellow or orange. The confusing repetition of the words mosaic, mottle, streak, ringspot, necrosis and yellows in common names of viruses is an unfortunate consequence of the frequency with which such leaf reactions are the predominant type of host reaction. Not only colour, but leaf form also often changes (Fig. 2–1). Size may be decreased or the shape changed, in some diseases only slightly, so that flat leaves become waved or puckered or the normal symmetry is somewhat modified, but in others drastically. In conditions described by such names as fern-leaf or shoe-string, the leaf laminae are so affected that what should normally be broad leaves consist of little more than the main veins and resemble tendrils rather than leaves. Leaves normally entire may become dentate, or, conversely, as in currant reversion, the indentations may be fewer than normal. Other effects common to several diseases are epinasty, the production of outgrowths (enations), often from the under surfaces of leaves, or for the leaf margins to roll upwards and inwards. Such rolling of the leaves is usually an external sign that they contain excessive amounts of carbohydrate. The occurrence of none of these symptoms can be taken as conclusive evidence that a plant is virus-infected, for similar leaf symptoms can have other causes. Most of the colour changes are at least simulated by lack of essential elements (deficiency diseases) or by toxins, or by infections with fungi or bacteria. Similarly, the leaf deformities caused by hormone weed-killers resemble those of some virus diseases, and leaf rolling can be caused by other conditions, such as damage to the bases of stems, that make carbohydrates accumulate excessively in leaves.

Of the many ways in which infection by viruses affects stems, probably the commonest is to shorten the internodes. When this happens uniformly and is not extreme, the habit of growth is not greatly changed and the end result is simply a shorter plant than usual. Often, though, the growth habit is affected, with the leaves bunched together to give a rosette instead of an open-type plant, and in grape-vines with fan-leaf disease whole internodes may be miss-

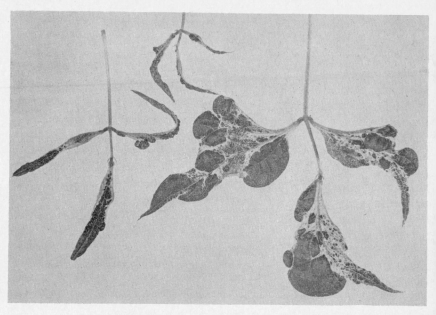

Fig. 2–1. Leaves of French bean (*Phaseolus vulgaris*) systemically infected with the cowpea strain of tobacco mosaic virus, showing mottling, deformity and blistering.

ing to produce the effect called double nodes (Hewitt and Gifford, 1956). The various changes in shape are exemplified by such names as fasciation of the vine, swollen shoot of cocoa, flat-limb of apples, and spindly sprout of potato, and the production of excessively many side shoots is characteristic of the various witches' broom diseases. The formation of tumours wherever stems are injured is a feature of plants infected with wound-tumour virus (Black, 1946), and loss of the usual spines from the stems of *Ceiba pentandra* is a novel sequel to infection by cocoa swollen shoot virus (Posnette, 1947). Mottling, ringspot and superficial necrotic streaks, resembling the effects of infection on leaves, are common symptoms in plants with green stems, and cankers or various changes in the character of the bark occur in some diseases of trees. Stems often die from their tops back (top-necrosis) when they become systemically infected by viruses that cause necrotic lesions in inoculated leaves. Potato tubers sometimes show superficial necrotic rings where they have been infected with tobacco necrosis viruses (Noordam, 1957), and internal rings and spots (spraing) when infected with tobacco rattle virus (Fig. 2–2); the production of many small tubers, sometimes

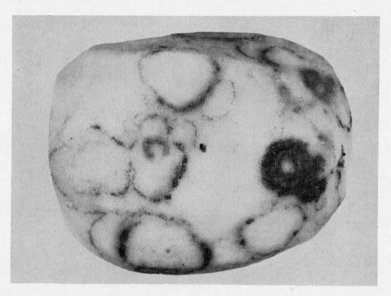

Fig. 2–2. Peeled potato tuber showing necrotic rings and patterns (spraing) caused by infection with tobacco rattle virus.

below and sometimes above ground, is a feature of potato witches' broom disease (Todd, 1958). Many of the effects of virus infections on stems, as with some on leaves, suggest disturbed hormone balance and that the usual apical dominance is destroyed.

Only few effects have been described on roots, whether because of the difficulty of seeing them, or because roots rarely show symptoms of infection, is unknown. That size of roots is decreased is evident from crops where the root is the economically important part of the crop, for example, yields of sugar beet are much decreased by infection with sugar beet yellows, and this is likely to be a general effect. The most striking root symptoms recorded are the tumours formed by various plants when infected with wound tumour virus (Black, 1946); these initiate in the pericycle wherever the roots are injured and then protrude through the cortex (Fig. 2–3). Root

Fig. 2–3. *Rumex acetosa* with wound tumour disease. Root system of old diseased plant showing many tumours of various sizes. (L. M. Black, Sixth Growth Symposium, 79, 1947).

swellings are also characteristic of tobacco clubroot (Valleau, 1947), tobacco necrosis viruses cause local necroses in roots (Bawden and Kassanis, 1946), and streaks of necrotic tissue are a feature of black root rot of snap beans (Jenkins, 1940, 1941). Death of the lateral roots is a common feature of many virus diseases of trees; in elms with phloem necrosis it seems to be a primary and direct effect of the virus (McClean, 1944), but with other diseases it is probably a secondary effect, a consequence either of the leaves failing to synthesise enough food to maintain all the roots or of the normal flow of food to the roots becoming interrupted. The death of sweet orange trees on sour orange stocks after infection with tristeza virus is a striking demonstration of an unusual interruption to the flow of food (Fawcett and Wallace, 1946). The trees apparently die from a foot rot without showing any of the leaf symptoms usually associated with virus infections, but the rot is a secondary effect, resulting from the inability of food to pass from the scion to the stock. The sweet orange is a symptomless carrier of the tristeza virus, whereas the sour orange is so intolerant that infected cells soon die, and with the movement of the virus from the sweet orange scion into the stock, the sour orange dies at the graft union, food no longer passes to the stock and the whole tree succumbs.

Two effects on flowers, variegation and phyllody, are characteristic enough of virus diseases to be diagnostically valuable. Variegation, or breaking, is best known in tulips; the self-coloured blooms characteristic of plants raised from seed become splashed or streaked with other colours after they become virus-infected. Propagating by bulbs perpetuates the variegated flowers, which used to be much admired and sought after, and virus-infected clones were often sold under different varietal names from the virus-free ones from which they derived. Only in tulip has the variegation of flowers been exploited commercially, but it happens in very many other species, as varied as chrysanthemum, carnation, gladiolus, wall-flower (Fig. 2–4), viola, and sweet pea. It is, indeed, almost a general effect of infection by viruses that cause leaf mottlings, and it has probably not been widely exploited because affected flowers of most species other than tulip are usually smaller than normal, less vividly coloured, deformed or fade and fall sooner than flowers from uninfected plants. Many flowers are, of course, variegated because of their genetic constitution, but when flowers show colour changes the fact should be taken as a strong hint that the plants have become virus-infected. Phyllody, or the change from a normal flower to leafy structures, is characteristic of infections by viruses that cause witches' broom diseases. The symptoms are well described by the names given to such conditions as false blossom of cranberry, green petal of strawberry, big bud and virescence of tomato. Any or all of the floral parts may be leaf-like and many flowers are sterile.

Fruits, too, show a wide variety of effects from infection with different viruses, ranging from a decrease in number or size, with no

Fig. 2–4. Breaking in wall-flower (*Cheiranthus cheiri*): left-hand plant showing variegated petals caused by infection with cabbage blackring virus; right-hand plant healthy.

other obvious abnormality, to changes in colour, shape, texture and flavour. Several viruses cause ringspots or mottles on tomato and cucumber fruits, and cucumbers are often mis-shaped and show wart-like out-growths. Cocoa pods from trees with swollen shoot are not only mottled, but are characteristically more nearly spherical than usual. Some effects on tree fruits are best indicated simply by listing the names given to them; star crack, chat fruit, rough skin and bitter pit of apples, little cherry, bitter cherry, plum pox, peach wart, stony pit of pear. Tomato fruits from plants infected with aspermy virus are often seed-less (Blencowe and Caldwell, 1949), and tobacco etch virus partially or wholly suppresses the spines that are normally such a feature of the thorn apple (*Datura stramonium*) (Blakeslee, 1921).

The sequence of symptoms. Viruses are economically important only in plants in which they cause systemic infection; that is to say, plants in which they can spread from an initial entry point, usually either in a leaf or root, through the main stem and into parts remote from it. Some spread extensively, and will invade almost every cell of tissues that are actively growing at the time the plant becomes infected; others, particularly those that cause necrotic lesions, are more restricted and, although they spread from their initial entry points, do not achieve a full systemic infection. Because systemic infection is the usual condition of virus-infected plants encountered in the open, it is widely considered to reflect a general ability of viruses in susceptible hosts, but whether it does is less certain. Experience with the tobacco necrosis viruses shows that they can infect very many species locally, but in very few do they become even partially systemic. Other viruses, too, may have much wider host ranges than now suspected, for they may multiply in directly inoculated cells but be unable to spread from these.

Viruses that become systemic commonly cause diseases with three phases. First, a lesion develops at the site of infection; secondly, systemic infection shows by symptoms developing on the young leaves around the stem apex, and thirdly the type of symptoms shown by systemically infected leaves often changes strikingly with increasing duration of infection. However, no general rule can be laid down, for there are great differences between the behaviour of different viruses in one species of plant and of one virus in different species of plants. The extent of these differences is perhaps best indicated by describing the behaviour of a few common viruses.

Tobacco mosaic virus often causes no clear local lesions in tobacco leaves, but may produce faint chlorotic spots. Systemic symptoms first show as a translucence around the veins of the young leaves (clearing of the veins), and then develop into an uneven pattern of various shades of green or yellow, often accompanied by some leaf deformity, and this syndrome is repeated in all the new leaves later produced. When plants are infected young, all their leaves that are fully formed at the time plants became infected may remain normal in appearance or they may become discoloured at their bases around the main veins. In tomato, events follow a simi-

lar sequence, except that inoculated leaves rarely show symptoms
and the first effects show often by a down curling of the young
leaves, to be followed by vein clearing and later by mottling and
perhaps leaf deformity. In striking contrast is the behaviour of
Nicotiana glutinosa, which gives only necrotic local lesions, the un
inoculated leaves remaining symptomless and virus-free. The lesion
develop in 2–3 days and slowly increase in size, some ultimately
reaching 0.5 cm in diameter (Fig. 2–5). Comparable necrotic loca
lesions are caused by many other viruses in some host or another and
they provide the basis for most assays of infectivity. As viruse
multiply only in living cells, their localisation in hosts that reac
necrotically has a plausible explanation, but death of infected cell
seems inadequate to explain whether or not a given virus become
systemic in a given host. Even tobacco mosaic virus in *Nicotiana
glutinosa* is not restricted to the first cells that collapse and die, for
neighbouring cells become infected and both the size and the viru
content of individual lesions continue to increase for some days. I
a host like *Datura stramonium*, tobacco mosaic virus causes necroti
local lesions, but nevertheless becomes systemic and kills the whol
plant. By contrast, it and tobacco necrosis viruses multiply only
in inoculated leaves of some hosts, though these leaves do not be
come necrotic and may remain symptomless. Also, in *Chenopodiun
amaranticolor*, several viruses produce white necrotic local lesion
of a very similar kind, but some become systemic and others do not

Potato virus Y produces a comparable range of reactions in differ
ent plants. In tobacco, the sequence of events resembles those
caused by tobacco mosaic virus, but with virus Y the same sequence
also occurs in *Nicotiana glutinosa;* inoculated leaves either show
nothing or faint chlorotic spots, and the first systemic symptom i
a clearing of the veins of the young leaves, which is succeeded by a
lasting syndrome of light green interveinal areas with the vein
banded by dark green lines. In potato plants, the effects differ
greatly in different varieties. In many, of which Majestic is typical
inoculated leaves show uniformly black necrotic lesions, but these
do not prevent systemic spread; the upper leaves become mottled
and crinkled with some necrotic spotting, and the older leaves de
velop necrotic streaks along the veins. Most of the leaves shrivel
and fall, leaving a largely bare main stem crowned by a few small
and crinkled leaves. This leaf-drop-streak is a syndrome of the first
year of infection only and plants grown from infected tubers show
few necrotic lesions, but are dwarfed, sprawl untidily, and the leaves
are small, mottled and crinkled. In other potato varieties, Arran
Victory for example, symptoms are much more similar in first and

Fig. 2–5. *Nicotiana glutinosa* leaves infected with the tobacco and bean forms of the cowpea strain of tobacco mosaic virus. *Left:* leaf from plant inoculated on left-hand half with the bean form, and right-hand half with tobacco form, and then kept at 20°; note much smaller lesions caused by the bean form. *Right:* leaf from plant inoculated with tobacco form on left-hand half, and bean form on right-hand half, and kept at 35°; the tobacco form at this temperature causes large chlorotic rings and the bean form multiplies without causing lesions.

subsequent years of infection; inoculated leaves show no local lesions, and systemic symptoms in the first year are a mottling and waving of the young leaves, whereas in later years these leaf symptoms are shown by all leaves and the plants lack vigour.

Similarly, potato virus X, perhaps the most prevalent of the many viruses of the potato, produces different diseases in different plants. In the potato varieties in which it is prevalent, it causes no local lesions and systemic symptoms are at most a faint mottle. In other varieties, it causes black necrotic local lesions, which may be the only symptoms or there may be systemic spread, when the young leaves develop black necrotic spots and shrivel, and the main stems also die back from their tops. Tubers set by systemically infected plants develop necrotic lesions and become fissured or may shrivel completely; most do not sprout and those that do usually produce only minute shoots, smothered with necrotic spots, which soon die. In tobacco and *Nicotiana glutinosa*, virus X gives local lesions, either white necrotic rings or chlorotic spots, and systemic symptoms either of the ringspot type or a bright interveinal mottle. The systemic symptoms usually become less severe as time passes.

Many diseases share the feature of being initially acute and then decreasing in severity, but it is especially characteristic of those with primary symptoms of the ringspot type. Tobacco ringspot virus in tobacco, for example, not only causes necrotic local lesions, but the initial systemic reaction is acute, for the leaves develop many necrotic lesions and become deformed and shrunken. The appearance of plants 2–3 weeks after inoculation suggests they would not survive, but new leaves are put out that show progressively fewer and less severe lesions, until a month or so later leaves are only faintly chlorotic or may show no obvious symptoms (Wingard, 1928). This change in reaction is accompanied by a fall in the virus content, and the leaves of "recovered" plants contain only one-fifth or so as much virus as do leaves showing necrotic lesions (Price, 1936); leaves initiated before a plant becomes infected with such viruses are apparently better fitted to provide a high population of virus than those initiated after infection. An initially severe disease, or "shock reaction" as it is often called, is common with tree infections, but with these it is unknown whether the decrease in symptoms as time passes also reflects a lower virus content.

Leaves that are fully grown when a plant becomes infected rarely show symptoms unless they are directly inoculated. Hence plants infected when half grown often show symptoms in their youngest leaves while the bottom parts look normal. Potato plants with leaf roll have strikingly different appearances in the first and subsequent years of infection. When growing plants become infected, their lower leaves remain normal, while the young leaves roll upwards and inwards, showing undersurfaces that are usually highly pigmented. By contrast, when plants come from infected tubers, rolling and pigmentation are most evident on the lowest leaves, and the main effects shown by the upper leaves are an interveinal pallor and a more erect habit than usual (Fig. 1–7).

These examples are enough to show the range of symptoms that can be caused by one virus and, consequently, the uncertainty there often is in diagnosing solely from the appearance of infected plants. One virus may kill one host, cause a lasting severe disease in a second, a mild disease in a third, and be harmless to a fourth. Also, in one host, the symptoms may change with time from acute ringspot to the apparently harmless condition of a symptomless carrier. There may be some viruses that have narrow host ranges and cause distinctive symptoms in all the plants they infect. However, most are not like this: they infect a wide range of species, cause many different kinds of symptoms and the symptoms they cause resemble those caused by other viruses. The names of many of these are merely historical accidents and serve as convenient tags, but as little else. Viruses such as tomato spotted wilt, cucumber mosaic, lucerne (alfalfa) mosaic and arabis mosaic, have host ranges extending to many plant families, and in some host or other they cause many other kinds of symptoms than the one for which they were named.

Differences between virus strains. In describing types of symptoms and the sequences of symptoms in the previous two sections, for simplicity viruses were treated as though they were single entities, which always produce the same result when they infect any given plant. This is very far from being true, for every virus that has been studied in any detail has been found to occur in a range of forms or strains that differ from one another in some property or other, and the differences most often reported are in virulence or host range. To describe a single disease as typical of infection by, say, tobacco mosaic virus is such an oversimplification as to be confusing rather than helpful in diagnosis. Any description of one syndrome can relate only to the effects of one strain of the named virus, and each virus must be expected to be made up of many strains that individually may cause very different symptoms in any given host.

The symptoms so far described as caused by tobacco mosaic virus in tobacco, *Nicotiana glutinosa* and tomato, are those caused by the type strain; some other strains behave similarly in these hosts, but still others behave very differently. Thus, in tobacco plants in which the type strain gives the systemic, mild mottling already described, some strains cause only necrotic local lesions, and some severe systemic diseases, with leaves greatly deformed, necrotic or bright yellow, whereas the masked strain produces few or no obvious effects. Except for strains that have cucurbitaceous plants as their prime hosts, all produce necrotic local lesions in N. *glutinosa,* but the type of the lesion, the time it takes to appear and its size, can all differ with different strains (Fig. 2–5). Similarly in tomato, some strains cause predominantly necrotic lesions (streak), others produce mottlings of different degrees of brightness, and still others have as their main effect the causing of leaf deformities, such as fern-leaf or enations. Nor do all strains behave alike in *Datura stramonium;* instead of the lethal systemic disease caused by the type strain, some strains produce only necrotic local lesions and still others become systemic without killing the whole plant.

Similarly the symptoms attributed in the preceding section to infection by potato viruses are not characteristic of all strains. Different strains of potato virus X, for example, cause in tobacco effects ranging from severe ringspot symptoms, through mottles of different intensities, to barely visible changes in leaf colour or vigour (Salaman, 1938). In one potato variety, say Majestic, some strains are carried symptomlessly, some cause faint mottles, some bright mottles, some crinkling with necrotic spots (Fig. 2–6), and some the systemically lethal disease, top-necrosis. Such differences in behaviour are often indicated by saying that one strain is more virulent than another, with the words virulent and avirulent being applied as though they reflected intrinsic and fixed properties of the individual virus strains. This is rarely justified. Virulence reflects the interaction between host and pathogen and should be attributed to a pathogen only in reference to a specified host. One virus strain may cause a severe disease in one host and be harmless in a second; whether the first host is regarded as more intolerant than the second, or the virus strain is regarded as more virulent towards it, is a matter of convenient terminology rather than making any true distinction. Strains of virus X will serve to illustrate the point. By their behaviour in tobacco, they can be graded in order of increasing virulence, but this order will not necessarily be repeated by their behaviour in potato plants. Of two strains that produce diseases of different severities in tobacco, the more virulent towards tobacco may also be the more virulent towards potato, but almost equally likely it will not be. One strain that causes slight effects in tobacco may be lethal in potato, whereas one that is virulent towards tobacco may cause only a mosaic disease in potato. However, to describe the effects of a strain of virus X in potato plants is meaningless without specifying the potato variety, because a strain can be virulent towards one variety and avirulent towards another. For example, one strain that is carried by the variety Majestic kills President, and there are others that reverse this behaviour.

Fig. 2–6. Comparable leaves from two shoots of one potato plant showing segregation of strains of potato virus X. Most of the plant showed only mild symptoms and contained an avirulent strain (left-hand leaf), but one shoot showed a severe mosaic with much necrosis and contained a virulent strain.

Strains of potato virus Y show the same kind of difference in behaviour. Although most strains produce the mosaic symptoms in tobacco already described, one is much more virulent, as implied by its name, tobacco veinal necrosis (Smith and Dennis, 1940; Nobrega and Silberschmidt, 1944). However, in most potato varieties this strain causes a much less severe disease than do many of the strains that cause only mosaic symptoms in tobacco. Behaviour in tobacco is no guide to behaviour in potato, and of strains that cause similar mosaic symptoms in tobacco, some cause only a faint mottling in the potato variety Majestic, others leaf-drop-streak diseases of different degrees of severity, and others top-necrosis. As a contrast, none causes necrotic lesions in the variety Arran Victory, in which different strains differ mainly in producing mottling and crinkling of different severities.

Enough has been said to show that two strains may be indistinguishable in one host, but produce strikingly different diseases in another. Also, it will be evident that diseases caused by different viruses may resemble one another more closely than diseases caused by different strains of one virus. The range of symptoms caused in potato varieties by potato virus X overlaps that caused by virus Y. In the variety Majestic, the necrotic streaks along the veins and the leaf fall are characteristic enough to diagnose infection with a strain of virus Y, but mottlings or top-necrosis may be caused by strains of this virus or of virus X, or by other viruses unrelated to either.

The range of symptoms caused by different strains of tobacco mosaic and of potato viruses X and Y indicate well enough the very different diseases that can be caused in one host by different strains of one virus. It is worth stressing that these three viruses are not exceptional. They have simply been used to illustrate what must be expected with every virus; namely that it will exist in clinically different strains and that in some plant or other some strain will cause a disease very like that caused by some quite unrelated virus. For some time, tomato bushy stunt virus seemed exceptional, in as much as it had been studied intensively and no clinically distinct strains described, but even this one has now come into line with the demonstration that not all single-lesion isolates give the same symptoms in *Datura stramonium* and tomato (Steere, 1953).

With the overwhelming evidence for the variability in viruses, it is odd that so many workers should persist with the idea of a virus as something that always produces the same effects. The idea presumably derives from work with one original isolate, studied and propagated in a limited range of hosts and in relatively constant environments. In such conditions, constancy and reproducibility of results are to be expected, but the expectation should not extend to other isolates, propagated in other hosts or in other environments. The literature on virus diseases contains many detailed descriptions of symptoms, often first accounts of viruses thought to be "new," in which differences from previously described syndromes are stressed as evidence of newness. How valueless such accounts can be is strikingly obvious from the number of times strains of such viruses as tobacco mosaic, cucumber mosaic, potato X and Y, lucerne (alfalfa) mosaic, and arabis mosaic have been described as "new" viruses. Nevertheless, many virus workers are reluctant to appreciate that variability, especially in symptomatology and host range, is normal ather than exceptional, and they continue to describe with a wealth of picturesque detail clinical conditions that may never again be precisely reproduced.

The environment and symptoms. Even when the particular strain of a virus and the variety of the host plant are both specified, categorical statements about symptoms still cannot be made safely unless the environment is also defined. Whether a given plant can be a host for a given strain of a virus, and whether infection can lead to symptoms or not, is presumably primarily determined by the genetic constitution of both the plant and the virus strain. However, within this over-riding limitation, phenotypic changes can have enormous effects, for the ability of a virus to infect, multiply in and affect the normal working of a potential host plant, depends greatly on the physiological condition of the plant. Indeed, many of the apparent contradictions in the literature on virus diseases originate in this fact. The physiology of plants responds rapidly and strikingly to changes in the environment and cultural conditions, so any environmental change may affect host physiology in a way that influences virus multiplication or the response to infection. This responsiveness is a troublesome complication when reproducible results are sought, but it provides excellent opportunities to study the factors that affect the course of infection and symptom development, opportunities that as yet have been barely exploited.

In latitudes where there are large climatic differences between the seasons, it is necessary only to infect plants through the year to see how greatly growing conditions affect their reactions. It is also obvious that seasonal changes affect different virus diseases differently; some, particularly the yellows types like sugar beet yellows and potato leaf roll, have much more obvious symptoms during summer than during winter, whereas many of the viruses that mostly cause mosaic or ringspot symptoms, such as potato X, tobacco necrosis, tobacco etch and tomato bushy stunt, cause much more severe reactions in winter than in summer. An extreme example of seasonal behaviour is provided by *Phaseolus vulgaris*, vars. Prince and Bountiful, when inoculated with cucumber mosaic virus; during the summer the beans are apparently immune, whereas during winter they produce black local lesions in numbers adequate for quantitative assays (Bhargava, 1951). However, other viruses are only slightly less affected; in summer, tomato bushy stunt virus often produces only a few local lesions in tomato plants, whereas in winter it rapidly becomes systemic and causes a crippling disease; similarly, it is common in winter for tobacco seedlings to become naturally infected with tobacco necrosis viruses, but rare in summer (Smith and Bald, 1935), and inocula that when rubbed over leaves during winter produce hundreds of lesions and kill rubbed leaves, in summer-grown plants produce only a few isolated lesions. The main factor determining these different reactions seems to be light intensity, because most of the winter-type reactions can be produced during summer in plants raised in appropriate shade (Bawden and Roberts, 1947), but temperature is also important.

Seasonal differences in the appearance of plants infected with sugar beet yellows or potato leaf roll viruses are also primarily determined by the light intensity, and giving extra illumination during winter intensifies the symptoms they show. So also does spraying infected beet leaves with solutions of sugar (Watson, 1955), and with these diseased plants, in which carbohydrate accumulates in leaves, it is reasonable to conclude that light intensity affects symptom expression because of its direct influence on the amount of carbohydrate photosynthesised. The fact that tomato plants survive infection by beet curly top virus when shaded but succumb in full light (Shapavalov and Lesley, 1931) may also be explained in the same way, but there is no such easy explanation for low light intensities suppressing the usual bright mottles caused by *Abutilon* mosaic (Baur, 1906), and by two strains of tobacco mosaic virus, tomato aucuba (Ainsworth, 1935) and cucumber 4 (Knight, 1941). The two last do not cause carbohydrate to accumulate, but decrease the normal carbon/nitrogen ratio, yet, in contrast to the other viruses already mentioned that cause mosaic symptoms, they cause less intense symptoms during winter than during summer. Infected plants that show only faint mottlings in winter develop bright yellow lesions when given artificial light for a few days. The explanation is unknown, but the extra light could work either by increasing the extent to which the strains multiply or perhaps affect the chlorophyll formation in a way that increases the extent to which it is affected by infection. Light intensity can affect the reaction of other organs than leaves; for instance, shading branches of cherry trees infected with the little cherry virus allows them to produce a crop of normal fruit (Welsh and Wilks, 1951).

The large effects on symptom expression that have been ascribed to changes in light intensity have mostly come from work at ambient temperatures of about 18°, either by work in glasshouses during winter or by shading plants in the open during summer. In the open, temperature and light intensity usually fluctuate together, and which variable is responsible for any effects noted on symptoms is less certain. However, temperature is likely most often to be the more important, because it rather than light intensity will usually be the factor limiting plant growth.

Like all biological processes, virus multiplication and movement are temperature-dependent, and are speeded by increases of temperature up to an optimum. Hence the most general effect of increasing temperature is to shorten the interval between infection and the production of lesions, both local and systemic. Changes in temperature can also affect the severity and type of symptoms, and may determine whether infection becomes systemic or not, but effects differ greatly with different viruses and, even with one virus, with different strains and different hosts. Symptoms of many diseases are most severe within a narrow range of temperature. The decrease in severity at temperatures above the optimum has, where studied, been usually found to be correlated with a decreased virus content. For example, increases in temperature from 16 to 28° increase the severity of symptoms shown by cabbage plants infected with cabbage black ring virus, which reaches its highest concentration at 28°, whereas they decrease those shown by plants infected with cauliflower mosaic virus, which achieves its highest concentration at the lower temperature, and above 24° plants show slight symptoms (Pound and Walker, 1945, 1945a). In contrast to the behaviour of cabbage, *Nicotiana glutinosa* reacts more severely when infected with cabbage black ring virus at 16–20° than at higher temperatures. The effect of temperature on virus concentration, therefore, seems not to be one on rate of virus multiplication alone, but to be more complex, possibly reflecting a balance between rate at which the virus multiplies and is inactivated by host mechanisms, which differ either quantitatively or qualitatively in different hosts. Different strains of cabbage black ring virus produce most severe symptoms at different temperatures, and one that is more virulent than another towards cabbage at 28° is less virulent at 20°. Similarly, some strains that can readily be differentiated by the diseases of different severities they cause in *Nicotiana glutinosa* at the higher temperatures cause very similar symptoms at 16–20°. Presumably the different strains either multiply optimally at different temperatures or differ in their susceptibility to inactivators in the host cells.

The behaviour of tobacco mosaic virus, especially in *N. glutinosa*, also depends on the temperature at which infected plants are growing. At temperatures below about 30°, the type strain produces only necrotic local lesions, but the speed with which these develop and the size they reach is increased by raising the temperature. At higher temperatures, the type of reaction changes, the local lesions are chlorotic instead of necrotic, and the plants become systemically infected and show mosaic symptoms (Samuel, 1931). When infected plants that have been at 35° for some days are placed at 20°, the virus content of the leaves increases rapidly and greatly, and the previously chlorotic areas die and collapse (Kassanis, 1952). A strain obtained from systemically infected leguminous plants also gives necrotic lesions at temperatures around 20°, although these are smaller, take longer to appear and are less well defined than those caused by the type strain, but at temperatures above 30° this one multiplies without causing any lesions, chlorotic or necrotic (Fig. 2–5). At the high temperature, like the type strain, it invades more cells than at 20°, and when plants that have been at 35° for some days are placed at 20°, the invaded areas quickly succumb (Bawden, 1958).

Tobacco plants with mosaic show similar symptoms over a wide temperature range, but when kept for long at over about 25° the symptoms often decrease in severity. This is not because their virus content has fallen, which is what happens with many other virus diseases that become less severe when the temperature is raised, but because the high temperature selects strains that are better able than the type one to multiply at high temperatures, many of which are less virulent towards tobacco (Holmes, 1934; Kassanis, 1957). The symptoms of some potato diseases, such as mosaic caused by virus X and crinkle caused by viruses A and X acting together, decrease with increasing temperature and above 20° may become so slight that the infected plants seem almost normal. An exception to this phenomenon, often called "heat-masking," is potato yellow dwarf: below 16°, infected plants look normal, but the typical symptoms soon develop when the temperature is raised; tubers that grow normally at low soil temperatures may fail to produce sprouts at high temperatures (Walker and Larson, 1939).

The growth of plants is so profoundly affected by soil conditions that these almost certainly affect the symptoms of many virus diseases, but these variables have been less studied than light intensity and temperature. The seasonal incidence of symptoms in strawberry plants with yellow edge seem to depend on both plenty of soil moisture and an air temperature above 16°, so that in Britain infected plants are most obvious in spring and autumn (King and Harris, 1942). Also excess water enhances both the prevalence and severity of mosaic in tomato crops, whereas symptoms are lessened by drought and by either a deficiency or an abundance of nitrogen (Selman, 1947). Perhaps the most general statement that can be made is that, the better the conditions are for the growth of a plant, the sooner symptoms will appear and the more characteristic they

ιill be, though no doubt there are many exceptions to this generali-
ation and plants are usually more crippled by infection when their
ιutrition is defective than when they are supplied with abundant
ιutrients.

Any account of symptoms caused by viruses would be incom-
ɔlete without mentioning the ways in which infection by one may
nfluence those caused by another. There are two main effects, de-
ɔending primarily on whether the two viruses are related or not.

Fig. 2–7. Tomato streak caused by simultaneous infection with tobacco
mosaic virus and potato virus X. Left-hand plant infected with an avirulent
strain of virus X and right-hand one with the mosaic virus; centre plant infected
with both. Photographs taken 14 days after infection.

First, a plant that is already systemically infected with one strain of
a virus that causes slight symptoms usually develops no further
symptoms when inoculated with a second, more virulent strain. For
example, tobacco plants infected with the type strain of tobacco
mosaic virus fail to produce necrotic local lesions when inoculated
with tomato aucuba mosaic virus, and tobacco plants showing the
mild mottling characteristic of infection by avirulent strains of
potato virus X continue unchanged after inoculation with strains that
alone cause ringspot diseases. Similarly, the symptoms shown by a
plant infected simultaneously with two strains that differ in virulence
towards it, are usually intermediate between those that would be
caused by either strain alone. In striking contrast to this phenomenon is the second one, in which simultaneous infection by two unrelated viruses gives a more severe disease, and perhaps one of a

different type, than either virus causes alone. Typical examples are
streak in tomato, caused by the combined action of strains of potatc
virus X and tobacco mosaic virus, which alone cause only mild
mosaic symptoms (Fig. 2–7), and the severe necrotic disease ir
tobacco, caused by the combined action of potato viruses X and Y
Again, virus concentration seems to be concerned, for tobacco plant;
infected with the two potato viruses contain more virus X than dc
plants infected with virus X alone (Rochow and Ross, 1955). Infection with a second virus sometimes restores severe symptoms tc
plants that have been through and recovered from an initially severe
disease. For example, tobacco plants that look normal after recover-
ing from the initial effects of infection with dodder latent virus, have
their symptoms restored as a result of infection with tobacco mosaic
virus; the concentration of dodder latent virus remains large anc
symptoms are maintained indefinitely by plants containing botl
viruses (Bennett, 1949).

The differences in severity of symptoms occasioned by changing
the environment seem, more often than not, to be correlated witl
the amount of virus in the plants. There is, though, no such genera
correlation between severity of host reaction and virus concentration; many viruses that reach only a small fraction the amount of
tobacco mosaic virus nevertheless cause much more severe disease:
in tobacco; similarly, because one strain of a virus is more virulen'
than another towards a given host does not necessarily mean that i'
occurs in greater amounts, and a host that reacts severely to a viru:
strain does not necessarily contain more virus than one that react:
moderately. Although we are woefully ignorant about the direc'
causes of symptoms, it is at least clear that symptoms reflect reaction:
between specific activities of both host and virus strain, activitie:
that, although primarily determined by the genetical constitutior
of both, are also affected in many different ways by phenotypic
changes.

REFERENCES

AINSWORTH, G. C. 1935. Ann. appl. Biol. 22: 55.
BAUR, E. 1906. S. B. preuss. Akad. Wiss. 1: 11.
BAWDEN, F. C. 1958. J. gen. Microbiol. 18: 751.
———, and B. KASSANIS. 1946. Ann. appl. Biol. 33: 46.
———, and F. M. L. ROBERTS. 1947. Ann. appl. Biol. 34: 286.
BENNETT, C. W. 1949. Phytopathology 39: 637.
BHARGAVA, K. S. 1951. Ann. appl. Biol. 38: 377.
BLACK, L. M. 1946. Nature, Lond. 158: 56.
BLAKESLEE, A. F. 1921. J. Genet. 11: 17.
BLENCOWE, J. W., and J. CALDWELL. 1949. Ann. appl. Biol. 36: 320.
FAWCETT, H. S., and S. M. WALLACE. 1946. Calif. Citrogr. 32: 50.
HEWITT, W. B., and E. M. GIFFORD. 1956. Bull. Dep. Agric. Calif. 45: 249.

HOLMES, F. O. 1934. Phytopathology 24: 845.
JENKINS, W. A. 1940. J. agric. Res. 60: 279.
———. 1941. *Ibid.* 62: 683.
KASSANIS, B. 1952. Ann. appl. Biol. 39: 358.
———. 1957. Virology 4: 187.
KING, M. E., and R. V. HARRIS. 1942. J. Pomol. 19: 212.
KNIGHT, C. A. 1941. Arch. ges. Virusforsch. 2: 26.
McCLEAN, D. M. 1944. Phytopathology 34: 818.
NOBREGA, N. R., and K. SILBERSCHMIDT. 1944. Arch. Inst. biol. (Def. agric. anim.)
    S. Paulo 15: 307.
NOORDAM, D. 1957. Tijdschr. PlZiekt. 63: 237.
POSNETTE, A. F. 1947. Ann. appl. Biol. 34: 388.
POUND, G. S., and J. C. WALKER. 1945. J. agric. Res. 71: 255.
———, and ———. 1945a. *Ibid.* 71: 471.
PRICE, W. C. 1936. Phytopathology 26: 503.
ROCHOW, W. F., and A. F. ROSS. 1955. Virology 1: 10.
SALAMAN, R. N. 1938. Phil. Trans. *B* 229: 137.
SAMUEL, G. 1931. Ann. appl. Biol. 18: 494.
SELMAN, I. W. 1947. J. Pomol. 23: 50.
SHAPAVALOV, M., and J. W. LESLEY. 1931. Phytopathology 21: 83.
SMITH, K. M. 1957. Textbook of Plant Virus Diseases. Churchill, London.
———, and J. G. BALD. 1935. Parasitology 27: 231.
———, and R. G. W. DENNIS. 1940. Ann. appl. Biol. 27: 65.
STEERE, R. L. 1953. Phytopathology 43: 485.
TODD, J. M. 1958. Proc. Sci. Conf. Stolbur and similar diseases causing sterility,
    1956, Bratislava, 77.
VALLEAU, W. D. 1947. Phytopathology 37: 580.
WALKER, J. C., and R. H. LARSON. 1939. J. agric. Res. 59: 259.
WATSON, M. A. 1955. Ann. appl. Biol. 43: 686.
WELSH, F. M., and J. M. WILKS. 1951. Phytopathology 41: 136.
WINGARD, S. A. 1928. J. agric. Res. 37: 127.

Symptomatology: Changes Within Infected Plants

The many and varied changes produced within plants by viruse
divide into two main kinds; one is the production, usually in th
cytoplasm but sometimes in the nucleus, of microscopically visibl
bodies that differ from any that occur in uninfected cells, and th
other is the destruction or modification of normal cells or cell con
tents. The first is the more specific, sufficiently so for the inclusio
bodies to have diagnostic value, for whereas they accompany man
different virus diseases of both plants and animals, nothing like ther
has been reported to accompany other types of infectious disease
It is always worth examining sections of, or epidermal stripping
from, leaves of plants suspected to be virus-infected, because findin
inclusion bodies is almost conclusive confirmation. Unfortunately
failure to find them has no significance, because they are not in
variably present in infected plants; some viruses produce them i
some hosts but not in others, and in hosts where they usually occu
they do not always persist for as long as the infected plants show
external symptoms. Also, the inclusions formed by different viruse
differ considerably from one another in size and in the ease wit
which they can be clearly distinguished from normal cell con
ponents, so that some kinds are readily seen whereas others can mon
easily be overlooked.

The composition and significance of the inclusion bodies were for ong uncertain and subjects of dispute and controversy, mainly be-ween those who considered them to represent stages in the life his-ory of pathogenic organisms and those who considered them to be imply host material changed by infection. Like many other con-roversies, this one has now been resolved and most workers are greed that the inclusion bodies found in virus-infected plants and nimals consist largely of virus particles which have come together 1 numbers large enough to produce bodies resolvable by light microscopes.

Intracellular inclusions formed by tobacco mosaic virus. Intra-ellular inclusions in plants were first reported in tobacco with nosaic and the inclusions formed by tobacco mosaic virus have been nore studied than any others. As early as 1903, Iwanowski described wo kinds, one an amoeboid-like entity and the other a crystalline late (Figs. 1–1 and 1–2). His observations were often confirmed, ut interest for long centred almost exclusively on the amoeboid inds, because these had superficial similarities to some organisms, whereas the crystals, although recognised as specific to infected lants, were largely neglected because then current ideas about vi-uses did not extend to the possibility that crystalline material could e etiologically significant. Goldstein (1924, 1926), who described oth kinds of inclusion in detail, reflected the general opinion of hat time when she concluded that the crystals were host reac-ion products and aptly summarised the conflicting ideas about the moeboid-like inclusions by naming them X-bodies.

Relating the virus directly to the crystals had to wait on knowl-dge about the behaviour of the virus itself. Iwanowski (1903) nd Goldstein (1924) observed that the crystals developed striations nd changed into masses of needle-shaped particles when acidified, phenomenon responsible for the crystals sometimes being referred o as "striate material," but the significance of this was apparent only when Beale (1937) showed that, in appearance and pH stability ange, these needles closely resembled those produced by acidifying urified virus preparations (Fig. 3–1). Confirmation that the crys-als consist largely of virus and a volatile solvent, presumably water, ame from electron microscopy combined with an elegant technique or removing crystals intact from cells. This is impossible from ormal cells, because disturbing them by pricking or cutting disrupts he crystals, but by freeze-drying hair cells Steere and Williams 1953) were able to dissect out individual dry crystals from the dry ells and show both that they are infective and contain little, if anything, other than virus particles. The crystals partially dissolve when moistened, yielding many of the characteristic rod-shape particles and nothing else resolvable by the electron microscop (Fig. 3–2).

The inclusions, both X-bodies and crystals, are usually mos abundant in the epidermal and hair cells and they are convenientl examined in living preparations made by stripping the epiderm from leaves or stems. The X-bodies resemble compact masses c

Fig. 3–1. Epidermal cells from Turkish tobacco plant infected with tobacco mosaic virus after treatment with dilute HCl. The crystalline plates previously present have been replaced with numbers of para-crystalline needles. × 660. (H. P. Beale, 1937, Contrib. Boyce Thompson Institute 8: 413).

cytoplasm, and are usually round or oval, but their shape can chang as they come into contact with the cell wall or nucleus during thei movement round the cell in the streaming cytoplasm. They are pai tially translucent and granular, usually have one or more clearl visible vacuoles and they sometimes contain oil globules and mitc chondria. In large cells they may reach a diameter of 30 μ, wherea in small cells they may be no more than 5 μ.

The X-bodies formed by different strains of the virus, or by on strain in different hosts, differ slightly in appearance, but all stain i the same way, break down when pricked with micro-needles an and unaffected by weak acid (Sheffield, 1931; 1934; Livingsto and Duggar, 1934). Those produced by tomato aucuba mosaic viru in *Solanum nodiflorum* are more sharply differentiated from th host cytoplasm than most others and their method of formation i

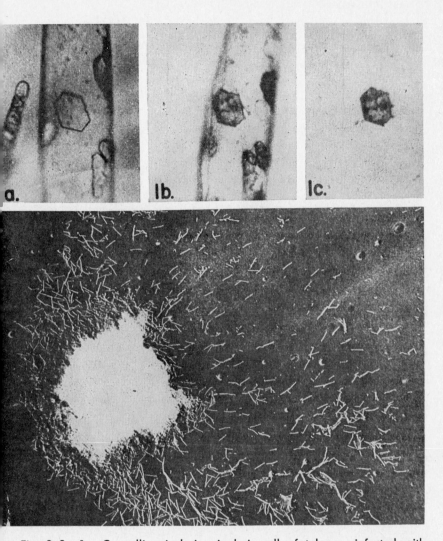

Fig. 3–2. *1a.* Crystalline inclusion in hair cell of tobacco infected with tobacco mosaic virus. *1b.* The same cell after freeze-drying. *1c.* The dried crystal removed from the cell. Bottom: Electron micrograph of partially dissolved crystal, showing opaque undissolved part and many dispersed particles of the virus. (R. L. Steere and R. C. Williams, 1953, Amer. J. Bot. 40: 81).

more readily observed. Sheffield (1931) made a cinema film whic]
showed that infection in cells of the host first makes the cytoplasn
stream faster and then leads to the cytoplasm developing an increas
ing number of small granules. The granules are carried passivel

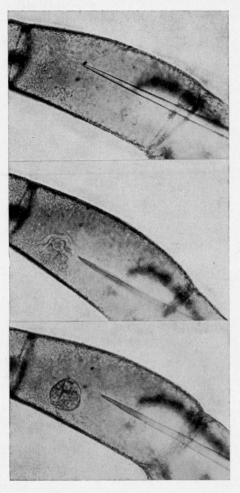

Fig. 3–3. Cell from hair (
Solanum nodiflorum infected wi'
aucuba mosaic virus. *Bottom:*
needle has been inserted throug
the transverse septum into the ce
leaving the inclusion body ui
affected. *Centre:* this photograp
was taken 15 seconds after tk
body was punctured by the needk
The body is rapidly changing i
consistency, forming a mass of cle(
bubbles in which a few granul(
are visible. *Top:* photographed 1
minutes later. The inclusion h(
almost disappeared, only a fe
scattered granules being visibk
× 300. (F. M. L. Sheffield, 193'
Proc. Roy Soc. B. 126: 529).

around the cell and fuse when they meet, a process that continue
until all are contained in one, or sometimes two, granular masse
which become rounded and vacuolate. The mature X-body is ofte
in contact with the nucleus, but this is accidental, a consequence c
the tendency circulating particles have to accumulate at the junctio
of cytoplasmic strands, several of which usually converge on th
nucleus. The association had led to the suggestion that the X-bod
was produced from the nucleus, but this is not so and Sheffield

bservations also explained other claims that the X-body was an
rganism, with autonomous movement, that grew, put out pseudo-
odia and divided by fission. The X-body moves no more than other
ell components, the fusion of a small aggregate of granules with a
arger one can simulate the appearance of a pseudopodium, and the
oming together or separation of two aggregates of similar size simu-
ates the appearance of binary fission.

The X-bodies are more stable than the crystals, withstand acid
nd are preserved by customary fixation methods. When stained,
hey give the usual colour reactions for protein, but they are un-
ffected by Feulgen's reagent, a test for deoxy nucleic acid, and so
an be sharply differentiated from the nuclei, which turn deep red.
he X-bodies are not destroyed by pricking or cutting cells that
ontain them, but they disintegrate when they are punctured with
 micro-needle, or when pressure is applied to the cells, giving rise
 granules resembling those that originally fuse to produce the
ature inclusion body and these soon disperse through the cell
Fig. 3–3). The X-bodies can be removed intact from fresh cells
nd kept intact in 0.1 M salt solutions, but at salt concentrations
elow 0.07 M they are soon dispersed. Sheffield extracted X-bodies
om *Solanum nodiflorum* infected with tomato aucuba mosaic
irus, washed them thoroughly in buffer solution, dissolved them
nd found that the preparations were about as infective as solutions
ontaining the same weight of purified virus as the computed weight
f the X-bodies. Later examinations of such preparations by elec-
on microscopy showed that they contained many of the character-
tic virus rods, but also other material of unknown composition
Sheffield, 1946). The development of techniques for cutting sec-
ons thin enough to be examined by electron microscopy has been
uch more exploited in studying inclusions in animal cells than in
lant cells, perhaps because plant tissues are more difficult to fix
nd cut, but it has been used enough to show that the bodies consist
rgely of virus particles (Black, Morgan and Wyckoff, 1950; Nixon
nd Sampson, 1954). Some pictures suggest that the body has a well
efined membrane, which contains fibrous masses of virus particles,
sually aligned parallelly. Whether the alignment is produced by
he methods of fixation or is a part of the original structure is uncer-
ain, but that particles can become regularly orientated in X-bodies
 still living cells is shown by the fact that, as the inclusions age,
mall birefringent crytsals often appear within them (Fig. 3–4)
Kassanis and Sheffield, 1941).

Not all the inclusions formed by strains of tobacco mosaic virus
all neatly into the characteristic X-bodies and flat crystalline plates,

and the kind most common differs at different times even with th«
same host and virus strain. At Rothamsted, for example, in 193«
and 1931 Henderson Smith and Sheffield found that tomato aucub;
mosaic virus produced many X-bodies and that crystals were usuall
produced only from disintegrating X-bodies; at that period they als«
often saw crystal-like spikes, some as long as the cell containin;
them. Between 1932 and 1940, they found no spikes and relativel
few X-bodies, but crystalline plates were abundant and were pro

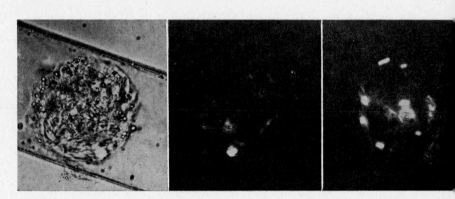

Fig. 3–4. A large X-body in hair cell of tomato infected with aucuba mosai
virus, showing the development of crystalline material. *Left:* photographed i
transmitted light shows a few crystals embedded in the body. *Centre:* photc
graphed in polarised light showing the presence of a little birefringent materia«
Right: photographed 30 hours later showing the presence of more birefringer
material. (B. Kassanis and F. M. L. Sheffield, 1941, Ann. appl. Biol. 28: 360.

duced as such and not indirectly from X-bodies. In 1940, the crys
tal-like spikes were again plentiful, and were accompanied by othe
forms not previously seen, birefringent spindle-shaped bodies, masse
of short fibres, and fibres many times as long as the cells so that the
were often curved into figures-of-eight (Fig. 3–5) (Kassanis an«
Sheffield, 1941). These changes seemed not to be related to change
in a virus strain, because at any one time several strains often pro
duced similar fibrous inclusions simultaneously. The environmen
of the growing plants affects their external symptoms, their composi
tion and the extent to which the virus multiplies, so the explanatio;
for the different types of inclusion body at different times also mos
likely lies in effects of the environment on host-plant metabolism
but there is little to be gained from speculating on this theme unti
the correlation between the types of inclusion formed and the grow
ing conditions of the host has been studied in greater detail.

Cytological work now seems to have become unfashionable, which is to be regretted for such a study might be rewarding, not simply to establish this correlation, but to provide a better explanation than can now be given for the production of inclusion bodies. It is abundantly evident that they consist largely of virus particles, but what remains unexplained is the mechanism responsible for the virus aggregating and separating out in solid or semi-solid states. From the behaviour of purified tobacco mosaic virus, it is easy to

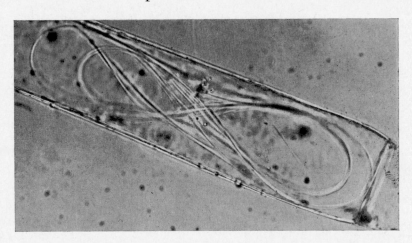

Fig. 3–5. A hair cell from tomato plant infected with aucuba mosaic virus containing long, fibrous inclusion bodies curved to form figures of 8. × 500. (B. Kassanis and F. M. L. Sheffield, 1941, Ann. appl. Biol. 28: 360).

explain the production of paracrystalline precipitates, the needles and fibres, because precipitates of this kind are readily produced *in vitro*, not only by treating virus preparations with acid or strong salt solutions, but by such varied substances as nicotine, protamines, histones, pancreatic ribonuclease and other proteins (Bawden and Sheffield, 1939). Hence there is no lack of substances in plant cells with which the virus might combine and be precipitated, and that such substances do occur is suggested by the paracrystalline fibres that settle out of infective plant sap left undisturbed (Best, 1940, 1947). Also, the fact that the inclusions often form and then disappear can be explained by postulating changes in the cells that alter the ratio of virus to substance with which it is combined, or the pH or the salt content, for *in vitro* some substances give precipitates only when they and the virus are combined in definite proportions and then only in limited pH ranges and salt concentrations (Kassanis and Kleczkowski, 1948). However, only a detailed cyto-chemical examination of cells with different kinds of inclusions is likely to show whether these plausible explanations are correct and to show what substances, if any, are acting as virus precipitants.

Possibly there are no precipitants concerned in producing the crystalline inclusions and for these there may be no need to postulate anything more than the usual forces that lead to crystal growth However, there is a striking contrast between the behaviour of the virus *in vivo* and *in vitro*. All solid precipitates of tobacco mosaic virus produced *in vitro* are paracrystalline, that is, they are regular in two dimensions only, with the rod-shaped particles arranged parallel to one another in the direction of their length but no regular arrangement along their length (Bernal and Fankuchen, 1937). In striking contrast, many inclusions are unquestionably true crystals with a full three-dimensional regularity; they have side and end faces and some are almost perfect hexagons, birefringent when viewed edge-ways but not when viewed flat. They probably contain about 60% water and seem to be built up from successive layers of virus particles, each layer as thick as the length of the virus particles and composed of particles aligned parallel to one another, but with an orientation not quite parallel to that in adjacent layers (Wilkins, Seeds, Stokes and Oster, 1950). Electron micrographs of virus in dried sap have sometimes been obtained at Rothamsted showing aggregates of virus particles side by side with their ends in straight lines at right angles to the length of the particles, suggesting these may be fragments of one layer from a crystal. Therefore, the crystals seem to contain particles of a uniform length able to pack into a true crystal lattice; whether this means that such particles are preferentially selected by the process of crystallisation, or whether all particles in the plant are of this length and the irregularity in length of particle characteristic of purified virus preparations is produced by the processes of purification, is uncertain. Bald and Solberg (1961) describe in recently infected cells material distinguishable by appropriate phase-contrast equipment, which they report as first associated with the nucleus. It first forms what they call grey plates, which they conclude are single or double layers of orientated virus particles, and these later aggregate to give the crystalline inclusions.

What makes the virus settle out in the form of X-bodies is also unknown. The virus combines with and is precipitated *in vitro* by many proteins and other materials that are oppositely charged to it; most of these produce paracrystalline precipitates, of which the virus is by far the greater component, but globin is an exception and produces an amorphous precipitate that is one-quarter globin (Kleczkowski, 1946). Tobacco mosaic virus also gives amorphous precipitates when it combines *in vitro* with antibodies produced in animals injected with it, and in such precipitates the ratio of antibody to virus can be very small. It is possible that living cells regularly contain, or produce when infected, proteins or other materials that are similarly able to combine with and precipitate the virus in other than paracrystalline forms, but if there are such, they await identification. Whether the formation of X-bodies or other inclusions is in any sense a defence mechanism of the host is similarly a matter of conjecture, but it is obvious that rendering the virus insoluble and localising it might lessen its pathogenic effects.

Inclusion bodies have been seen in roots, stems, leaves and flowers of infected plants, and in most tissues of these organs except the phloem sieve elements (Esau, 1941; Zech, 1952). They are perhaps most common in the epidermal cells of leaves and stems, but they are not always present in every infected cell and one part of a leaf may have them in almost every cell while a nearby part has none. In systemically infected leaves, they begin to form at about the same time as symptoms first show and reach their maximum number in about a month, when the X-bodies often disappear though the crystals may remain for much longer. X-bodies and crystals have been reported to form in uninoculated cells of large leaf hairs within 3 to 6 days of another cell in the hair being inoculated (Zech, 1952). Most descriptions refer to inclusions in systemically infected tissues, but they can also occur in local lesions (Milicic, 1962). Statements about the correlation between the external symptoms of leaves and the distribution of inclusions are conflicting, for whereas some workers have reported finding them only in chlorotic areas, others have found them in the intervening green areas. The distribution of inclusions may differ with different strains or depend on the extent of virus multiplication; in tobacco leaves infected with the masked strain, Beale (1937) found crystalline inclusions only in the occasional areas that showed external symptoms, from which more virulent strains than the parent type can sometimes be isolated.

Most workers have found that tobacco mosaic virus produces inclusions only in the cytoplasm, and electron microscopy of sections of cells infected with the type strain showed no abnormalities, or virus particles, in the nucleus (Black, Morgan and Wyckoff, 1950; Nixon and Sampson, 1954), but Woods and Eck (1948) described one strain that produced fibrous and crystalline inclusions in the nuclei. Zech (1954) and Zech and Vogt-Köhne (1955) also report that, at an early stage in infection of leaf hairs by the type strain, the nucleus becomes surrounded by material that absorbs ultraviolet radiation strongly, and that this material later diffuses into the cytoplasm. This material may be the same as that reported by Bald and Solberg (1961) to form grey plates as a first step in making crystalline inclusions.

Intracellular inclusions formed by other viruses. It seems likely that most viruses form inclusions in some conditions, for some that had apparently been studied exhaustively enough to preclude the possibility have nevertheless later been found to form them. The third edition of this book, for example, listed potato leaf roll and tomato spotted wilt viruses among those that apparently fail to form inclusions, but both were shortly afterwards reported to produce vacuolate inclusions (Bald, 1949). There is, though, no doubt that different viruses differ greatly in the frequency with which they produce inclusions, in the type of inclusion they produce, and in the kind of tissue where they produce them. Few of these differences can be correlated with any known differences in properties between the viruses. Potato virus Y has very similar particles, flexible threads, to tobacco etch and henbane mosaic viruses, and *in vitro* all three precipitate in much the same conditions, yet whereas virus Y produces only very few ill-defined cytoplasmic inclusions, tobacco etch virus produces many, both in the cytoplasm and the nucleus, and henbane mosaic virus, which also produces many, does so in the cytoplasm only. There is the obvious implication for these differences that, if the inclusions are insoluble complexes of virus and some host component, the other component may be a product specific to infections by individual viruses.

The inclusions produced by some viruses are so well defined that their identity is unequivocal, but others are less sharply differentiated from host cell components and this raises two problems. One is to get conditions so that inclusions can be revealed if they exist and the other to ensure that any abnormality seen is an inclusion body and not a disarranged host component. For instance, though cells usually contain only one nucleus, virus-infected cells sometimes have two (Sheffield, 1936; Salaman, 1938), and it may be necessary to stain with Feulgen's reagent to ensure that an additional body in a cell is not a second nucleus. This is a relatively easy task, but unfortunately there is no specific stain for viruses and differentiating between small inclusion bodies and clumped cytoplasm or pieces of disrupted plastids is more difficult, though Bald (1949) described techniques for fixing and staining which he concludes identifies not only properly formed inclusions, but virus in the cytoplasm.

Whether inclusions are formed, and their character when they are, depends on the identity of both the infecting virus and the host nfected. Thus, tomato spotted wilt seems not to produce inclusion bodies in many species that react to infection by developing necrotic esions but it produces them in the epidermal layers of plants that react by becoming mottled (Bald, 1949). However, the formation of inclusions cannot be generally correlated with any particular kind of external symptoms, and it is not precluded by a necrotic reaction of the host, for tobacco ringspot virus produces many, both of the

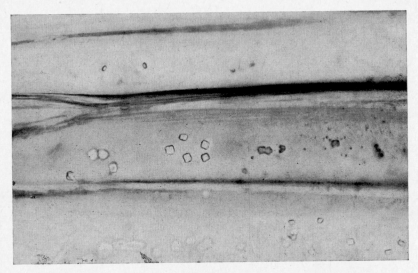

Fig. 3–6. *Nicotiana tabacum* infected with tobacco ringspot virus, epidermal cells from beneath a vein containing many small crystalline blocks. × 450. (F. C. Bawden and F. M. L. Sheffield, 1939, Ann. appl. Biol. 26: 102).

X-body type and crystals (Fig. 3–6), in tobacco, whereas it causes only few and ill-defined X-bodies in cucumber, which is also severely affected but has fewer necroses (Woods, 1933; Bawden and Sheffield, 1939). Some viruses produce inclusions in otherwise symptomless leaves. Indeed, Salaman (1938) reported that a strain of potato virus X that produced no external symptoms in tobacco produced inclusions more abundantly than did some other strains that cause severe mottling. Bawden and Sheffield (1939) also found inclusions in otherwise symptomless potato plants infected with some strains of virus X, though in this host inclusions were produced most abundantly in leaves with a yellow mottle and few or no necroses. The sizes and numbers of the X-bodies differed considerably with different strains and hosts; in tobacco they were relatively small, no larger than the nucleus, whereas in potato they were many times the size of the nucleus, some occupying half the total volume of the leaf cells. In potato leaf epidermis, the inclusions were equally abundant in green and yellow areas, whereas in the palisade cells and the spongy parenchyma they were abundant in the yellow areas but rare in the green areas.

Except for apical meristems, inclusions have been described in most kinds of plant tissues, including the abnormal tumourous tissue produced by plants infected with wound tumour virus (Littace and Black, 1952). Some viruses form them almost equally abundantly in many different tissues, whereas others form them more abundantly in one tissue than another, sugar beet yellows virus, for example, primarily and most abundantly in the phloem parenchyma and companion cells (Esau, 1960a; 1960b), and tomato spotted wilt virus in the epidermal cells (Bald, 1949). On the assumption that inclusions all contain virus particles and that a minimum amount of virus will therefore be needed to produce a visible body, the relative abundance of inclusions in different tissues is plausibly explained by postulating that it reflects the relative concentration of the virus in these tissues; if this is so, then it seems that different viruses multiply preferentially in different tissues, and that some are favoured by conditions in the epidermis, others by leaf parenchyma or the phloem, whereas still others do almost equally well in most types of mature cell.

All the X-bodies that have been examined have given the usual protein reactions and been Feulgen negative. The development of only a few has been studied in any detail, but those formed by henbane mosaic and tobacco etch viruses (Sheffield, 1934; 1941), potato virus X (Clinch, 1932; Salaman and Hurst, 1932), cabbage black ring virus (Rubio, 1956) and sugar beet yellows virus (Esau, 1960b), have all been reported to be built up from many granules that form in the cytoplasm and coalesce when they meet. Several workers have suggested that plastids are concerned in X-body formation and Rubio (1956) states that inclusions in plants infected with turnip yellow mosaic virus are made by the clumping together of material from degenerating plastids.

The typical spherical or ovoid X-body with its granular structure and vacuoles usually has a limited life and changes its appearance before disintegrating. Some change into obvious fibrous or semi-crystalline forms (Fig. 3–7). Those formed by henbane mosaic form thin needles, which seem not to be birefringent but possibly only because they are too small to show it clearly, and old cytoplasmic inclusions in tobacco plants infected with severe etch virus form needles or fibres that are birefringent (Sheffield, 1941). Similarly, the initially granular X-bodies formed by sugar beet yellows virus later become fibrous or banded and faintly birefringent (Esau, 1960b). The electron microscope has been surprisingly little used to study the structure of X-bodies, but it has shown that the inclusions formed by tobacco etch (Sheffield, 1946) and cabbage black ring and turnip yellow mosaic viruses (Rubio, 1956) contain particles of the same shape and size as the virus particles; electron micrographs show particles of cabbage black ring virus aligned in

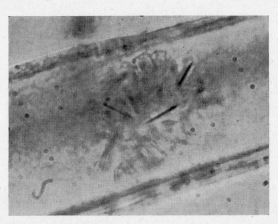

Fig. 3–7. An epidermal cell from a malformed leaf of a tobacco plant which was infected with severe etch virus when a young seedling. The cytoplasmic inclusion body has crystallised and contains needles; these are birefringent when viewed in polarised light. × 900.

parallel, which suggests that the common development of birefringence as X-bodies age probably means that the elongated particles are initially at random but later become increasingly concentrated and orientated.

With most viruses, fibrous or crystalline inclusions derive from aging X-bodies, but a few resemble tobacco mosaic virus in also producing crystals as a distinct type of inclusion. Cells of solanaceous plants infected with tobacco ringspot often contain many biaxial crystals (Fig. 3–6), rectangular blocks, which are birefringent along all axes (Bawden and Sheffield, 1939). Other forms of crystals have been reported in oats, millet, barley and maize suffering from mosaic (Sukhov and Vovk, 1938); most are small needles, but the epidermal cells often contain large protein crystals that sometimes break down into needles. Electron micrographs of sectioned cells infected with tomato bushy stunt (Smith, 1956) and rice dwarf virus (Fukushi, Shikata, Kimura and Nemoto, 1960) show regularly arranged particles of the size and shape of the two viruses, but whether these represent incipient crystal formation in the cytoplasm or within X-bodies is uncertain. Sections of *Zea mays* infected with an unindentified virus also show regularly arranged particles, 242 mμ long and 48 mμ wide in the cytoplasm (Herold, Bergold and Weibel, 1960).

Unlike animal viruses, many of which produce intranuclear in-clusions, most plant viruses produce inclusions in the cytoplasm

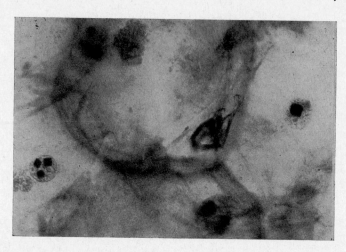

Fig. 3–8. Pith cells from *Nicotiana tabacum* infected with severe etch virus, stained with haematoxylin. All the nuclei contain darkly stained, plate-like inclusions. × 500. (Photograph by B. Kassanis).

only. Three reported exceptions are tobacco etch virus (Fig. 3–8) (Kassanis, 1939; Bawden and Kassanis, 1941), and pea virus 2 and Phaseolus virus 2 (McWhorter, 1940), all of which produce crystal-line inclusions in the nuclei. The intranuclear crystals are so regular and characteristic an effect of infection with strains of tobacco etch virus that they are valuable diagnostically. Most of those formed by severe etch virus are thin plates, of various sizes, birefringent when viewed edgeways. They begin to appear about a week after systemic symptoms become obvious and reach their maximum a month or so later; they occur in all tissues except the growing points, and a single nucleus may come to contain as many as thirty. Infec-tion with mild etch virus produces fewer but larger crystals, some of which seem to be eight-sided bi-pyramids. In contrast to the crystals formed from old X-bodies in plants infected with etch viruses, the intranuclear inclusions are very stable and when extracted from the nuclei their structure remains unaltered by pH changes between 2 and 10 or by ethyl alcohol. The nucleoli of nuclei containing crystals seem to be unaffected and the nuclei can still divide; infection with tobacco etch virus seems to stimulate mitosis in some mature cells, producing binucleate cells, and when this happens the nuclear inclusions are extruded from the dividing nuclei into the cytoplasm, and new crystals later form in the daughter nuclei (Sheffield, 1941).

Pea virus 2 and Phaseolus virus 2 differ from etch virus in that they produce isometric crystals and produce similar ones in both the cytoplasm and within the nucleoli. Five or more may occur in one nucleolus, but some nucleoli are almost filled by a single large crystal. These inclusions are also stable enough to be extracted from cells intact, they give the usual protein staining reactions and vary in size from 0.3 to 4 μ in diameter.

Histological changes other than intracellular inclusions. The macroscopic effects of viruses on plants are the end products of effects at the cellular or sub-cellular level, so it is only to be expected that the range of external symptoms shown by plants will be equalled or excelled by the range of cytological or histological changes. Some of these changes are common to infections by many different viruses and provide the immediate, though not the ultimate, explanation for the external symptoms. Thus, in mottled or crinkled leaves, the mottled areas are usually thinner than the green, with the palisade cells shorter, intracellular spaces smaller, and the chloroplasts fewer and smaller, less regular in outline and containing less chlorophyll (Clinch, 1932; Esau, 1956). Electron micrographs of sectioned chloroplasts in cells infected with tobacco mosaic virus show more intimate effects; instead of being composed of distinct grana, each with a characteristic layered structure, as are normal chloroplasts, the affected ones appear almost uniformly granular. The granules have a diameter approximately the same as the width of the virus particles, but whether this is what they are still remains to be determined (Nixon and Sampson, 1954).

Cells from leaves infected with viruses that cause mosaic diseases usually have much less starch than normal, but those from leaves infected with yellows type viruses, such as potato leaf roll, aster yellows, sugar beet curly top and yellows, contain more, and chloroplastids may be so gorged with starch that they burst (Clinch, 1932). It is characteristic of infections by all the yellows-type viruses for the phloem to be deranged, usually for the sieve tubes and companion cells to die (Quanjer, 1913; 1931; Artschwager and Starrett, 1936; Sheffield, 1943; Clinch and Loughnane, 1948). Phloem necrosis is often to be found before any leaf symptoms appear and it is obviously tempting to attribute the excessive accumulation of carbohydrate in the leaves to this disturbance in the food-conducting tissue, but in darkness sugars seem to move out of beet leaves infected with yellows virus as readily as out of uninfected leaves (Watson and Watson, 1953). With most of these infections, only the phloem elements die, but in sugar beet plants with curly top the necrosis may extend into the pericycle, when hypertrophy and hyperplasia around the affected areas lead to the veins becoming thickened and distorted (Esau, 1938). In some infected plants the phloem seems to be killed by the direct action of the virus, but in others death may be indirect, the result of hyperplasia of nearby cells crushing the sieve tubes and companion cells. Phloem necrosis of the elm seems to be one of the second type; it starts in the fibrous roots, spreads to the larger roots and into the trunk, when the tree dies (McClean, 1944). The affected phloem turns first yellow, then brown and smells faintly of wintergreen.

As is obvious from the external symptoms of infected plants, not all viruses restrict their lethal effects to the phloem and immediately adjacent cells. Indeed, we need consider only diseases of the potato to see that different viruses differ greatly in their ability to kill different types of tissue. Potato leaf roll has already been mentioned and serves to illustrate the type of virus that kills only phloem elements, which it may do in all parts of the plant, including tubers. The disease top-necrosis, caused in different varieties by several unrelated viruses, also starts by the phloem dying, but the necrotic lesions rapidly spread to all other tissues except the xylem. The tuber especially shows typical wound reactions, with phellogens forming around the necrotic tissues that sometimes succeed in localising a lesion. The disease leaf-drop-streak, caused by potato virus Y, is strikingly different, for the phloem is unaffected; the necrotic lesions initiate in the leaf mesophyll, spread along the veins, into the petioles and main stems. The collenchyma is the main sufferer, but the whole cortex may be destroyed while the vascular tissue remains intact (Quanjer, 1931; Bawden, 1932). Still other viruses may cause obvious necroses mainly in the leaf parenchyma or in leaf and tuber parenchyma (Fig. 2–2), as does tobacco rattle (Cadman, 1959). Many of the potato viruses cause degenerative changes that are not easily recognised by examining unstained tissues, but become evident with appropriate stains, which are widely used in some countries to identify infected tubers. Staining with phloroglucinol and hydrochloric acid, for instance, will make small lesions produced in leaf roll plants evident by colouring the damaged phloem yellowish red (Sheffield, 1943). The use of fluorescence in ultra-violet light to diagnose infection of potato tubers (Sanford and Grimble, 1944) probably depends on the accumulation of the substance scopoletin in and around necrotic spots (Best, 1944). Stains have also been proposed for diagnosing infections in fruit trees and these seem to be based on the idea that polyphenols are more plentiful in infected than in uninfected tissues (Lindner, Weeks and Kirkpatrick, 1951).

Degenerative changes are not the only ones caused by viruses. The swellings from which cocoa swollen shoot virus takes its name result from excessive activity of the cambium at certain times, but the extra phloem and xylem produced show no obvious abnormalities (Posnette, 1947). Excessive development of the phloem also occurs in sugar cane with Fiji disease, but the extra tissue is abnormal, with long galls being formed by the proliferation of the sieve tubes (Kunkel, 1924). Similarly, in tomato plants with big bud, there is much more internal phloem than usual and much of it is abnormal, for sieve tubes are rare and it mostly consists of small cells with prominent nuclei (Samuel, Bald and Eardley, 1933). In tobacco plants with kroepoek disease, not only does the primary phloem increase, but so also does the pericycle, in which new cambium arises and produces new vascular tissue. The leaf anatomy also changes greatly, for the spongy parenchyma is replaced by palisade tissue and palisade tissue forms in the lobed veins and proliferates to produce new leaflets or "enations."

Only a few abnormalities in xylem have been reported, of which the commonest is the formation of tyloses; this is especially common in plants infected with the virus that causes Pierce's disease of the grapevine, in which the first signs are tylose and gum development in the vessels, which later may be filled with products from disintegrating cells (Esau, 1948). An effect so far unique is the failure of apple trees with rubbery wood to form lignin.

Equally, except for intranuclear inclusions, there are few reports of infections affecting the nuclei of cells, though that they are often stimulated to divide when they otherwise would have ceased to do so is evident from the abnormal tissues, enations, tumours, and the like, that are so common. Tomato aspermy virus, however, disturbs both meiosis and mitosis in tobacco and *Nicotiana glutinosa* (Caldwell, 1952; Wilkinson, 1953), and causes mitotic failure in enations that develop on stems of infected *Petunia* (Wilkinson, 1960).

The current fashions in virus work are to study the structure of viruses and the sequence of events concerned in virus multiplication, and the property that makes viruses practically important, their ability to cause diseases, receives little attention. From the account given in this chapter it will be only too clear that we are pitifully ignorant of the ways in which viruses produce their effects, and the time seems overdue for a revival of symptomatology. The need, though, is for something other than simple observations of morbid anatomy, because, whether macroscopic or microscopic, these can do nothing except describe the end products of reactions whose nature they cannot disclose. Only by introducing new techniques into comparisons of infected and healthy cells, the use of electron microscopy, and refined chemical and enzymological methods, is knowledge likely to be gained on all such basic problems as the sites where viruses infect and multiply, the ways they affect cell metabolism, how they move from cell to cell, what determines whether a given plant can act as a host to a given virus and, if it can, what determines whether or not the plant becomes diseased.

REFERENCES

ARTSCHWAGER, E., and R. C. STARRETT. 1936. J. agric. Res. 53: 637.
BALD, J. G. 1949. Amer. J. Bot. 36: 335.
———, and P. A. SOLBERG. 1961. Nature, Lond. 190: 651.
BAWDEN, F. C. 1932. Proc. roy. Soc. B. 111: 74.
———, and B. KASSANIS. 1941. Ann. appl. Biol. 28: 107.
———, and F. M. L. SHEFFIELD. 1939. Ibid. 26: 102.
BEALE, H. PURDY. 1937. Contr. Boyce Thompson Inst. 8: 413.
BERNAL, J. D., and I. FANKUCHEN. 1937. Nature, Lond. 139: 923.
BEST, R. J. 1940. Aust. J. exp. Biol. med. Sci. 18: 307.
———. 1944. Ibid. 22: 251.
———. 1947. Ibid. 25: 283.
BLACK, L. M., C. MORGAN, and R. W. G. WYCKOFF. 1950. Proc. Soc. exp. Biol. N.Y. 73: 119.
CADMAN, C. H. 1959. Eur. Potato J. 2: 165.
CALDWELL, J. 1952. Ann. appl. Biol. 39: 98.
CLINCH, P. 1932. Sci. Proc. R. Dublin Soc. 20: 143.
———, and J. B. LOUGHNANE. 1948. Ibid. 24: 307.
ESAU, K. 1938. Bot. Rev. 4: 548.
———. 1941. Hilgardia 13: 437.
———. 1948. Ibid. 18: 423.
———. 1956. Amer. J. Bot. 43: 739.
———. 1960a. Virology 10: 73.
———. 1960b. Ibid. 11: 317.
FUKUSHI, T., E. SHIKATA, I. KIMURA, and M. NEMOTO. 1960. Proc. imp. acad. Japan 36: 352.
GOLDSTEIN, B. 1924. Bull. Torrey bot. Cl. 51: 261.
———. 1926. Ibid. 53: 499.
HENDERSON SMITH, J., and F. M. L. SHEFFIELD. 1930. Nature, Lond. 125: 200.
HEROLD, F., G. H. BERGOLD, and J. WEIBEL. 1960. Virology 12: 335.
IWANOWSKI, D. 1903. Z. PfKrankh. 13: 1.
KASSANIS, B. 1939. Ann. appl. Biol. 26: 705.
———, and A. KLECZKOWSKI. 1948. J. gen. Microbiol. 2: 143.

———, and F. M. L. SHEFFIELD. 1941. Ann. appl. Biol. 28: 360.
KLECZKOWSKI, A. 1946. Biochem. J. 40: 677.
KUNKEL, L. O. 1924. Bull. Exp. Sta. Hawaiian Sugar Plant. Assoc. 3: 99.
LINDNER, R. C., T. E. WEEKS, and H. C. KIRKPATRICK. 1951. Phytopathology 41: 897.
LITTACE, U. C., and L. M. BLACK. 1952. Amer. J. Bot. 39: 87.
LIVINGSTON, L. G., and B. M. DUGGAR. 1934. Biol. Bull. 67: 504.
MCCLEAN, D. M. 1944. Phytopathology 34: 818.
MCWHORTER, F. P. 1940. Ibid. 31: 760.
MILICIC, D. 1962. Phytopath. Z. 44: 282.
NIXON, H. L., and J. SAMPSON. 1954. Proc. Intl. Conf. on Electron Microscopy, London, 251.
POSNETTE, A. F. 1947. Ann. appl. Biol. 34: 388.
QUANJER, H. M. 1913. Meded. LandbHoogesch, Wageningen 6: 41.
———. 1931. Phytopathology 21: 577.
RUBIO, M. 1956. Phytopathology 46: 553.
SALAMAN, R. N. 1938. Phil. Trans. No. 559, 229, 137.
———, and C. C. HURST. 1932. J. R. Micr. Soc. 52: 237.
SAMUEL, G., J. G. BALD, and C. M. EARDLEY. 1933. Phytopathology 23: 641.
SANFORD, G. B., and J. G. GRIMBLE. 1944. Canad. J. Res. 22: 162.
SHEFFIELD, F. M. L. 1931. Ann. appl. Biol. 18: 471.
———. 1934. Ibid. 21: 430.
———. 1936. Ibid. 23: 498.
———. 1941. J. R. Micr. Soc. 61: 30.
———. 1943. Ann. appl. Biol. 30: 131.
———. 1946. J. R. Micr. Soc. 66: 69.
SMITH, K. M. 1956. Virology 2: 706.
STEERE, R. L., and R. C. WILLIAMS. 1953. Amer. J. Bot. 40: 81.
SUKHOV, K. S., and A. M. VOVK. 1938. C. R. Acad. Sci. U.R.S.S. 20: 745.
WATSON, D. J., and M. A. WATSON. 1953. Ann. appl. Biol. 40: 1.
WILKINS, M. H. F., A. R. STOKES, W. E. SEEDS, and G. OSTER. 1950. Nature, Lond. 166: 127.
WILKINSON, J. 1953. Nature, Lond. 171: 658.
———. 1960. Ann. Bot., Lond. 24: 516.
WOODS, M. W. 1933. Contr. Boyce Thompson Inst. 5, 419.
———, and R. V. ECK. 1948. Phytopathology 38: 852.
ZECH, H. 1952. Planta. 40: 461.
———. 1954. Exp. Cell Res. 6: 560.
———, and L. VOGT-KÖHNE. 1955. Naturwissenschaften 11: 337.

Symptomatology: Effects on Host-Plant Metabolism

The changes in colour, shape, size and habit of growth of plants produced by virus infections are, of course, all gross manifestations of disturbance in cellular metabolism, but the nature and direct causes of these disturbances are mostly unknown. In seeking explanations, there seems little to be gained from analogies with diseases caused by pathogens that use their hosts simply as a source of food, which they obtain and metabolise with their own enzyme systems. Current knowledge about viruses makes it highly improbable that they have any independent metabolic activities comparable to those of micro-organisms, and their parasitism seems to be at a different level of dependence, in which the host cells seem to provide, not only their substance, but also the mechanisms whereby they are synthesised. In effect viruses become parts of their host cells, to which they impart new patterns of synthesis; whether symptoms occur, and what kind, will presumably depend on what other syntheses are disturbed by the intrusion of the additional ones.

All the viruses whose gross constitution is known consist largely of protein and nucleic acid, and none has yet been found to contain any of the many enzymes, proteases, oxidases and the like, contained by organisms. However, this does not necessarily mean they are enzymically inactive, for they may contain other kinds of enzymes.

The protein of bacteriophages dissolves the walls of susceptible bacteria; similarly, the proteins of viruses from flowering plants may also be enzymes that act on substrates in their host cells, but there is as yet no evidence for this. Obviously, if the proteins can destroy essential host constituents, such actions would be of prime importance in causing symptoms, but any such enzymes, unlike those in bacteriophages, are not needed to initiate infection, which happens when leaves are inoculated with disrupted virus from which most of the protein has been removed. As the nucleic acid on its own seems to be infective, virus infections must be regarded as being primarily disturbances in the nucleic acid metabolism of infected cells. The intrusion of the new nucleic acid into a host cell imposes a new pattern of nucleic acid synthesis, which leads to a new pattern of protein synthesis, culminating in the formation of new virus and, often, a range of materials that resemble virus particles in some property or other. Although these other materials, which in infections with some viruses are protein only and with others nucleoprotein, are not infective, they are not necessarily wholly inactive, and they may to some extent determine the host's reaction to infection.

Accommodating a new pattern of nucleoprotein synthesis can be expected to impose stresses and strains on the normal functioning of cells and it is not surprising that the usual control mechanisms of cellular metabolism often fail to keep things balanced in infected cells. However, some hosts (symptomless carriers) can accommodate virus multiplication without being noticeably inconvenienced. This poses what is certainly one of the most important and fascinating problems of virus research: what makes a virus harmless to one host and pathogenic towards another? Unfortunately, almost all that can now be said in answer is that the relative virulence of different viruses, or of different virus strains, is not determined by the amounts to which they accumulate in infected plants. Some viruses are lethal or crippling towards tobacco, for example, although they do not reach a thousandth the concentration of tobacco mosaic virus, which can amount to half of the total leaf protein of plants that nevertheless continue to grow and, depending on the identity of the infecting strain, may not even be greatly harmed. Hence, pathogenicity seems not to be correlated with the total extent to which infecting viruses sequestrate their component parts, purines, pyrimidines and aminoacids, from their host cells. This, perhaps, is not surprising, because the protein content of uninfected leaves can vary within wide limits, depending on the nutrition and the environment of the plants, and much of the "normal" protein produced by richly fed plants seems dispensable.

With no reason to attribute symptoms to direct metabolic fatigue from host materials being diverted into virus particles, it seems necessary to seek their causes in specific virus-host interactions. The nature of any such interactions is obscure, but it is clear that the occurrence of a given symptom can be determined equally by the genetic constitution of the virus or the host, for a change in either may abolish or restore the symptom. Thus, one strain of potato virus X may be lethal to one potato variety and harmless to another, whereas a second strain may reverse this behaviour. Such differences in host reaction to infection by individual virus strains are often determined by single genes, and there is no reason to assume that the different behaviour of different virus strains towards one variety are controlled by more complex genetical differences. This carries the clear implication that such differences in the outcome of infection of one variety by different strains, or of different varieties by one strain, represent the consequences of reactions between highly specific components of host and virus, for the different virus strains have similar gross constitutions and the different varieties may also resemble one another closely. It is reasonable to seek the cause of such differences between host-virus reactions in some host component able to vary in structure and in some configuration of the virus equally able to vary, so that some structures provide substrates for some configurations and other structures for other configurations. The "Yale" lock and key provide a simple analogy; slight changes in a lock prevent it from being unlocked by a key that previously fitted it, but equally slight changes in the key can make it effective with the changed lock.

There is no need to assume that viruses are directly responsible for all the changes infection produces in cells, in the sense that they attack components of all the systems that become affected or that, in hosts where infections are lethal, they are the immediate killers. All they may need to do is to interfere with one system and put it out of balance with others and so disturb the whole working of the cell; similarly, any interference with a sequence of syntheses that allowed toxic intermediaries to accumulate could be lethal, without the virus particles themselves being directly able to attack and destroy any major cell structure.

Changes in enzymic activities. As no enzymes have been identified in preparations of plant viruses that have been carefully purified, the many reports in the literature about changed enzymic activities caused by infection presumably reflect the extent to which the normal enzymes of the host are thrown out of balance. Few general principles emerge from the reports, except that most workers who have studied oxidases have concluded that their activity is increased. Even with these, however, there has been considerable disagreement in detail. As early as the turn of the century, Woods (1899, 1900) commented on disturbances of the oxidase and peroxidase systems in tobacco plants with mosaic; that such disturbances are not peculiar to infections with viruses causing mosaic type diseases was early shown by Bunzel (1913), who found that sugar beet leaves infected with curly top virus had more than twice the normal oxidase activity, and by Rouzinoff (1930), who reported increased oxidase activity in potatoes as a result of infection with the leaf roll virus. Best (1937) found that sap from tomato leaves infected with tomato spotted wilt virus contained an oxidase undetectable in sap from leaves of uninfected plants, although detectable in their roots. It was not detected in infected plants of all host species.

Woods and Dubuy (1942) described complex effects of tobacco mosaic virus on the oxidase system of tobacco leaves; they distinguished three cyanide-sensitive systems, and claimed that, within 2–3 days of infection, one system is suppressed, the second is unaffected and the third stimulated. However, Takahashi (1947) failed to confirm these conclusions and detected no differences between the effects of cyanide on infected and uninfected leaves.

Polyphenol oxidase has been reported to be increased by infection with several different viruses in many different host plants (Martin, 1958; Hampton and Fulton, 1961). Farkas, Kiraly and Solymosy (1960) found that tobacco mosaic, cucumber mosaic or tobacco necrosis viruses increased polyphenol oxidase activity more, and more rapidly, in hosts that reacted by developing necrotic local lesions only than in those that became systemically infected. They attribute necrotic local lesions to the oxidation of polyphenols, and report that *Nicotiana glutinosa* leaves inoculated with tobacco mosaic virus form no lesions when they are supplied with high concentrations of ascorbic acid. Ascorbic acid is thought not to inhibit polyphenol oxidase but to keep the phenols from being oxidised. However, whether this, or the smaller virus content achieved in the leaves infiltrated with ascorbic acid, explain the lack of necrosis, is an open question. Inoculated *N. glutinosa* kept at 36° produce yellow lesions instead of the necrotic ones produced at lower temperatures. Farkas, Kiraly and Solymosy (1960) found that polyphenol oxidase activity is only slightly stimulated when infected plants are at 36°, and they interpret this as further evidence that oxidation of polyphenols causes the necrosis. However, such evidence cannot be conclusive, for oxidised polyphenols and necrosis will be equally correlated whether their oxidation is the cause or consequence of the cells dying. Many other things will also be different in infected leaves at 36° than at lower temperatures; in particular the virus content of individual cells is much less (Kassanis, 1952), and there may be no need to look further than this for the less severe symptoms.

Farkas, Kiraly and Solymosy (1960) also report that cells surrounding the necrotic lesions have greater dehydrogenase activity than usual, and they suggest this may be a defense mechanism of the host that helps to prevent the phenolic compounds from becoming oxidised. If it is, there is presumably no need to assume that it is specific to virus infections, but a generalised wound reaction comparable to the formation of cork cambia and consequent changes in neighbouring cells around the necrotic lesions produced in potato tubers by some viruses (Bawden, 1932).

It is perhaps worth stressing that necrotic lesions are not all of one type. This is obvious enough from their external appearance, for some, such as those produced by potato virus X or tobacco necrosis viruses in tobacco, are whitish rings or spots, whereas others, such as those produced by tobacco mosaic virus in N. *glutinosa* or by tobacco necrosis viruses in French bean, are darkly coloured. Infection in inoculated leaves may be localised in either type of lesion, but neither type can be relied on to prevent systemic infection. The white lesions consist of collapsed cells with few remaining contents, whereas the cells of the coloured lesions not only contain much deeply staining material, but they also reflect infra-red

Fig. 4–1. The under surface of a tobacco leaf showing systemic invasion by the virus causing tomato spotted wilt. *Above:* the necrotic lesions photographed by daylight on a panchromatic plate. *Opposite:* the fluorescence when photo-

radiation (Bawden, 1933) and fluoresce in ultra-violet radiation (Fig. 4–1) (Best, 1936). Best (1944) identified the fluorescent material as 6-methoxy-7-hydroxy-1:2 benzo-pyrone (scopoletin), which he also found in small amounts in uninfected plants, and he suggests that it is normally an intermediate product in a chain of reactions and accumulates in cells where this chain is broken. Scopoletin accumulates in infections with widely different viruses and is responsible for the fluorescence of some potato tubers when infected with potato leaf roll virus (Andreae, 1948).

The commonest symptom of virus diseases is for leaves that should be uniformly green to become variegated or mottled, and it is surprising that the mechanisms underlying the effects on chlorophyll have been so little studied. Peterson and McKinney (1938) reported changes in chlorophyllase produced by three strains of tobacco mosaic and another mosaic-causing virus, probably potato virus Y. In uninfected leaves, chlorophyllase activity and chlorophyll content were directly proportional, whereas in infected leaves chlorophyllase was greatest in the leaves that contained least chlorophyll. Similarly, yellow areas from mottled leaves contained more chlorophyllase but less chlorophyll than green areas. As chlorophyll, carotene and zanthophyll were all decreased by the same proportion, Peterson and McKinney suggested that chlorosis is a consequence of chlorophyll failing to mask the yellow pigments as it normally does. However, Elmer (1925) found that infection with tobacco mosaic virus doubled the concentration of carotene while

graphed under filtered ultra-violet light, with an aesculine filter placed between the leaf and camera to absorb any reflected ultra-violet. (R. J. Best, 1936, Austral. J. Exp. Biol. and Med. Sci. 14: 199).

lessening the amounts of both chlorophyll and xanthophyll, so in some conditions the yellow pigment may be increased. The degree of yellowing produced by type tobacco mosaic virus depends greatly on the nutrition and growing conditions of plants and is enhanced by a lack of nitrogen, although virus content is less than in greener leaves with abundant nitrogen (Bawden and Kassanis, 1954). Correspondingly, Zaitlin and Jagendorf (1960) found that, whereas infecting leaves of tobacco plants from which nitrogenous fertilisers were withheld decreased the chlorophyll from 0.5 mg/g fresh weight to 0.35, with plants receiving nitrogen the decrease was only from 0.79 to 0.68 mg.

Zaitlin and Jagendorf further found that the nitrogen nutrition of the host affects the *in vitro* photochemical activities of the chloroplasts isolated from infected leaves: in conditions of nitrogen stress, the photochemical activity started to decrease within a week of inoculating tobacco leaves and after 9 days had fallen to 60% of the activity of uninfected leaves, but in plants receiving abundant nitrogen the photochemical activities of the chloroplasts were almost equal to those from uninfected leaves. Spikes and Stout (1955) had previously found that chloroplasts from sugar beet leaves infected with beet yellows virus had only half the photochemical activity of those from uninfected leaves, so this effect seems common to infection by viruses of both the mosaic and yellows type. The effect is not solely one of decreasing the amount of chlorophyll, but also on its activity per unit weight. Again, though, Zaitlin and Jagendorf (1960) found that effects of infection with tobacco mosaic virus on the amount of ferric cyanide reduced per weight of chlorophyll depends on the nitrogen status of the leaves; it is least in infected nitrogen-deficient leaves, intermediate in uninfected nitrogen-deficient leaves, and very similar in infected and uninfected leaves with abundant nitrogen. These results suggest that tobacco mosaic virus does not directly attack chloroplasts or chlorophyll, for effects do not depend on the virus content of cells, but that chloroplasts and chlorophyll are affected indirectly by the extent to which virus multiplication creates conditions of nitrogen stress in the cells.

There are scattered reports of virus infections affecting other kinds of enzymes, but there have been few comprehensive studies in which infected and uninfected plants have been compared in a wide range of different growing conditions. Plants are highly responsive to changes in nutrition and environment, and infection with a given virus may well affect enzymic activities differently in plants grown under widely different conditions. The amount of a given carbohydrate or protein in a plant at any time reflects a balance between its synthesis and breakdown: in some conditions the amounts will be greatly in excess of needs, whereas in others they may be limiting. It is only to be expected that the effects of infection, on both the amounts of substances and on the enzymes responsible for their synthesis and breakdown, will depend on the state of the plants at the time of infection. Also, as growing conditions affect the ratios at which different substances occur in leaves, the results of comparing infected with uninfected plants may depend on the basis used for the comparison, that is, on whether the enzyme activity is measured on the basis of total fresh weight, total dry weight, per unit volume of sap, nitrogen content, or some other basis. These expectations are fully confirmed by the results from the only experiments comparing uninfected tobacco plants grown with a wide range of fertiliser treatments with plants otherwise similar but infected with tobacco mosaic virus (Holden and Tracey, 1948, 1948a). Although infection affected both the protease and pectase activity, it did so no more than did changing the nutrition and, as is shown by Table 4–1, which summarises the main effects analysed by Holden and

TABLE 4–1

Some Effects of Tobacco Mosaic Virus on Systemically Infected Tobacco Leaves

Decrease in:	Wet weight of plants
	Wet weight of leaves
	Total dry matter
	Total phosphorus
	Dry matter as % wet weight
	Sap sediment N as % non-fibre N
	Protease/g. protein N of sap
	Pectase/g. N of fibre
Increase in:	Total N as % dry matter
	Fibre N as % dry matter
	Sap N as % dry matter
	Total P as % dry matter
	Fibre P as % dry matter
	Sap N/ml.
	Protein N/ml.
	% total dry matter as fibre
	Total protease/g. dry weight
	Fibre protease/g. dry weight
No significant change in:	Total N
	% total N on fibre
	% total P on fibre
	Sap P as % dry matter
	Total units protease/g. total protein N
	Fibre protease/g. N.
	Pectase/g. dry matter of fibre

Tracey, whether protease is considered to have been increased or decreased by infection depends on whether its activity is measured on the basis of total dry weight or on the amount of protein in the sap.

Carbon : nitrogen ratios. It has long been appreciated that virus infections usually change the carbon:nitrogen ratio in leaves and that, whereas some viruses increase it, others decrease it (True and Hawkins, 1918; Jodidi *et al,* 1920; Campbell, 1925). Dunlap (1930) suggested that viruses divide into two types, those causing mosaic-type diseases, which increase nitrogen content and decrease carbohydrate, and those causing yellows-type diseases, which increase carbohydrate content and decrease nitrogen. However, it is doubtful whether there is need to conclude that the two groups of viruses necessarily affect both carbohydrate and nitrogen differently, because the C/N ratio would move in opposite directions if one type of disease increased the amount of carbohydrate in leaves and the other decreased it.

Since Quanjer (1913) first reported phloem necrosis in potato plants with leaf roll, this type of lesion has been found to be characteristic of yellows diseases and it has been widely accepted that carbohydrates accumulate in the leaves because the collapsed sieve tubes prevent the normal movement of sugars. Although this idea was early contested (Murphy, 1923), it continued to be held largely because when diseased and healthy plants are kept in the dark for suitable lengths of time, leaves of diseased plants still stain strongly with iodine after those from healthy plants have lost their starch. However, to attribute this difference to phloem necrosis meant neglecting the fact that mosaic viruses, which do not kill phloem elements, also slow the rate at which starch is lost from infected leaf cells. This fact is evident from the use of iodine-staining to reveal infections in inoculated leaves that otherwise show no local lesions. Two methods can be used (Holmes, 1931): the leaves can be decolourised and stained in the evening after the plants have been in the light during the day, when the infected areas show as lighter spots on a dark background; or they can be stained in the morning after some hours in darkness, when the infected areas show as dark spots against a light background. The staining at different times of the day shows that infection with this type of virus slows both the rate at which starch accumulates during daylight and the rate at which it disappears in darkness. The first could be simply that the rate of photosynthesis is slowed but the second must demand some intracellular change in the parenchymatous cells that either directly affects the hydrolysis of starch or the rate at which sugars produced from the starch diffuse away. Wynd (1943) suggested that it is a general effect of infections by mosaic- and yellows-type viruses to alter the permeability of cytoplasm so that soluble substances diffuse more slowly than in uninfected cells, but there is no critical evidence of this.

Staining for starch cannot give information about the rate at which carbohydrates move out of leaves, but shows only the relative amounts of starch in leaves at different times. The actual amount of carbohydrate that moves from infected and uninfected leaves seem to have been measured only in sugar beet, with and without yellows (Watson and Watson, 1951, 1953); the results seem to make untenable the idea that phloem necrosis causes starch to accumulate in the yellow leaves, for comparable leaves of infected and uninfected plants lost the same amount of total carbohydrate over-night, showing that translocation is not impeded by some of the phloem being necrotic. The leaves of the plants with yellows had more carbohydrate at the end of the period in darkness simply because they had more at the start. Whether after prolonged periods in the dark yellowed leaves still contain starch, has yet to be determined and should be to see whether conditions there preclude its complete dissolution. However, the greater part of the increased content of carbohydrate in the yellowed leaves is not starch but glucose and fructose, which may amount to 20% of the total dry weight—more than five times as much as in uninfected leaves. Watson and Watson (1953) suggest that, as the translocation rate is unchanged by infection, the rise in carbohydrate content of the leaf possibly results from increased resistance to the movement of sugars through the leaf lamina. The fact that much of the increase is in the forms in which carbohydrate probably moves through the vascular system is compatible with the idea that these sugars must reach a higher concentration than in uninfected leaf lamina before they move into the veins.

With leaf roll of potato, also, there is evidence that phloem necrosis and accumulation of carbohydrates in the leaves may be independent effects, rather than cause and effect. Murphy (1923) reported that starch accumulates in the leaves before phloem necrosis is detectable and Wilson (1955) found no correlation between severity of leaf symptoms and phloem necrosis. Thung (1928) also found that starch accumulation precedes phloem necrosis, but concluded that the two were correlated in as much as changes in the phloem that end in necrosis also restrict the movement of sugars. He found that rolled leaves contained both more sugar and more starch than healthy leaves, and Barton-Wright and McBain (1932) concluded that, whereas the sugar of translocation in healthy potatoes is sucrose, in plants with leaf roll it is hexose.

Effects of potato leaf roll (Barton-Wright and McBain, 1933b) and sugar beet yellows (Watson and Watson, 1953) on the nitrogen content of leaves were no greater than could be accounted for by changes in the carbohydrate content. Schweizer (1930), however, concluded that leaf roll virus does derange the protein metabolism: he found that nitrogen passes into young shoots more rapidly from infected than from uninfected tubers, and he suggests that infection decreases diastase activity in the tubers, so that much starch remains unhydrolysed and infected tubers remain hard longer than uninfected ones. Sreenivasaya and Sastri (1928) reported that spike disease of sandal increases the contents of both carbohydrate and nitrogen, which makes it an anomaly among yellows diseases; they suggest that lack of calcium, which is characteristic of diseased plants, may affect the movement of carbohydrate. Diseased plants contain mannitol, which is not detectable in healthy sandal (Sreenivasaya, 1930).

Of the few mosaic diseases that have been studied, beet mosaic (Watson and Watson, 1953) and potato crinkle (Barton-Wright, 1941) had little or no effect on the carbohydrate content of leaves, but leaves of Arran Victory potatoes with paracrinkle (Barton-Wright and McBain, 1933a) had more carbohydrate than uninfected leaves, though the excess was much smaller than in plants with leaf roll. No consistent pattern emerges from the reports of effects of mosaic-type viruses on nitrogen content. Potato plants with crinkle had more nitrogen and protein than uninfected plants (Barton-Wright, 1941) and beet mosaic virus increased the nitrogen content of all parts of beet plants not given nitrogenous fertilisers, but not of those that were fertilised (Watson and Watson, 1953).

Reports about effects of tobacco mosaic virus are many and conflicting. Dunlap (1930) and Cordingley et al (1934) reported increases in nitrogen content of about 10%, whereas Stanley (1937) reported twice the usual amount of nitrogen and protein. Martin, Balls and McKinney (1938) failed to confirm this and pointed out that Stanley's results showed large effects only on the extractable protein and not on total protein. They found no differences between the total nitrogen and total protein of healthy plants and plants infected separately with three strains of tobacco mosaic virus. Other workers have also found large effects on the extractable protein (Table 4–1), but relatively little on the total protein (Holden and Tracey, 1948). Tobacco mosaic virus accumulates to such an extent that it becomes an analytically significant component of the leaf. The actual amount in systemically infected tobacco leaves depends on the nutrition of the plants, and may be more than twice as much in well-fed as in poorly-fed plants. As a proportion of the total nitrogen, the variation is much greater than this, from 10% in well-fed plants to 60% in plants receiving abundant phosphorus but no nitrogen (Holden and Tracey, 1948). Obviously, effects on the normal proteins are likely to depend on the nutritional state of the infected leaves. The virus will multiply in detached leaves given no extra supply of nitrogen; in such conditions there can be no increase in total nitrogen and in these circumstances the virus presumably multiplies by using materials from autolysed normal proteins, but this need not be so when supplies of nitrogen are abundant.

Although effects of infection by tobacco mosaic virus on total nitrogen are insignificant compared with those produced by varying plant nutrition, effects on the amount of protein that remains in solution after leaf sap has been clarified are considerable. When studied electrophoretically, sap from uninfected tobacco leaves shows one predominant component, but infected leaves show another with the characteristic mobility of the virus. Wildman, Cheo and Bonner (1949) reported that the amount of the normal component decreased as the amount of the virus increased and advanced this as evidence that "virus protein is synthesised at the direct expense of the normal protein." However, others have not confirmed this, although Takahashi and Ishii (1952) also reported that infection decreased the amount of soluble normal protein. By contrast, Holden and Tracey (1948) found that the increased protein content of sap from infected leaves was sometimes more than could be accounted for by the amount of virus, and Commoner et al (1952) found no consistent effects but that the amount of normal protein varied erratically. Bawden and Kleczkowski (1957) found that the number and concentration of electrophoretically distinguishable components in sap from uninfected tobacco leaves depended on the position of the leaf on the stem, the age of the plants, their nutrition and conditions of growth, but these components were not consistently affected by infection with any of four mosaic-type viruses, which cause diseases of different severity and which reach very different concentrations in sap. Neither potato Y, which causes a slight disease, nor tobacco etch, which causes a severe disease, reaches an amount detectable electrophoretically in sap; usually neither affected the concentration of normal proteins in sap, but sometimes decreased it slightly. Potato virus X and tobacco mosaic virus are readily detectable electrophoretically, for they may exceed in quantity the nor-

mal proteins; infection with them sometimes decreased the amoun
of normal proteins, usually in young rapidly growing plants whicl
produced much virus, but even in these conditions the amount wa:
often unaffected. Simultaneous infection with both viruses, each o:
which reached the same concentration as when present alone, hac
no more effect on the amount of soluble normal proteins than dic
infection with one or other alone. Thus, if there are any protein:
that autolyse in infected leaves and provide aminoacids or othe›
nitrogen sources for building virus particles, these seem largely tc
be other than those that remain in solution when sap is clarified.

Photosynthesis and respiration. Although effects on photosyn
thesis have been studied with only a few viruses, enough has beei
done to show that the different carbon-nitrogen ratios characteristi‹
of plants with yellows and with mosaic diseases are not attributabl‹
to the two diseases affecting either photosynthesis or respiration dif·
ferently. Photosynthesis has been found to be decreased by potatc
leaf roll (Thung, 1928; Barton-Wright and McBain, 1932; Watsor
and Wilson, 1956) and by infection with the mosaic type viruses,
tobacco mosaic, potato X and tobacco etch (Owen, 1958a, 1957a
1957b). Respiration has been found to be increased by infectior
with several yellows-type and many mosaic-type viruses, and thi:
is presumably responsible for infected leaves having higher tempera·
tures than uninfected ones (Yarwood, 1953).

Only with tobacco mosaic virus has there been conflicting report:
about effects on respiration, and with this every possible result ha:
been described, that is, increases, decreases and no change. These
seemingly irreconcilable reports are now at least in part explicable
First, infection only slightly increases the respiration of tobaccc
leaves and, because it also decreases the water content which detached leaves attain when kept in conditions of minimum wate›
stress, the conclusion drawn can depend on whether the results are
expressed on the basis of dry weight, or initial or final fresh weights,
also, the effect on respiration depends on the age of the leaves when
they become infected and on the length of time they have been infected when the measurements are made (Owen, 1955a, b, 1956
1958b). The most striking effect is that, in directly inoculated
leaves, respiration increases by 10% within an hour after the inoculation (Owen, 1955a); it continues at this slightly enhanced level for
some days while the virus content of the leaves is increasing rapidly,
but then falls below the level in comparable uninfected leaves.
Leaves that become invaded systemically also at first respire more
than uninfected ones, but then later respire less, perhaps because

when the virus has reached its maximum amount it represents about 10% of the dry weight of the leaves that is divorced from respiration (Owen, 1956).

The almost immediate increase in the respiration of tobacco leaves produced by inoculation with tobacco mosaic virus is unique among the virus-host combinations yet tested. Owen (1957a, 1958a) did not find it in tobacco leaves inoculated with potato virus X or tobacco etch virus, or in *Nicotiana glutinosa* leaves inoculated with tobacco mosaic virus; these three infections produced greater effects on respiration rates—increases of 20–40%—but did not produce these effects until soon before symptoms started to appear. Similarly, with these virus-host combinations photosynthesis was also unaffected until symptoms were starting to develop, when it decreased by about 20%, whereas in tobacco leaves inoculated with tobacco mosaic virus photosynthesis decreased by about 15% within an hour of inoculation (Owen, 1957b). To affect photosynthesis, cells below the epidermis must presumably be affected, but in what way is unknown and it is usually assumed that virus rubbed over the leaf penetrates only the epidermis. Also, changes in the physiology of leaves within an hour of inoculation cannot reflect virus multiplication, because it is several hours before new virus appears and one hour before any change in the state of infecting virus particles has been detected. However, the effects on respiration, photosynthesis and water content seem not to be a reaction of cells to virus protein in the inoculum, because tobacco leaves rubbed with tobacco mosaic virus inactivated by ultraviolet radiation were unaffected (Owen, 1957b). The effects are uninterpretable and demand further study, but do so in their own right rather than because they have any general significance, because other viruses in tobacco, and tobacco mosaic virus in other hosts, behave differently, with effects on respiration correlated with virus multiplication and symptom production (Weintraub, Kemp and Ragetli, 1960).

When a virus such as tobacco etch can decrease photosynthesis by as much as 20% and increase respiration by 40%, there is little need to look further for its crippling effect on growth (Owen, 1957a), and the different extents to which different viruses affect the net assimilation rate of leaves, that is the rate of increase of dry matter per unit leaf area, may go far to explain their different effects on yield. However, there are other effects, such as changes in leaf area, shape of leaf, length of internodes, numbers of side shoots and the like, that suggest disturbances in the functioning of hormones. The amount of free auxins has been reported to be decreased by infecting a range of plants with various viruses (Grieve,

1943; Pavillard, 1954), but applying auxins usually enhances instead of diminishing the twistings and deformities of diseased plants. However, giving gibberellic acid overcomes the stunting of tobacco plants caused by infection with tobacco etch virus (Chessin, 1957) and of asters, maize and clover infected respectively with aster yellows, corn stunt and wound tumour viruses (Maramorosch, 1957), but the other symptoms of infection remain.

Too few of the many known virus diseases have been studied physiologically for any confident generalisation to be made. Nevertheless, it is worth comment that the few that have been studied are reasonably representative of diseases caused by viruses known to have widely differing properties and that, despite this, they do show many similarities. Increased respiration, decreased photosynthesis, abnormal hormone balance, a decreased water content and solutes diffusing more slowly, seem to be features of leaves suffering from both yellows-type and mosaic-type diseases. There is no clear indication that any virus specifically attacks or affects any specific cell constituent. Instead, the picture that emerges is of a comprehensive disturbance to the normal metabolic processes. The fact that respiration and photosynthesis are simultaneously disturbed is clearly evidence of more than one effect, for these metabolic activities are normally independent of one another and proceed at different sites in leaf cells. Because so many metabolic processes are disturbed, the physiological studies provide no clue to the cell components that are primarily invaded by infecting virus particles or concerned in virus multiplication. Perhaps these components will have to be identified by other kinds of work before the reasons for the metabolic disturbances will be understood.

REFERENCES

ANDREAE, W. A. 1948. Canad. J. Res. C. 26: 31.
BARTON-WRIGHT, E. 1941. Ann. appl. Biol. 28: 299.
——, and A. M. McBAIN. 1932. Trans. roy. Soc. Edinb. 57: 309.
——, and ——. 1933a. Ann. appl. Biol. 20: 525.
——, and ——. 1933b. Ibid. 20: 549.
BAWDEN, F. C. 1932. Proc. roy. Soc. B. 111: 74.
——. 1933. Nature, Lond. 123: 168.
——, and B. KASSANIS. 1954. Ann. appl. Biol. 37: 215.
——, and A. KLECZKOWSKI. 1957. Virology 4: 26.
BEST, R. J. 1936. Aust. J. exp. Biol. and Med. Sci. 14: 199.
——. 1937. Ibid. 15: 191.
——. 1944. Ibid. 22: 251.
BUNZEL, H. H. 1913. Bull. U.S. Dep. Agric. 277.
CAMPBELL, E. G. 1925. Phytopathology 15: 427.
CHESSIN, M. 1957. Proc. 3rd Conf. Potato Virus Diseases (Lisse-Wageningen, Netherlands, 1957).

COMMONER, B., P. NEWMARK, and S. D. RODENBERG. 1952. Arch. Biochem. Biophys. 37: 15.
CORDINGLEY, H., J. GRAINGER, W. H. PEARSALL, and A. WRIGHT. 1934. Ann. appl. Biol. 21: 78.
DUNLAP, A. A. 1930. Amer. J. Bot. 17: 348.
ELMER, O. H. 1925. Res. Bulletin Iowa Agric. Exp. Sta., 82.
FARKAS, G. L., Z. KIRALY, and F. SOLYMOSY. 1960. Virology 12: 408.
GRIEVE, B. J. 1943. Aust. J. exp. Biol. and med. Sci. 21: 89.
HAMPTON, R. E., and R. W. FULTON. 1961. Virology 13: 44.
HOLDEN, M., and M. V. TRACEY. 1948. Biochem. J. 43: 147.
——, and ——. 1948a. Biochem. J. 43: 151.
HOLMES, F. O. 1931. Contr. Boyce Thompson Inst. 3: 164.
JODIDI, S. L., S. C. MOULTON, and K. S. MASKLEY. 1920. J. Amer. chem. Soc. 42: 1061.
KASSANIS, B. 1952. Ann. appl. Biol. 39: 358.
MARAMOROSCH, K. 1957. Science 126: 651.
MARTIN, L. F., A. K. BALLS, and H. H. McKINNEY. 1938. Science 87: 329.
MARTIN, M. C. 1958. C. R. Acad. Sci. Paris 246: 2026.
MURPHY, P. A. 1923. Sci. Proc. R. Dublin Soc. 17: 163.
OWEN, P. C. 1955a. Ann. appl. Biol. 43: 114.
——. 1955b. Ibid. 43: 265.
——. 1956. Ibid. 44: 227.
——. 1957a. Ibid. 45: 327.
——. 1957b. Ibid. 45: 456.
——. 1958a. Ibid. 46: 198.
——. 1958b. Ibid. 46: 205.
PAVILLARD, J. 1954. Proc. 2nd Conf. Potato Virus Diseases (Lisse-Wageningen, Netherlands, 1954.)
PETERSON, P. D., and H. H. McKINNEY. 1938. Phytopathology 28: 329.
QUANJER, H. M. 1913. Meded. LandbHoogesch., Wageningen 6: 41.
ROUZINOFF, P. G. 1930. Morbi Plant. Leningrad 19: 148.
SCHWEIZER, G. 1930. Phytopath. Z. 6: 557.
SPIKES, J. D., and M. STOUT. 1955. Science 122: 375.
SREENIVASAYA, M. 1930. Nature, Lond. 126: 438.
——, and B. N. SASTRI. 1928. J. Indian Inst. Sci. 11: 23.
STANLEY, W. M. 1937. Phytopathology 27: 1152.
TAKAHASHI, W. N. 1947. Amer. J. Bot. 34: 496.
——, and M. ISHII. 1952. Nature, Lond. 169: 419.
THUNG, T. H. 1928. Tijdschr. PlZiekt. 33: 1.
TRUE, R. H., and L. A. HAWKINS. 1918. J. agric. Res. 15: 381.
WATSON, D. J., and J. H. WILSON. 1956. Ann. appl. Biol. 44: 390.
WATSON, M. A., and D. J. WATSON. 1951. Ann. appl. Biol. 38: 276.
——, and ——. 1953. Ibid. 40: 1.
WEINTRAUB, M., W. G. KEMP, and H. W. J. RAGETLI. 1960. Canad. J. Microbiol. 6: 407.
WILDMAN, S. G., C. C. CHEO, and J. BONNER. 1949. J. biol. Chem. 180: 985.
WILSON, J. H. 1955. Ann. appl. Biol. 43: 273.
WOODS, A. F. 1899. Zbl. Bakt. 5: 745.
——. 1900. Science 11: 17.
WOODS, M. W., and H. G. DUBUY. 1942. Phytopathology 32: 288.
WYND, F. L. 1943. Bot. Rev. 9: 395.
YARWOOD, C. E. 1953. Phytopathology 43: 675.
ZAITLIN, M., and A. T. JAGENDORF. 1960. Virology 12: 477.

chapter

5

Methods of Transmission

Viruses multiply only intracellularly, so their continued existence demands that they infect a continuous series of cells. This they achieve in two ways; first by their ability to spread unaided from one cell to another inside individual plants, so that infection of one cell initially can later lead to most cells of a large plant becoming infected; secondly, by spreading from one plant to another, which they rarely do unaided, except from parent plants to their offspring. The cuticle of plants seems a barrier that viruses cannot penetrate and transmission from one growing plant to another requires the active help of some agent able to cause an appropriate wound through which the virus can enter. What is an appropriate wound for one virus, however, is not necessarily appropriate for another and different viruses make use of very different agents for their spread. The three main methods whereby viruses can be transmitted to a healthy plant are: (1) by grafting with a scion from an infected plant; (2) by rubbing with juice from an infected plant; (3) by a specific animal feeding on it after having fed on an infected plant. A fourth method, too recently discovered for its importance yet to be known, is by a soil-borne fungus.

Some viruses have been transmitted by all three methods, others by only one or two, and the methods whereby a virus has been transmitted usually loom large in diagnostic descriptions. The knowledge that a virus has been transmitted by a given method is obviously valuable, but negative results are less valuable than has usually been admitted. There is no doubt that many viruses that as et have been transmitted experimentally only by grafting do have animal or other vectors awaiting discovery and it is becoming increasingly obvious that failure to transmit by inoculation with sap is often determined more by the properties of the host plant in which the virus is encountered than by properties intrinsic to the virus. Finding the specific animal vector can take a long time: *Abutilon* variegation, for example, had been known to be graft transmissible for more than 71 years before it was found to be transmitted by the white-fly *Bemisia tabaci* (Orlando and Silberschmidt, 1946); similarly, some of the oldest known viruses of the vine, for which grafting has till recently been the only known method of transmission, have now been transmitted both by a nematode, *Xiphinema index* (Hewitt, Raski and Goheen, 1958) and by inoculation with sap (Cadman, Dias and Harrison, 1960).

Vegetative propagation and grafting. Plants in which viruses are economically important are those in which the viruses become established systemically, that is, from a single entry point spread through most or all of the vegetative parts of the plant. Plants have no antibody-forming mechanism comparable with those by which animals combat viruses and infection of a plant that becomes systemically invaded usually gives a continuing source of virus for as long as any vegetative parts of the plant remain viable. It is, perhaps, worth stressing that not all hosts provide conditions equally favourable to the survival of a virus. A host that becomes infected only locally or is rapidly killed by infection provides only a brief period of multiplication compared with one that is invaded systemically and survives the infection. Should a host of the second type be a perennial plant or one propagated vegetatively, a virus is supplied with a continuous series of susceptible cells year after year without ever being exposed to the risks inseparable from the process of transmission from one individual to another. Often, indeed, such perennial or vegetatively propagated plants are the main sources of viruses for annual plants. The persistence of viruses in perennial or vegetatively propagated plants was commented on in Chapter 1 and there is little need to do more here than to stress the great importance of vegetative propagation, not only in perpetuating viruses but also in aiding their spread; any method of vegetative propagation, whether by tubers, bulbs, corms, runners, suckers, or by rooting cuttings, is likely to produce virus-infected progeny if the parent plant was infected, and against the undoubtedly great virtues of clonal varieties must be set the harsh fact that their use has disseminated many important viruses widely.

Grafting is, of course, simply a method of vegetative propagation, whereby a part of one plant becomes established on another instead of on its own roots. Transmission of viruses by grafting is an inevitable sequel to their ability to survive in vegetative cells and to spread between vegetative cells inside plants. Once organic union is established between scion and stock, the two are effectively one plant, and viruses able to move between cells will pass from one into the other. It is axiomatic that viruses will be transmitted by grafting between individual plants of a type which they can infect systemically, and such transmission, taken together with the failure to find a visible pathogen, has long provided the main criterion for establishing an abnormal condition as a virus disease.

Any grafting method that ensures organic union between an infected piece of one plant and the uninfected tissues of another will lead to trasmission. With herbaceous plants, a good method is to cut off the top of the healthy test plant, preferably at or immediately above a node, and slit the stem down the center for 2–3 cm. An apical shoot cut from the diseased plant is trimmed to a few small leaves, its stem cut to a wedge shape and inserted into the slit stock so that the cambium of scion and stock meet, when the junction is lightly bound. The plant is then kept warm and humid and out of bright light, conditions which not only encourage union between scion and stock but make the stock produce succulent side shoots, often excellent material for contracting infection and showing symptoms rapidly.

With woody plants or trees, budding may be more successful than cleft grafting. A bud should be cut from the diseased plant so that it carries with it cortical tissue and phloem; two slits at right angles to one another are made in the stem of the stock reaching down to the cambium, and the bud is inserted into the opening so that the cambium of bud and stock are in contact. A bud is not always necessary. The virus causing spike disease of sandal, which has not been transmitted by inoculating healthy plants with juice from infected ones, is transmitted when pieces of stem tissue from infected trees are inserted between the wood and bark of healthy trees; callus forms between the two and this apparently suffices for the virus to pass from infected to healthy cells (Sreenivasaya, 1930). Similarly, peach mosaic (Cochran and Rue, 1944) and psorosis of citrus (Wallace, 1947) can be transmitted by placing cut pieces of infected leaves under the bark of healthy trees; uncut leaves are ineffective, for the transmission apparently depends on callus formed between the cut edges and the cambium of the stock. Grafts between any kinds of tissue, roots, tubers, bulbs and corms, no less than conventional stems, will lead to transmission, provided only that organic union is achieved.

Transmission by grafting often gives different results from transmission by inoculation of sap or by an animal vector. There can be two reasons for this: one, the more common, is that the plant from which transmission is being made is infected by more than one virus, all of which will be transmitted by grafting whereas not all may be by the other method; the second reason is that transmission by grafting will often lead to systemic infection in hosts that react only with necrotic local lesions when inoculated by rubbing their leaves. For example, potato varieties that produce only black local lesions when inoculated with some strains of potato viruses X and Y die from top-necrosis when the strains are introduced by cleft grafts. Similarly, *Nicotiana glutinosa* plants stem-grafted with scions from tobacco or tomato systemically infected with tobacco mosaic virus will die from a systemic disease; black necroses first appear around the growing points of newly produced side shoots, which would remain healthy in comparable plants infected by rubbing their older leaves.

Grafting is now increasingly less used than it was in work with viruses, for many of the viruses for which this was the only known method of transmission can now be transmitted in other ways. However, it still remains an important method whereby viruses are spread in horticultural crops, such as fruit trees, roses and other flowering plants, where it is general practice to graft one variety onto a root stock of another variety. The unwitting use of either infected root stocks or of infected plants to supply scions or bud wood has undoubtedly been a major reason for many viruses of these plants becoming widely distributed. The actual practice of grafting can sometimes create the conditions for a serious virus disease, even though both scion and stock were uninfected at the time of grafting. Decline or tristeza of sweet orange trees, which presented some features that for long prevented it being recognised as caused by a virus, provides the classic example (Fawcett and Wallace, 1946). Sweet orange grafted onto sour orange stocks often wilt and die, apparently because of a root rot. If pieces of the wilting sweet orange are established as cuttings, they will grow and if the sweet orange is removed from the stock before it dies the sour orange will also grow again. This happens because of the different reactions of the two varieties to infection; the sweet orange can tolerate the virus, but the sour orange is so intolerant that infected cells soon die. Hence when the sweet orange scion becomes infected, the leaves show few effects, but when the virus passes into the scion-stock union it kills the sour orange cells, prevents the normal movement of food from leaves to roots and so both roots and shoots soon die unless the two are separated.

Dodder. Transmission of viruses by grafting is, of course, limited to transmission between plants whose tissues can form organic union with one another, which often means only within one genus. An ingenious method of transmission that can be regarded as an extension of grafting that overcomes this limitation is the use of the plant parasite dodder (*Cuscuta* sp.) to form a union between infected and healthy plants (Bennett, 1940; Johnson, 1941). Dodder is most reliable in transmitting viruses for which it is itself a host; such viruses are simply transmitted by allowing dodder first to establish itself on the infected plant, then breaking pieces of the parasite off and allowing them to become established on the healthy plant. Viruses that do not multiply in the dodder may still be transmitted from infected to healthy plants, but this entails establishing the dodder on both plants so that it makes a conducting channel between the two; transmission in these circumstances is helped by pruning the dodder keeping the infected donor plant in bright light and the healthy recipient in shade, presumably because this encourages the flow of food from donor to recipient and the viruses move in the food stream (Cochran, 1946). Different species of dodder are susceptible to a wide range of different viruses and Bennett (1944) found that symptomless *Cuscuta californica* is often infected with a previously undescribed virus, which he called dodder latent mosaic, and which causes serious diseases in many plants as varied as sugar beet, potato and cantaloupe. In using dodder to transmit a virus, therefore, it is important to show that the stock of dodder used does not already contain a virus that infects the test plants.

The main value of the transmissions by dodder has been to show that viruses previously thought to be restricted to one kind of plant do have wide host ranges and to transmit such viruses to other plants where they may be more amenable to study and able to be compared with other viruses. For example, Kunkel (1943, 1945) transmitted cranberry false blossom virus from cranberry, its only previously known host and a most inconvenient experimental plant, to 28 different species, belonging to 10 different families and including such convenient experimental plants as tobacco and tomato. Similarly, he transmitted potato witches' broom and peach mosaic viruses, both till then thought to have narrow host ranges, to such plants as *Vinca rosea*, tomato and sugar beet. The possibilities of extending host ranges by transmitting with dodder seem almost limitless, for there are many *Cuscuta* sp. with different host ranges and the single species *C. campestris* can parasitise more than 100 kinds of plants, so here are probably few higher plants that cannot be simultaneously parasitised by one *Cuscuta* sp. or another.

Transmission through seed. Most of the viruses that are said to infect a host systemically in fact fall short of infecting all its tissues; in particular, although all or most of the vegetative cells become invaded, the cells engaged in sexual reproduction do not. Consequently, most viruses are not seed-borne. The contrast between the health of progeny produced by sexual and asexual reproduction from infected parent plants is so striking in many species that it has given asexual reproduction the undeserved reputation of being intrinsically debilitating. What prevents most viruses from entering the seeds of their host plants is unknown, but the rate at which clonal varieties of some plants lose their vigour obviously makes some such cleansing process an evolutionary necessity, otherwise species in which virulent viruses spread rapidly could not survive. In discussions of the evolutionary significance of sexual reproduction, too, only the genetical advantages are usually mentioned, but the expulsion of viruses, at least in hosts that are harmed by infection, may well deserve more attention. However, although exceptional, seed-transmission is far from insignificant, for seed-borne virus is not only the main source of infection that leads to economically important diseases of several crops, but it can also greatly aid the dispersal of viruses that only rarely manage to infect seed.

Among theories advanced to explain what prevents seed from becoming infected are disturbances to cell division, the anatomical isolation of the embryo, and the inactivation of viruses by their adsorption onto the seed proteins or by the maturation of the seed, but none is supported by any convincing evidence. Certainly, inactivation within the seed seems implausible, for some of the viruses that are seed-transmitted are unstable *in vitro*, whereas those that are not are among the most stable. Also, the failure to be seed-transmitted seems to come, not from virus reaching the embryo and inactivating there, but from the failure to enter the pollen or egg mother cells. No virus that is not seed-transmitted has yet been demonstrated in the pollen set by infected plants (Caldwell, 1934; Bennett and Esau, 1936; Gratia and Manil, 1936), whereas pollen from bean plants (*Phaseolus vulgaris*) infected with bean mosaic virus (Reddick, 1931) and from barley with false stripe virus (Gold *et al*, 1954), both of which are transmitted through a high proportion of seeds, is infected. It may be significant in this context that many viruses that reach high concentrations in differentiated vegeta-

tive cells not only fail to infect seeds but also seem unable to infect
the meristematic cells at stem growing points (Morel and Martin
1952, 1955; Kassanis, 1957a). This suggests that the nucleic acid
metabolism of most cells when undergoing nuclear division may be
such as to preclude the multiplication of viruses, and seed-transmission may indicate the ability of a virus to implant its pattern of
nucleic acid synthesis on host cells even when these are actively engaged in providing their own needs for extra deoxy and ribose nucleic acids. The anatomical isolation of the embryo, already mentioned, may prevent viruses unable to survive in cells undergoing
meiosis or mitosis from entering the seeds after cells have stopped
dividing.

Except for virus causing mosaic of *Phaseolus lunatus* and *Phaseolus vulgaris,* which were early shown to be seed-transmitted (Mc-
Clintock, 1917; Reddick and Stewart, 1919), none of those studied
at all intensively in the early days of virus research were perpetuated
through seed. This fostered the idea that leguminous plants were
exceptional and that reproduction by seed of plants in other families
could safely be assumed to provide virus-free progeny, even though
the parent was infected. Unfortunately, later experience showed
this assumption to be unjustified, for although seed-transmission is
unusual, it is a much commoner event than was generally supposed.
Also, it is by no means restricted to leguminous plants, although
some viruses seem to be transmitted to a much higher proportion of
seed set by leguminous than by other infected plants. For example,
seed set by Lincoln Soybean infected with tobacco ringspot virus
gave 50–80% infected seedlings (Desjardins, Latterell and Mitchell,
1954), whereas Henderson (1931) got no seed-transmission in tobacco but about 20% in *Petunia* sp.; Valleau (1941) reported some
seed-transmission in tobacco, and also that infection in this host
made much of the pollen sterile. By no means all the viruses that
infect leguminous plants are seed-transmitted in them, and those
that are infect different proportions of the seeds.

Many of the apparent contradictory reports about the seed-transmission of some viruses probably come from different workers having
worked with different hosts or, perhaps, having taken seed from
plants that have been infected for different lengths of time. It seems
likely that some viruses are rarely, if ever, seed-borne in any of their
hosts; some are seed-borne in some hosts but not in others and in
some hosts they may be seed-borne much more often than in others.
The ability to invade and survive in seed, like the ability to cause a
given type of clinical syndrome, is not an absolute property of a
virus or virus strain but depends equally on the identity of the host

plant. It possibly also depends on the physiology of the host at the time of flowering, for even in a host where a virus is often seed-transmitted, the proportion of seeds that becomes infected can differ greatly in different plants. For instance, not all the seeds set by *Phaseolus vulgaris* plants infected with bean mosaic virus contain virus and the same pod may have infected and uninfected seeds. One thing that affects the proportion of seeds that become infected is the length of time for which the parent plant has been infected; the proportion is greatest with plants themselves raised from infected seeds and plants that remain uninfected until after their blossom has set produce all uninfected seeds (Fajardo, 1930; Nelson, 1932; Harrison, 1935). Similarly, the proportion of seeds infected with lettuce mosaic virus depends on when the parent lettuce plants become infected; it may be up to 14% in those infected young, is much less in those infected soon before flowering and falls to 0% in plants first infected after flowering has begun. The virus is not seed-borne in the lettuce variety Cheshunt Giant, apparently because infection kills the pro-cambium of the first-formed florets and secondary ones seem not to become invaded by the virus (Ainsworth and Ogilvie, 1939; Grogan *et al*, 1952; Couch, 1955).

Although most plants that are virus-free until the time they flower are probably free from the danger of setting infected seeds, this cannot always be safely assumed. At least two viruses, namely those causing mosaic of *Phaseolus vulgaris* (Reddick, 1931) and false stripe of barley (Gold *et al*, 1954) are pollen-transmitted and fertilising the pistils of uninfected plants with pollen from an infected one will give some infected seed. Most of the examples of seed transmission are from virus that invades the embryo, but only with false stripe of barley has virus been demonstrated in all parts of the seed (Gold *et al*, 1954). Most workers are agreed that tobacco and tomato seedlings produced from seed set by plants infected by tobacco mosaic virus are virus-free, but a few have described infections which they attribute to seed-borne virus. These infections possibly come, not from virus inherited through the embryo, but by infection of the young seedling with virus which contaminates the seed coats and can often be recovered from them even after the seed has germinated (Ainsworth, 1933). Tobacco etch virus also seems to enter the seed coats, for these but no other part of the seed contain the characteristic intranuclear inclusions; seedlings raised from such seed are virus-free, and this virus, which is much more unstable than tobacco mosaic, seems soon to inactivate, for whereas immature seeds give infective extracts fully mature seeds do not (Sheffield, 1941).

Not all viruses that enter the embryos seem able to survive for a long as seed retains its ability to germinate; two batches of musk melon seed, for example, gave 93% and 28% infected seedlings when sown soon after harvest but gave only 3% and 6% when sown after three years in store (Rader, Fitzpatrick and Hildebrand, 1947). In fection of melon and squash seeds by squash mosaic virus, which can also survive in seed for at least three years, often produces ligh and deformed seed, which can be removed by careful winnowing only 2% of the plump seed from a batch gave infected seedlings, in contrast to 37% of the light-weight seed (Middleton, 1944). Seed transmission has been reported in many cucurbitaceous plants, but as with leguminous plants, no generalisations are possible, because one virus may be seed-borne in one species but not in another, and a second may reverse this procedure. This determining effect of the host species is also evident with plants from other families; for example, dodder latent mosaic virus was transmitted through 5% of the seed set by infected *Cuscuta campestris*, but not through seed set by cantaloupe, pokeweed or buckwheat, all of which show symp- toms when infected (Bennett, 1944); similarly, tomato spotted wilt virus seems not to be seed-borne in most of its many hosts, but is in *Cineraria* sp. (Jones, 1944). Tomato black ring virus, however seems exceptional in as much as it was transmitted through a high proportion of the seed set by all nine species of plants tested, be- longing to the families Leguminosae, Rosaceae, Cruciferae, Papav- eraceae, Compositae and Solanaceae; two other soil-borne viruses raspberry ringspot and arabis mosaic, were seed-borne in some species but not others (Lister, 1960). Seed transmission is not re- stricted to herbaceous plants, and many (up to 30%) of the seeds set by cherry trees with necrotic ringspot or yellows produce infected seedlings (Cation, 1949).

Soil-borne viruses. There is nothing novel in the idea that viruses may be soil-borne, for Mayer suggested in 1886 that the cause of tobacco mosaic virus should be sought in the soil and Beijerinck showed in 1898 that tobacco seedlings became infected when grown in soil collected some months earlier from around the roots of dis- eased plants. Similarly, Behrens concluded in 1899 that the cause of the disease now usually called tobacco rattle persisted in the soil, a conclusion amply confirmed by recent work. Despite this early attention, however, the study of soil-borne viruses languished for many years. The subject may well have suffered from the fact that tobacco mosaic virus was the first to be recognised as soil-borne; it remains infective for many years in plant extracts or dead tissues, so it was not surprising that it should also survive in soil. There also seemed nothing subtle about its ability to infect plants, for it readily enters through wounds and there was need only to postulate that roots become injured while growing through contaminated soil to get an acceptable explanation for the infections. There is good evidence that soil-borne virus often initiates outbreaks of mosaic in tobacco (Johnson and Ogden, 1929) and tomato (Doolittle, 1928), but outbreaks can initiate in other ways and the fact that tobacco mosaic virus can also spread rapidly above ground may have diverted attention from infections below ground and created the impression that other soil-borne viruses also had other and more important methods of spread. The failure to realise the potentialities of soil-borne viruses has undoubtedly led to false claims of viruses arising "spontaneously" in insect-proof glasshouses and has possibly also led to false claims of seed-transmission, for few workers have taken adequate precautions to ensure that the soil in which their test plants are grown is virus-free.

Plants will contract tobacco mosaic virus from recently sterilised soil to which the virus is added and the simple mechanical explanation long held for its survival and method of infection may be true. Certainly, if any organism plays a part it must be a prevalent one that soon establishes itself again in sterilised soil. The condition is different with most other soil-borne viruses. For instance, the group of viruses that cause the cereal mosaics and wheat rosette, which are prevalent in many parts of the U.S.A. and Japan (McKinney, 1923, 1925, 1953; McKinney et al, 1925, 1957; Webb, 1927, 1928; Sill, 1958; Sawada, 1927; Wada and Fukano, 1934), infect plants grown in soil containing roots from naturally infected plants but not in soil containing only leaves or sap from infected plants. Infective soil free from cereals, or indeed free from any higher plants, can remain infective for up to four years when dry. As these viruses are highly unstable in leaf extracts and are difficult to transmit mechanically, their persistence in the soil and the readiness with which they infect plants from infective soil, strongly suggests that there is some soil-borne organism that acts both as an alternative host for the virus and as a vector able to introduce them into plant roots. Various organisms have been tested without success, but the most obvious kind of suspect from existing information about the behaviour of the viruses in soil is perhaps a fungus able to form resting spores when conditions do not favour its growth and acting as a superficial parasite of cereal roots when it is active. This type of vector, or another kind of organism readily carried in water, would also explain the spread of chlorotic streak virus from infected to healthy sugar-cane plants growing in separate containers but receiving the same lot of circulating nutrient solution (Bird, Cibes and Tio, 1958).

The idea that cereal mosaic virus may be transmitted by a soil-borne fungus gains credence from the correlations reported between *Olpidium brassicae* and tobacco stunt (Hidaka *et al,* 1956; Hidaka, 1960), lettuce big-vein (Fry, 1958; Grogan *et al,* 1958) and tobacco necrosis (Teakle, 1960), and from recent experimental evidence that this fungus transmits tobacco necrosis (Teakle, 1962) and lettuce big-vein viruses (Campbell, Grogan and Purcifull, 1961; Campbell, 1962; Tomlinson and Garrett, 1962). These two differ greatly in their other behaviour, so it is not unexpected that they also seem to be transmitted differently by *O. brassicae.* The tobacco necrosis viruses get their name from the shrivelling of the lowest leaves of tobacco seedlings grown under glass during winter (Smith and Bald, 1935); for long this was the only disease they were known to cause, although they were known to multiply locally in the leaves of almost any species to which they were inoculated, usually causing necrotic lesions, and to occur commonly in the roots of plants with symptomless tops. At first, too, only one virus was thought to be concerned, but serological and other studies showed there were several, some of which also occur in distinctive strains (Bawden, 1941; Bawden and Pirie, 1942). They have now been found causing systemic necroses in tulip (Kassanis, 1949; de Bruyn Ouboter and van Slogteren, 1949), *Phaseolus vulgaris* (Bawden and van der Want, 1949; Quantz, 1956; Natti, 1959) and cucumber (McKeen, 1959); also lesions on potato tubers (Noordam, 1957). Presumably all these, and perhaps the satellite virus that often accompanies them, are spread by *O. brassicae,* but this is not yet established. Roots become infected when exposed to mixtures of tobacco necrosis virus and zoospores, and the zoospores may do little except acquire virus on their surface and carry it into cells they invade. Things are different with lettuce big-vein, a systemic disease caused by a virus transmitted by grafting but not by inoculation of sap; transmission occurs only with *O. brassicae* coming from virus-infected plants, and the virus is probably carried inside the spores. This virus seems to survive for long periods in the resting spores, but there is no critical evidence to show whether it multiplies in them; however, it is lost when fungus cultures are propagated in plants insusceptible to the virus.

Another group of soil-borne viruses is being increasingly identified as causing many diseases long-known but thought to be distinct. Until techniques were developed that allowed viruses to be transmitted from fruit crops and studied in herbaceous plants, such diseases as raspberry leaf curl, strawberry mosaic, peach yellow bud mosaic, cherry rasp leaf and fanleaf of grapevine, seemed to have nothing in common, but it has gradually become evident that they are caused by similar viruses that also infect other crops as diverse as tomato, potato, turnip, sugar beet and oats, in addition to a very wide range of weed plants. Some of these viruses occur in land that has never been cultivated, so they cannot be attributed to the too frequent growing of susceptible crops. They all have isometric particles and similar general properties, but differ from one another antigenically and in other details. Soil loses its infectivity when dried or when treated with nematicides, and they are probably all transmitted by nematodes. The identification of a nematode vector

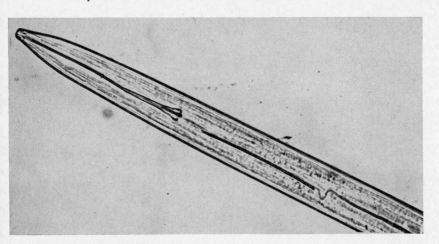

Fig. 5–1. The head of a larva of the spear-bearing nematode, *Xiphinema diversicaudatum*, the vector of the soil-borne virus, arabis mosaic.

(*Xiphinema index*) was first achieved by Hewitt, Raski and Goheen (1958), working with fanleaf disease of grapevine, since shown by Cadman, Dias and Harrison (1960) to be caused by a strain of arabis mosaic virus. Other nematodes that have been identified as vectors are: *X. diversicaudatum* (Fig. 5–1) of the arabis mosaic virus itself (Jha and Posnette, 1959, 1961; Harrison and Cadman, 1959); *X. americanum* of peach yellow bud mosaic virus (Breece and Hart, 1959), since shown to be a strain of tomato ringspot virus (Cadman and Lister, 1961) and of tobacco ringspot virus (Hendrix, 1961); *Longidorus elongatus* and *L. attenuatus* of strains of tomato black ring virus (Harrison, Mowat and Taylor, 1961). Nematode transmission is not restricted to these viruses that cause ringspot symptoms in many of their hosts, for tobacco rattle, which differs from them in many ways and has rigid rod-shaped particles, is transmitted by *Trichodorus pachydermus* (Sol, van Heuven and Seinhorst, 1960).

It is characteristic of crops that are harmed by these viruses to have diseased plants occurring in patches, the width of which increases only slowly with increasing time, not more than a foot or so a year. Within the patches all the plants may be affected, and replanting usually leads to the new plants succumbing within a year or two. Surveys in the United Kingdom show a remarkable correlation between the distribution of infected plants and of the specific nematode vector in the soil, for not only is the vector always in the soil where diseased plants are growing, but it is rare to find it elsewhere. That the nematodes seem able to become infective almost anywhere has a plausible explanation from the discovery that the ringspot viruses are seed-transmitted in many of the weeds and some of the crop plants they infect. As the weeds include many free-seeding ones, such as groundsel, which have very efficient methods for dispersing their seeds, the opportunities for the viruses to reach most plots of soils infested by their nematode vector are obvious. In soil free from the specific vector, the introduction of the virus by weed seeds will be unimportant and pass unnoticed, but where the vector occurs the virus will be spread from infected weeds to crop plants and initiate disease outbreaks. The nematodes can remain infective for long periods, more than 30 days even when prevented from feeding (Jha and Posnette, 1959; Harrison and Winslow, 1961), but the viruses seem not to be transmitted through the eggs from female nematodes to their progeny (Raski and Hewitt, 1960), so presumably each generation of nematodes has to acquire virus by feeding on infected plants.

Inoculation with plant extracts. Knowledge about the physico-chemical properties of viruses derives largely from the study of those that are readily transmitted by inoculating healthy plants with sap from infected ones and such a method of transmission is almost a pre-requisite to the study of *in vitro* properties. Some viruses are probably not transmitted in this way because of some intrinsic property, perhaps ability to multiply only in deep-seated tissues such as the phloem, but these are certainly many fewer than has been generally assumed till very recently. They are mostly those transmitted by leafhoppers or whitefly, though they include a few aphid-transmitted viruses, characterised by potato leaf roll, which behave in their vectors much like some leafhopper-transmitted viruses. The failure to infect plants by mechanical inoculation with these cannot be attributed to the fact that they are unstable *in vitro*, for several of them have been transmitted by injecting their insect vectors with extracts from infected plants.

Except with the minority of viruses, all of which cause diseases of the "yellows" rather than the "mosaic" or "ringspot" type, it is doubtful whether the many reported failures to infect plants by inoculation with extracts from infected ones reflect the intrinsic behaviour of the infected virus. Most probably these failures occurred because the properties of either the plant yielding the extract or the one inoculated prevented infection. With increasing appreciation of the factors that affect mechanical transmission, more and more of the viruses long thought to be transmitted only by grafting or by a specific vector have been transmitted mechanically: this has allowed their properties to be studied, which in turn has sometimes shown that two diseases long assumed to be etiologically distinct, in fact, have the same cause.

Many workers, particularly those studying virus diseases of trees and shrubs, have been slow to appreciate that transmitting a virus by inoculation between two plants may depend less on the identity of the virus than on the species (and the physiological state) of either the plant from which the extract is made or the one to which it is to be inoculated. Consequently, knowledge about these viruses has lagged, and has mostly been restricted to symptomatology and epidemiology. It is, therefore, well worth considering in some detail the various factors that can prevent infections by viruses that are potentially transmissible by inoculation.

The first obvious essential for transmission is a virus concentration in the inoculum adequate to establish infection in the inoculated plant. Neither the virus content of extracts from infected hosts, nor the minimum amount of virus needed to infect, is a constant. The virus content of sap from different host species, or from plants of one species in different physiological states, can differ greatly; also the concentration of inoculum required to establish infection depends on the identity and physiological state of the plant inoculated. Failure to transmit a virus by inoculating healthy plants with extracts from a diseased one, therefore, may mean only that the virus content of the extract is below that required to infect the test plant. Dandelion yellow mosaic virus, for example, has not been transmitted from infected to healthy dandelion plants, but it has occasionally from dandelion to lettuce and from lettuce to dandelion; from infected to healthy lettuce it is transmitted readily, because lettuce not only supports a higher virus concentration than dandelion, but is also more susceptible to infection (Kassanis, 1947).

The virus content of the inoculum, however, is far from being the only factor affecting mechanical transmission; establishing infection can depend equally on what other substances are present. Some viruses are rapidly inactivated by components of sap, particularly by oxidising enzymes, but of more general importance is the fact that extracts of many plants contain substances that although not virus inactivators inhibit infection (Bawden, 1954). The nature of these inhibitors in most plants still remains undetermined, but the potent one in *Phytolacca decandra*, the first plant found to have virus-inhibiting properties (Allard, 1914, 1918; Doolittle and Walker, 1925; Duggar and Armstrong, 1925), is a glycoprotein containing 14 to 15% nitrogen and 8 to 12% carbohydrate (Kassanis and Kleczkowski, 1948). Tannins are common components of plants and their presence in sap often explains failure to transmit a virus by mechanical inoculation. The fact that, until recently, no virus from strawberry plants had been so transmitted obviously had no necessary bearing on the properties of viruses infecting this plant, for extracts from strawberry leaves contain up to 1% tannin, are protein-free and prevent tobacco mosaic virus from infecting *Nicotiana glutinosa* (Bawden and Kleczkowski, 1945). Tannins behave rather differently from other materials that inhibit infections by viruses. These other materials usually produce their full inhibiting effect immediately they are mixed with a virus; the size of their effect may depend more on the identity of the host inoculated than of the virus used, and their ability to inhibit is proportionally much greater at high than at low concentrations, so that diluting non-infective mixtures of concentrated inhibitor and virus often allows them to infect (Table 5–1). The consequences of different effects on different

TABLE 5–1

Recovery of Infectivity by Diluting a Mixture of Virus and Inhibitor

Original Solution	Infectivity			
	Average Number of Lesions per Leaf with Solution Diluted			
	1/1	1/10	1/100	1/1000
Tobacco mosaic virus 0.05 g/1 in				
Water	110	64	20	4
Sap from *Phylacca esculenta* diluted 1/10 ..	0	3	6	4

hosts, and of there being no fixed ratio between inhibitor and virus that neutralises infectivity, show in such facts as that cucumber mosaic virus can be transmitted by inoculation with undiluted sap from infected to healthy beet but not to healthy tobacco plants, and that tobacco plants will become infected when the beet sap is diluted 1/10 or more with water before being used as inoculum (Hoggan, 1933; Bhargava, 1951).

Gendron and Kassanis (1954) showed that it is a general feature of plant extracts to interfere less with infection of species producing the extracts than of other species. Hence Allard's early (1914, 1918) failure to infect tobacco with cucumber mosaic virus from *Phytolacca decandra*, although he infected healthy *P. decandra*. However, infection of some species seems generally less affected than of others by inhibitors, and the increasing use of such plants as cucumber and *Chenopodium amaranticolor* as test plants in part explains the increasing number of viruses that have recently been transmitted mechanically. How the inhibitors of infection act is unknown, but they are so varied chemically, ranging from large molecules such as proteins and polysaccharides to substances of small molecular weight, that it is extremely unlikely they all do precisely the same things. Some of the substances combine with virus particles *in vitro*, but not all do, so the combination is probably irrelevant to the inhibition of infection, which may depend on some effect on the host cells rather than a direct action on the viruses. An exception to this may be pancreatic ribonuclease, for on the assumption that the nucleic acid of virus particles becomes free as an initial step in the infection process, its action can be plausibly interpreted as hydrolysis of the free nucleic acid (Casterman and Jeener, 1955). However, even its action perhaps lies in some metabolic disturbance it causes in leaf cells, for not only do some substances with no nuclease activity behave similarly in inhibiting infection, but preparations of leaf ribonucleases equally able to hydrolyse nucleic acid *in vitro* inhibit infection much less than does pancreatic ribonuclease. The only common attribute to the various materials that inhibit infection may be that they differ from normal components of the cells they affect and their entry into the cells provokes some metabolic change that makes the cells temporarily resist infection. Comparable effects can happen in other ways than by rubbing leaves with solutions of specific substances. For example, exposing leaves that are normally susceptible to a virus to ultraviolet radiation can make them insusceptible, permanently if the leaves are kept in darkness after irradiation but only temporarily if they are kept in daylight (Bawden and Kleczkowski, 1952).

The different behaviour of tannins from other inhibitors shows in several ways. Their inhibitory action depends less on the identity of the plant inoculated than on the identity of the virus; for each virus, there is a fixed ratio between the amount of virus and the amount of tannin that is needed to lower infectivity to a given amount; their inhibitory action also increases with increasing time they are left in contact with viruses *in vitro* before inoculation to test plants (Cadman, 1959). In dealing with extracts that contain tannin, the inhibitory effects can be largely overcome by grinding leaves in the presence of nicotine sulphate, which combines with and precipitates the tannins (Limasset *et al*, 1950; Thung and van der Want, 1951). Raising the pH of leaf extracts by grinding the leaves in alkaline buffer solutions, or by grinding the leaves with solid Na₂HPO₄ also decreases the inhibitory action of tannins. Raising the pH sometimes produces infective extracts from some leaves, such as those of the grapevine, which normally yield such acid extracts that viruses are likely to be precipitated or inactivated.

Although most additions to an inoculum decrease the chances of infection, a few increase them. The phosphate ion has been the most studied and used, but still without any clear understanding of how it acts. The extent to which it increases infections is determined less by the identity of the virus being transmitted than by that of the host being inoculated, and is much greater with French beans than with *Nicotiana glutinosa* (Thornberry, 1935; Stanley, 1935), so it probably also acts by affecting the susceptibility of the host plant, presumably by doing the opposite of inhibitors and making conditions in cells temporarily more favourable to the survival of introduced virus particles. Extracts of New Zealand spinach (*Tetragonia expansa*) leaves contain both an inhibitor, probably a protein, and an augmenter of infection, a soluble oxalate salt. Benda (1956) suggests that the prime effect of both the oxalate and phosphate ions may be to precipitate calcium in leaf cells, which might aid infection by decreasing the viscosity of the cytoplasm or by increasing the permeability of the wounded cell membrane.

The biggest augmenters of infection are substances usually called abrasives. In early work with viruses, mechanical transmission was usually attempted by injecting sap into healthy plants or by placing drops of sap on leaves and scratching through them with needles. These methods succeeded with some viruses, but gave erratic results with others and they are now rarely used. Instead of being scarified, leaves are wetted with inoculum and gently rubbed, with the pestle used to grind leaves in a mortar, with the fore-finger, with a muslin pad, a brush, or something else according to personal preferences: unwounded leaves seem immune from infection, though people have claimed infections when leaves simply had virus suspensions atomised over them (Duggar and Johnson, 1933; Smith and Bald, 1935), but the kind of wound that most favours infection still remains to be determined. As viruses multiply only in living cells, lethal injuries can obviously be expected to prevent infections, and this probably explains the ineffectiveness of the early scratching methods. The breaking of hair cells is often thought to be the most important type of wounding, but Boyle and McKinney (1938) found that the number of infections obtained with tobacco mosaic virus is independent of the number of hair cells on leaves and as many infections occur on parts of pepper leaves without as with hairs. Inoculations by methods that damaged only the leaf hairs produced few infections, and Boyle and McKinney suggest that bruising the epidermal cells is more important than damaging hair cells. The simplest explanation of the action of abrasives is that their use increases the number of cells that become damaged, but not irreparably so, when leaves are rubbed. Their use was first shown with viruses that were not easily transmitted by rubbing leaves with sap only but became so when sand was incorporated in the inoculum (Fajardo, 1930; Samuel and Bald, 1933). Sand, though, is relatively ineffective compared to 400–500 mesh carborundum (Rawlins and Tompkins, 1934, 1936; Costa, 1944) and appropriate grades of diatomaceous earths, such as "Celite," or animal charcoal (Kalmus and Kassanis, 1945). These are usually dusted over the leaf surfaces, which are then gently rubbed with the inoculum, or mixed with the inoculum.

The effect of adding carborundum to an inoculum depends on the species and the physiological state of the plant being inoculated; as Table 5–2 shows, it can increase the infection end-point of a virus

TABLE 5–2

Effect of Carborundum 400-Mesh on the Dilution End-Point of
Tobacco Mosaic Virus

	Average Number of Lesions per Leaf at Different Virus Concentrations (g./ml.)				
Inoculum:	10^{-5}	10^{-6}	10^{-7}	10^{-8}	10^{-9}
With carborundum	407	166	26	5	1
No carborundum	24	4	2	0	0

preparation by 100 times. This probably explains its usefulness in transmitting some viruses otherwise difficult to transmit by inoculation with plant extracts, for these are probably viruses that occur in the extracts in amounts approaching the infection end-point. The behaviour of potato viruses A and Y in transmission tests between potato and tobacco plants will serve to illustrate the point. Virus Y is readily transmitted between both plants without the aid of an abrasive, but whereas sap from infected tobacco will usually infect tobacco seedlings when diluted to more than 1/10,000, it ceases to infect potato when diluted to about 1/500. With carborundum, the dilution end point for each host is increased 50–100 times. Potato virus A is transmitted from potato to tobacco without abrasives, but only with sap not diluted less than 1/50, whereas potato is rarely infected by inoculation with undiluted sap, unless an abrasive is used. If, as with virus Y, about 50 times as much virus A is needed to infect potato as to infect tobacco, the failure of virus A to infect

Fig. 5–2. Effect of abrasives in facilitating transmission and in increasing permeability of leaves. Left-hand half-leaves rubbed with water; right-hand half-leaves rubbed with water and Celite. Leaf *at left* sprayed with suspension of tobacco mosaic virus and leaf *at right* treated with ammoniacal silver hydroxide (argentaffin test). Note many more lesions and much more uniform staining of half-leaves rubbed with Celite. (H. Kalmus and B. Kassanis, 1945, Ann. appl. Biol. 32: 230).

potato plants unless an abrasive is used is simply explained by the fact that the virus content of sap is just below the infection endpoint for this host without carborundum and slightly above with.

Fig. 5–2 shows two effects of rubbing a *Nicotiana glutinosa* leaf with a diatomaceous earth: (1) the increase in number of local lesions produced by a dilute solution of tobacco mosaic virus; (2) the increase in permeability shown by treating the leaf with ammoniacal silver hydroxide, which turns dark when it reacts with reducing substances during exposure to light. Unwounded leaves placed in the reagent do not blacken, and leaves rubbed with the forefinger become only stippled with black spots, whereas after rubbing with an abrasive leaves become almost uniformly blackened. The abrasive removes the cuticle and the hairs, and temporarily makes the leaves highly susceptible to infection when virus solutions are simply sprayed over them, a result not obtained by rubbing with the forefinger alone. Within 3–4 hours of rubbing with the abrasive, the leaves regain their resistance to infection by sprayed virus solutions, but remain permeable to salts, presumably because their cuticle is not repaired (Kalmus and Kassanis, 1945).

Some plant species, although hosts for a virus introduced by some other method, such as by a feeding vector, are highly refractory to infection when their leaves are rubbed with inocula that readily infect other host species. All species of *Rosaceae* seem to come into this refractory category, as do many trees and shrubs of several other families. This may be because their cuticles are especially tough, or their epidermal cells are rich in substances that inactivate virus in the inoculum, but whatever the reason it seems that they might become susceptible if they were grown in conditions widely different from those now generally practised. This is suggested by the fact that the ease with which species that are not in the refractory category become infected by mechanical inoculation depends greatly on their physiological state when they are inoculated, which in turn depends on their nutrition and the environment in which they have been raised. In general, young actively growing seedlings are the best receptor plants, but the conditions that most favour infection by one virus are not those that necessarily most favour infection by another. For example, when a *Nicotiana glutinosa* with 8–10 well developed leaves has opposite halves of these leaves rubbed with tobacco mosaic and tomato bushy stunt viruses, the former will cause lesions on all leaves, but more on the middle and lower ones than on the upper ones, whereas tomato bushy stunt virus will produce no lesions on the lowest leaves, a few on the middle ones and most on the upper. Even the type of inoculum used can determine which leaves produce most lesions, for preparations of nucleic acid from tobacco mosaic virus, like tomato bushy stunt virus, and unlike tobacco mosaic virus itself, will produce more lesions on the upper than on the lower leaves of *N. glutinosa*. Susceptibility to infection can alter rapidly as plants age; during summer French bean plants about 10 days from sowing will give many infections with inocula of tobacco necrosis and some other viruses, but 3–4 days later may give none.

Probably the environmental variants that most affect the susceptibility of a given species to infection are light intensity and temperature. Plants raised in low light intensity are more susceptible than plants raised in bright light and remain susceptible until they are much older (Fig. 5–3); susceptibility is also increased by keeping plants in darkness for some time immediately before they are inoculated (Bawden and Roberts, 1948). Keeping plants at temperatures around 37° for some time before inoculation similarly

Fig. 5–3. Leaves of *Nicotiana glutinosa* showing effect of shade in increasing susceptibility to tomato bushy stunt virus. *Left:* leaf from shaded plant. *Right:* leaf from unshaded plant. Left-hand half-leaves inoculated with virus at 10 mg./l. and right-hand halves with virus at 1 mg./l.

greatly increases the numbers of lesions produced by a given inoculum (Kassanis, 1952, 1957b). No time can be specified, either for keeping plants in darkness or at 37°, that will produce maximum susceptibility, for this depends on the species of plant and its physiological state at the time. One or two days are usually enough to produce a considerable effect, and longer than this may damage some plants and make infections fewer. The effects have applied with all hosts and all viruses yet tested, though their magnitude differs with different plants and viruses. Table 5–3 shows that their magnitude also depends on the type of the inoculum, for although intact tobacco mosaic virus and its nucleic acid both produce more lesions in plants kept at 37° or in darkness for 2 days before they were inoculated than in plants kept in daylight at 20°, the increase is much greater with the inoculum of nucleic acid (Bawden and Pirie, 1959). In striking contrast to the effect of high temperature before inoculation, keeping plants at 37° after inoculation decreases the number of infections obtained and can completely

TABLE 5-3

Effect of Preconditioning Test Plants on the Relative Infectivity of Tobacco Mosaic Virus and Its Nucleic Acid *

Inoculum	Treatment of Plants			
	Control	2 Days at 37°	Control	2 Days in Darkness
Virus 5 mg./l	100	160	100	160
1	43	79	28	45
0.2	15	42	3.5	9
Nucleic acid 5 mg.P/l	20	152	4	64
1	3	35	1.5	15
0.2	0.4	10	0.3	3

* The virus and nucleic acid at the specified concentration were inoculated to opposite halves of the same leaves. The control plants were left in normal glasshouse conditions and the treated ones were at 37° or in darkness for the 2 days before they were inoculated; afterwards they were all put in the glasshouse. The results are expressed as the % of the number of lesions produced by the half-leaves of the control plants inoculated with virus at 5 mg./l; the actual numbers produced by these 12 half-leaves were 512 and 620.

prevent infection by some viruses (Kassanis, 1952). Plants that have been conditioned by a period at 37° should therefore be put at 20° after inoculation.

Extracts from many plants contain substances that injure leaves of herbaceous plants, particularly of actively growing seedlings raised in low light intensity or at high temperatures, unless they are quickly removed by washing with water. Although washing is necessary, it also can decrease the number of infections, possibly as Yarwood (1955) suggested because water removes ions that aid the process of infection, but the deleterious effect of washing can be decreased by drying the leaves quickly, for example, in currents of air (Yarwood, 1957).

Knowledge about the factors affecting the mechanical transmission of virus can perhaps be most usefully summarised in the form of recommended practices when attempting the transmission of an unknown virus from a plant with unknown properties. First, grind the leaves in the presence of phosphate and a reducing agent, such as sulphite, and use the inoculum immediately. Secondly, inoculate only rapidly growing plants that have been raised in low light intensities, and preferably pretreated by a period in darkness or at 37°. Thirdly, inoculate not only to the same species as the original hosts, but to plants such as cucumber and *Chenopodium amaranti color* that are less affected than many others by inhibitors of infection. Fourthly, dust the leaves to be inoculated with carborundum or kieselguhr. Fifthly, wash the leaves in a stream of water, and then dry them as rapidly as possible. Sixthly, test the extract to see whether it inhibits infection by readily transmissible viruses such as tobacco mosaic. If it does, failure to transmit the unknown virus has no significance in defining its properties. If extracts inhibit infection, it may also be worth trying another method of inoculation simply cutting or breaking leaves of the infected plant and rubbing their cut edges over leaves of the test plants previously dusted with an abrasive (Yarwood, 1957). Indeed, the method has advantages even with plants whose sap does not inhibit infection or rapidly inactivate viruses, for it is quick and obviates the need for a pestle and mortar or mincing machine to release sap. Should leaf extracts contain inhibitors, it is worth trying inoculum from other tissues such as petals or roots, for these may give infective extracts although leaves do not.

When transmission fails or is difficult using sap as the inoculum, it sometimes becomes easy with inoculum prepared by grinding infected leaves with phenol. The phenol denatures proteins and when the leaf extracts partition into a water phase and a phenol phase, the virus protein and any inhibitors of infection pass into the water phase whereas the nucleic acid passes into the phenol phase and gives effective inocula after the phenol has been removed. This extraction with phenol not only gives infective inocula from leaves that contain inhibitors of infection, but also of some virus strains that are either unstable in sap or occur in such conditions in leaf cells that they are not liberated into sap when leaves are macerated in conventional ways. Grinding with borate buffer at high pH, or with bentonite, treatments that inhibit the action of ribonuclease, also give highly infective inocula of some viruses which are not easily transmitted by inoculating with sap.

Although of prime importance in experimental work, mechanical transmission is by no means negligible in spreading viruses in crop plants. Tobacco mosaic virus, for example, often contaminates implements, hands and clothes, and from such sources can infect plants; once established by this method in one or a few plants in tobacco or tomato crops, it can spread readily by the rubbing together of healthy and infected plants or by operations, such as disbudding, which involve handling (Johnson, 1937). Similarly, potato virus X can survive on implements, clothes and other materials, and can be introduced into virus-free crops by such varied agencies as tractors, ploughs, spraying machines, hoes, and people or animals that have previously become contaminated by being in an infected crop (Todd, 1958); again, once established it can spread from infected to healthy plants when their leaves rub together (Loughnane and Murphy, 1938). Virus X can also spread from infected to healthy plants when their leaves are not in contact (Roberts, 1946); this has been assumed to happen by mechanical contact between roots, but the possibility of some soil-inhabiting organism acting as a vector has not been excluded. Potato spindle tuber is another disease that can be spread when tractors pass through crops (Merriam and Bonde, 1954); it is also transmitted from infected to healthy tubers on cutting knives, as can be some viruses of tulip (van Slogteren and Ouboter, 1941, a, b) and cymbidium (Jensen and Gold, 1955) when cutting flowers. Spread in such ways may well be much commoner than is now assumed and could account for some disease outbreaks in plants susceptible to infection by mechanical inoculation that now seem inexplicable. However, in total, the infections they cause in field crops are probably few compared with those caused by the insect and other vectors of viruses whose behaviour is described in Chapter 6.

REFERENCES

AINSWORTH, G. C. 1933. Ann. Rep. Cheshunt exp. Sta. 62.
———, and L. OGILVIE. 1939. Ann. appl. Biol. 26: 279.
ALLARD, H. A. 1914. Bull. U.S. Dep. Agric. No. 40.
———. 1918. Phytopathology 8: 51.
BAWDEN, F. C. 1941. Brit. J. exp. Pathol. 22: 59.
———. 1954. Advanc. Virus Res. 2: 31.
———, and A. KLECZKOWSKI. 1945. J. Pomol. 21: 2.
———, and ———. 1952. Nature, Lond. 169: 90.
———, and N. W. PIRIE. 1942. Brit. J. exp. Pathol. 23: 314.
———, and ———. 1959. J. gen. Microbiol. 21: 438.
———, and F. M. ROBERTS. 1948. Ann. appl. Biol. 35: 418.
———, and J. P. H. VAN DER WANT. 1949. Tijdschr. PlZiekt. 55: 142.
BEHRENS, J. 1899. Landw. VersSta. 52: 442.
BEIJERINCK, M. W. 1898. Verh. Akad. Wet., Amst. 6: 3.
BENDA, G. T. A. 1956. Virology 2: 438.
BENNETT, C. W. 1940. Phytopathology 30: 2.
———. 1944. Ibid. 34: 77.
———, and K. ESAU. 1936. J. agric. Res. 53: 595.
BHARGAVA, K. S. 1951. Ann. appl. Biol. 38: 377.
BIRD, J., H. CIBES, and M. A. TIO. 1958. Tech. Pap. P. R. Agric. Exp. Sta. 27.
BOYLE, L. M., and H. H. McKINNEY. 1938. Phytopathology 28: 114.

BREECE, J. R., and W. H. HART. 1959. Plant Dis. Reptr. 43: 989.
CADMAN, C. H. 1959. J. gen. Microbiol. 20: 113.
————, H. F. DIAS, and B. D. HARRISON. 1960. Nature, Lond. 187: 577.
————, and R. M. LISTER. 1961. Phytopathology 51: 29.
CALDWELL, J. 1934. Ann. appl. Biol. 21: 191.
CAMPBELL, R. N. 1962. Nature, Lond. 195: 675.
————, R. G. GROGAN, and D. E. PURCIFULL. 1961. Virology 15: 82.
CASTERMAN, C., and R. JEENER. 1955. Biochim. biophys. Acta. 16: 433.
CATION, D. 1949. Phytopathology 39: 37.
COCHRAN, G. W. 1946. Ibid. 36: 396.
COCHRAN, L. C., and J. L. LA RUE. 1944. Phytopathology 34: 934.
COSTA, A. S. 1944. Phytopathology 34: 288.
COUCH, H. B. 1955. Phytopathology 45: 63.
DESJARDINS, P. R., R. L. LATTERELL, and J. E. MITCHELL. 1954. Phytopathology 44: 86.
DOOLITTLE, S. P. 1928. Phytopathology 18: 155.
————, and M. N. WALKER. 1925. J. agric. Research. 31: 1.
DUGGAR, B. M., and J. K. ARMSTRONG. 1925. Ann. Mo. bot. Gdn. 12: 359.
————, and B. JOHNSON. 1933. Phytopathology 23: 934.
FAJARDO, T. G. 1930. Phytopathology 20: 469.
FAWCETT, H. S., and S. M. WALLACE. 1946. Calif. Citrogr. 32: 50.
FRY, P. R. 1958. New Zealand J. agric. Res. 1: 301.
GENDRON, Y., and B. KASSANIS. 1954. Ann. appl. Biol. 41: 188.
GOLD, A. H., C. A. SUNESON, B. R. HOUSTON, and J. W. OSWALD. 1954. Phytopathology 44: 115.
GRATIA, A., and P. MANIL. 1936. R. Soc. Biol. Paris 123: 509.
GROGAN, R. G., J. E. WELCH, and R. BARDIN. 1952. Phytopathology 42: 573.
————, F. W. WINK, W. B. HEWITT, and K. A. KIMBLE. 1958. Phytopathology 48: 292.
HARRISON, A. L. 1935. Tech. Bull. N.Y. St. agric. Exp. Sta. 236.
HARRISON, B. D., and C. H. CADMAN. 1959. Nature, Lond. 184: 1624.
————, W. P. MOWAT, and C. E. TAYLOR. 1961. Virology 14: 480.
————, and R. D. WINSLOW. 1961. Ann. appl. Biol. 49: 621.
HENDERSON, R. G. 1931. Phytopathology 21: 225.
HENDRIX, J. W. 1961. Ibid. 51: 194.
HEWITT, W. B., D. J. RASKI, and A. C. GOHEEN. 1958. Phytopathology 48: 586.
HIDAKA, Z. 1960. Rep. Scot. hort. Res. Inst. 1960–61, p. 76.
————, C. HIRUKI, K. NAKANO, T. SHIMIZU, and T. UOZUMI. 1956. Bull. Hatano Tobacco exp. Sta. 40: 1.
HOGGAN, I. A. 1933. Phytopathology 23: 446.
JENSEN, D. D., and A. H. GOLD. 1955. Phytopathology 45: 327.
JHA, A., and A. F. POSNETTE. 1959. Nature, Lond. 184: 962.
————, and ————. 1961. Virology 13: 119.
JOHNSON, F. 1941. Phytopathology 31: 649.
JOHNSON, J. 1937. J. agric. Res. 54: 239.
————, and W. B. OGDEN. 1929. Res. Bull. Univ. Wis. agric. Ex. Sta. 95.
JONES, L. K. 1944. Phytopathology 34: 941.
KALMUS, H., and B. KASSANIS. 1945. Ann. appl. Biol. 32: 230.
KASSANIS, B. 1947. Ann. appl. Biol. 34: 412.
————. 1949. Ibid. 36: 14.
————. 1952. Ibid. 39: 358.
————. 1957a. Ibid. 45: 422.
————. 1957b. Advanc. Virus Res. 4: 221.
————, and A. KLECZKOWSKI. 1948. J. gen. Microbiol. 2: 143.
KUNKEL, L. O. 1943. In Virus Diseases. Cornell University Press, Ithaca.
————. 1945. Phytopathology 35: 805.
LIMASSET, P., P. CORNUET, and C. MARTIN. 1950. C. R. Acad. Sci., Paris, 231: 913.

LISTER, R. M. 1960. Virology 10: 547.
LOUGHNANE, J. B., and P. A. MURPHY. 1938. Sci. Proc. R. Dublin Soc. 22: 3.
McCLINTOCK, J. A. 1917. Phytopathology 7: 60.
McKEEN, C. D. 1959. Canad. J. Bot. 37: 913.
McKINNEY, H. H. 1923. J. agric. Res. 23: 771.
———. 1925. Bull. U.S. Dep. Agric. 1361.
———. 1953. Yearb. U.S. Dep. Agric. 1953, 350.
———, W. R. PADEN, and B. KOEHLER. 1957. Plant Dis. Reptr. 41: 256.
———, R. W. WEBB, and G. H. DUNCAN. 1925. Bull. Ill. agric. Exp. Sta. 264: 273.
MAYER, A. E. 1886. Landw. VersSta. 32: 450.
MERRIAM, D., and R. BONDE. 1954. Maine Fm. Res. 1: (4), 7.
MIDDLETON, J. T. 1944. Phytopathology 34: 405.
MOREL, G., and C. MARTIN. 1952. C. R. Acad., Sci. Paris 235: 1324.
———, and ———. 1955. C. R. Acad. Agric. Fr. 41: 472.
NATTI, J. J. 1959. Plant Dis. Reptr. 43: 640.
NELSON, R. 1932. Tech. Bull. Mich. agric. Exp. Sta. 118.
NOORDAM, D. 1957. Tijdschr. PlZiekt. 63: 237.
ORLANDO, A., and K. SILBERSCHMIDT. 1946. Arch. Inst. biol. (Def. agric. anim.),
    S. Paulo 17: 1.
OUBOTER, M. P. DE B., and E. VAN SLOGTEREN. 1949. Tijdschr. PlZiekt. 55: 262.
QUANTZ, L. 1956. Nachrbl. deut. Pflanzenschutzdienstes (Braunschweig) 8: 7.
RADER, W. E., H. F. FITZPATRICK, and E. M. HILDEBRAND. 1947. Phytopathology
    37: 809.
RASKI, D. J., and W. B. HEWITT. 1960. Nematologica 5: 166.
RAWLINS, T. E., and C. M. TOMPKINS. 1934. Phytopathology 24: 1147.
———, and ———. 1936. Ibid. 26: 578.
REDDICK, D. 1931. Extr. Deux. Congr. Int. Path. Comp. 363.
———, and V. B. STEWART. 1919. Phytopathology 9: 445.
ROBERTS, F. M. 1946. Nature, Lond. 158: 663.
SAMUEL, G., and J. G. BALD. 1933. Ann. appl. Biol. 20: 70.
SAWADA, E. 1927. J. Pl. Prot., Tokyo 14: 12.
SHEFFIELD, F. M. L. 1941. J. R. micr. Soc. 61: 30.
SILL, W. H. 1958. Plant Dis. Reptr. 42: 912.
SLOGTEREN, E. VAN, and M. P. DE B. OUBOTER. 1941a. Publ. No. 64, Lab. Bloem-
    bollenonderzoek, Lisse.
———, and ———. 1941b. Meded. LandbHoogesch., Wageningen 45.
SMITH, K. M., and J. G. BALD. 1935. Parasitology 27: 231.
SOL, H. H., J. C. VAN HEUVEN, and J. W. SEINHORST. 1960. Tijdschr. PlZiekt.
    66: 228.
SREENIVASAYA, M. 1930. J. Indian Inst. Sci. 13: 113.
STANLEY, W. M. 1935. Phytopathology 25: 899.
TEAKLE, D. S. 1960. Nature, Lond. 188: 431.
———. 1962. Virology 18: 224.
THORNBERRY, H. H. 1935. Phytopathology 25: 618, 931.
THUNG, T. H., and J. P. H. VAN DER WANT. 1951. Tijdschr. PlZiekt. 57: 173.
TODD, J. M. 1958. Proc. 3rd Conf. Potato Virus Diseases, Lisse-Wageningen, 1957,
    132.
TOMLINSON, J. A., and R. G. GARRETT. 1962. Nature, Lond. 194: 249.
VALLEAU, W. D. 1941. Phytopathology 31: 522.
WADA, E., and H. FUKANO. 1934. Agric. and Hort. (Tokyo) 9: 1778.
WALLACE, J. M. 1947. Phytopathology 37: 149.
WEBB, R. W. 1927. J. agric. Res. 35: 587.
———. 1928. Ibid. 36: 53.
YARWOOD, C. E. 1955. Virology 1: 268.
———. 1957. Advanc. Virus Res. 4: 243.

Transmission by Animals While Feeding

Although the ways in which viruses can be spread are many and varied, the great majority of plants that become naturally infected undoubtedly do so because they are fed on by infective animals. This broad statement, however, calls for immediate qualification, to correct the possible but wrong implication that transmission is a casual process and inevitably occurs whenever any kind of animal chances to feed on an uninfected host plant after feeding on an infected one. On the contrary, the transmission of most viruses is a highly specific process, something that not only demands feeding by a given type of animal but, often, the fulfilling of other exacting conditions. It is true that a few viruses, notably potato spindle tuber (Schultz and Folsom, 1925; Goss, 1931) and tobacco mosaic (Hoggan, 1931; Walters, 1952; Newton, 1953), have been reported to be transmitted by widely different kinds of animals, some with biting and some with sucking mouth-parts. These reports may well represent examples of viruses that are readily transmitted by manual inoculation with plant sap being conveyed between plants unspecifically as chance contaminants on the animals' mouths, but they are exceptions that do little to disturb the generalisation that transmission usually depends on specific interactions between individual viruses and their animal vectors. Indeed, what is more unexpected than the few reported successes with tobacco mosaic virus are the many failures to transmit this, and other readily inoculable ones such as

110

otato X, by many species of insects that are efficient vectors of other viruses much less readily transmitted by manual inoculation. Failures with such viruses, which *a priori* might be expected to be transmitted by almost any feeding animal, emphasise the specific association between the other viruses and their vectors.

There are two categories of specificity. First, and most obvious, s group specificity, which can be defined by saying that a virus with a vector in one group of animals, say the aphids, rarely also has vectors in other groups, such as the leaf hoppers, thrips or nematodes. One that does is *Centrosema* mosaic virus, which is transmitted almost as readily by two species of plant bugs of the genus *Nyscies* as by its two known aphid vectors (Van Velsen and Crowley, 1961). Another is sowbane mosaic virus, which has been transmitted, though not very readily by any, by the leaf miner fly *Liriomyza langei*, the beet leafhopper *Eutettix tenellus* and the aphid *Myzus persicae* (Bennett and Costa, 1961). Secondly, and this different viruses how to very different extents, is species specificity. Some viruses, especially some of those with aphid vectors, can be transmitted by many different species, though few rival onion yellow dwarf for which 50 different vector species have been described (Drake, Harris and Tate, 1933). In contrast, are other viruses mainly among those transmitted by leaf-hoppers, white-flies, thrips and nematodes, for which only one vector species is known. Such extreme specificity is probably often apparent rather than real, reflecting ignorance rather than knowledge, and additional vectors for some of these no doubt await discovery. However, past experience suggests that any extra vectors that are discovered are likely to be found in whatever group of animals contains the already known vector rather than in different groups; this expectation is strengthened by recent discoveries that some viruses are transmitted by nematodes, a group not previously known to contain vectors, for those so transmitted have all been viruses for which no vector was previously known. Within this group, too, there is already ample evidence of species specificity, for of the soil-borne viruses already shown to be nematode-transmitted different ones are transmitted by different species. There is also ample evidence of species specificity even with aphid-transmitted viruses that have many vectors, for rarely have all the species that have been tested with a given virus been found to transmit it. Table 6–1 shows the results of transmission tests using two closely related aphid species; *Myzus persicae* transmitted seven of the eight viruses used, and *M. ascalonicus* four, but these four included the one not transmitted by *M. persicae* (Doncaster and Kassanis, 1946). Specificity, however, can be greater than that unrelated viruses are trans-

PLANT VIRUSES AND VIRUS DISEASE

TABLE 6–1

Comparative Transmission of Different Viruses by *Myzus persicae* and
Myzus ascalonicus

Virus	M. persicae	M. ascalonicus
Potato Y	19/20 *	0/47
Cucumber mosaic	18/20	41/50
Henbane mosaic	10/10	20/35
Tobacco etch	10/10	0/30
Lettuce mosaic	24/24	0/38
Sugar beet mosaic	10/10	0/10
Dandelion yellow mosaic	0/30	7/33
Sugar beet yellows	10/10	5/10

* Numerator is the number of plants infected, denominator number colonised
With each virus, the numbers of individual insects used per test plant was the same
for both aphid species.

mitted by different species, for a species of aphid (Bawden and
Kassanis, 1947; Watson, 1956), leafhopper (Black, 1953a) or nema
tode (Harrison, Mowat and Taylor, 1961), may transmit some strains
of a given virus but not others; changes in a strain of cucumber
mosaic (Badami, 1958) led to loss of transmissibility by *M. persicae*
which transmits most strains more readily than do other aphids that
are vectors, while retaining the ability to be transmitted by these
other species.

Most of the animals that have been found to transmit viruses feed
by sucking plants and not by biting them. Indeed, about half the
viruses for which vectors are known are aphid-transmitted and one
third leafhopper-transmitted. Biting animals perhaps do more trans
mitting than is currently thought, for it is difficult to see how they
can avoid sometimes getting their mouths contaminated with stable
viruses that are easily transferred mechanically. However, biters
have obvious limitations as vectors. Biting not only damages leaves
excessively, but it is a method of infecting likely to succeed only with
viruses that are easily spread by mechanical inoculation with plant
sap. Also, should a voracious feeder chance to introduce virus into a
leaf with one bite, there is the obvious possibility that a later bite
will remove the infected piece of leaf. There is little enough con
solation to be got from contemplating the damage wrought by a
plague of locusts, but it is something that they are unlikely to be
spreading viruses to the plants they defoliate.

Factors affecting spread. In seeking a vector for a virus, par
ticularly one that spreads rapidly and extensively, it is under
standable that the common pests of the host should first be tested

Iowever, the vector will often not be among them, for animals that re rarely numerous enough to be damaging pests can still be the 1ain vectors of important viruses. For example, many peach or- hards in the U.S.A. have been ruined by peach yellows, which is cansmitted by *Macropsis trimaculata*, a leafhopper with only one rood a year, which is active for only a few weeks in the summer and 5 never abundant (Kunkel, 1933). Even when a common pest is ound experimentally to be a vector, it may still be relatively unim- ortant in spreading a virus in field crops. For example, when com- ared in experiments, *Aphis fabae* is as efficient as *Myzus persicae* n transmitting sugar beet yellows virus (Watson, 1946), but the irus often spreads little in beet crops heavily infested with *A. fabae,* vhereas light infestations of *M. persicae* can lead to whole crops recoming infected. It is important to remember that transmission means moving and that, in experiments, animals are moved from lant to plant by the experimenter, whereas in crops movement is roluntary. Hence, spread of viruses in a crop is not something that 1eed necessarily reflect the total population of potential vectors, for t also depends on their activity. A few actively mobile individuals vill do more transmitting than many sluggards. In part, the pre- minence of *M. persicae* as a field vector of many viruses, which other 1phids can also transmit, reflects its greater restlessness. Even with his species, the spread of viruses is much less closely correlated with he total population that develops on a potato crop than it is with the 1umber of winged individuals trapped in the crop (Broadbent, .950), and most spreading of viruses is done, not by the wingless ndividuals that form the bulk of the population, but by the small ninority with wings (Broadbent and Tinsley, 1951).

The spread of viruses in crops demands three things: first, a ource of the virus; secondly, the presence of vector species; thirdly, he movement of the vector. Regional and seasonal differences be- ween the incidence of individual virus diseases in part reflect dif- erences between numbers of virus sources, but they mainly reflect lifferences between the numbers and activity of the vector species. Thus, whether or not such viruses as potato leaf roll and beet yel- ows spread extensively in the United Kingdom depends on whether or not the season favours the multiplication and movement of *Myzus* persicae, and potato viruses usually spread much more extensively n the south and east than in the north and west because the weather here more often encourages this aphid early in the year and more often supplies the still warm air that encourages it to fly.

The fact that different virus diseases spread at very different rates can have other explanations than that their vectors differ in

number or mobility. Even though their host plants become heavil
infested with mobile vectors, some viruses spread only slowly be
cause the plants are unfavourable hosts, either intrinsically difficul
to infect, or supporting only a small virus concentration and so bein
poor sources of virus for the vectors, or both. Differences in th
behaviour of different viruses in these respects are readily show
experimentally by the fact that, whereas some viruses are trans
mitted to almost every plant colonised by a single vector that ha
fed on an infected plant, others are rarely transmitted unless plant
are colonised with many individuals. The importance of the hos
plant is evident because the same virus often behaves very differ
ently in different hosts. Dandelion yellow mosaic virus, for ex
ample, is readily acquired from and transmitted to lettuce plants b
Myzus ornatus but aphids rarely acquire virus while feeding on in
fected dandelion plants and aphids infective for lettuce rarely infec
dandelions on which they feed (Kassanis, 1947).

The difficulties in discovering vectors do not arise solely becaus
there are very many possible animals to be tried, although this i
problem enough, for vectors are often among species of animal
that are not recognised pests of the particular crop, and may eve
not colonise it, but be only visitors that feed on the crop in passing
Difficulties also arise because certain limited conditions must b
fulfilled before a potential vector will transmit. In general, th
chances of success in transmission experiments are increased b
using as sources of virus plants showing severe symptoms and usin;
as test plants young actively growing seedlings. However, plant
with the most obvious symptoms are not always the best sources o
virus, for Kassanis (1952) found that aphids fed on young symptom
less shoots from potato tubers infected with leaf roll virus becom
infective much more readily than when fed on older plants wit
their leaves chlorotic and rolled. When testing most kinds of ani
mals as possible vectors, it is well to allow them to feed for as lon;
as possible on an infected plant before transferring them to the tes
plants, on which in turn they should again be allowed to feed a
long as possible. However, with aphids, in addition to this kind o
protracted test, it is always desirable to make another kind in whicl
the aphids are first prevented from feeding for some hours and the
allowed to feed for only 1–5 minutes on the infected plants before
they are transferred to the test plants.

An odd property of some viruses is that they are insect-trans
mitted when they occur in plants simultaneously infected with an
other virus for which the insect is a vector, but not otherwise. Thi
phenomenon was first encountered when potato aucuba (tube

blotch) virus, which is not transmitted by *Myzus persicae* from plants infected with it alone, was found to be transmitted from plants simultaneously infected with potato virus A (Clinch, Loughnane and Murphy, 1936), and has since been described with others, but an adequate explanation for it is still awaited. The transmission of potato virus C by *M. persicae* from plants simultaneously infected with potato virus Y is, perhaps, explicable by genetic recombination (Watson 1960), for these two are serologically related strains, but such an explanation is unlikely to hold for the similar ability of tobacco vein-distorting virus to make tobacco mottle virus transmissible (Smith, 1946). These two viruses together cause tobacco rosette. The vein-distorting virus is transmitted by *M. persicae*, but not by mechanical inoculation of sap, whereas the mottle virus is readily sap-inoculable and is not transmitted by *M. persicae* that feed on plants infected with it alone. However, aphids transmit mottle virus from plants with rosette, and after feeding on the doubly infected plants aphids can remain infective with both viruses for several days. When transferred at intervals to a series of healthy plants, individual aphids may infect some plants with both viruses and others with either vein-distorting or mottle virus. Hence, it is the ability to acquire mottle virus from infected plants that seems to be conferred by the vein-distorting virus and not the ability to be transmitted to healthy plants. Presumably the ability to be acquired could be conferred simply by the two viruses associating *in vivo*, so that when the aphid acquired one it is also likely to acquire the other; alternatively, acquisition may depend on phenotypic changes in the mottle virus, which when produced in cells where the vein-distorting virus is also multiplying has incorporated in it protein components of the vein-distorting virus that allow it to be acquired by the aphid. Other possibilities are that infection with vein-distorting virus alters the distribution or amount of mottle virus, so that in mixedly infected but not in singly infected leaves it is readily obtained by aphids. There are several examples of viruses reaching higher concentrations in leaves simultaneously infected with another virus than they do when on their own. However, although Kassanis (1961) found that the concentration of potato aucuba mosaic virus is influenced by the presence of potato virus A or Y, its transmissibility by aphids was not correlated with its concentration. None of the 12 strains of aucuba mosaic virus tested was transmitted by *M. persicae* from plants infected with them alone, some but not all were transmitted readily from plants also infected with virus A, and some were transmitted only from plants also infected with potato virus Y. Hence, the ability to become transmissible differs with different strains, and different strains acquire the ability from association with different viruses, a nice demonstration of the specificity of interactions between viruses and vectors on which transmission depends. The phenomenon deserves much further study for the light it might shed on the mechanisms involved in transmission. It would, too, be interesting to know whether strains that do not become transmissible by *M. persicae* when together with virus A become transmissible by some other species of aphid.

Types of behaviour. How to categorise and label viruses according to the features they show in transmission by vectors has long been controversial. Everybody is agreed that there are two extremes of behaviour that of necessity imply very different mechanisms of transmission; at one extreme are viruses that can be acquired from an infected plant and transmitted to a healthy one all within a minute or so, and vectors of these viruses cease to be infective within hours of leaving an infected plant; at the other, are viruses whose vectors do not become infective until some days after acquiring virus by feeding on an infected plant but, once infective, the vectors remain so for long periods, often for the rest of their lives. These two types have often been called mechanical and biological transmission (Doolittle and Walker, 1928; Huff, 1931; Hoggan, 1933; Kunkel, 1938; Leach, 1940; Cook, 1947); such names carried implications quite unjustified by knowledge, and there has long been ample evidence that many viruses said to be mechanically transmitted had specific associations with their vectors that conflicted ill with the idea that they simply contaminated their vector's stylets as they might contaminate a needle. As more and more viruses have been studied, it has become increasingly obvious that there are many grades of behaviour between the two extremes, and this has led Day and Fenner (1953) to suggest modifications of the old terminology, with mechanical transmission divided into three groups, labelled "simple mechanical," "delayed mechanical" and "modified mechanical." By mechanical seems to be meant simply that the virus does not pass through the tissues of the vector (Day, 1955a), but this is not something readily determinable from results of transmission tests and can only be postulated for most viruses whose behaviour is intermediate between the extremes.

Any criteria for naming groups of viruses according to their behaviour when transmitted by vectors are obviously more soundly based on measurable phenomena than on interpretations of phenomena. However, the most suitable phenomena to use are by no means obvious. In different editions of this book, different ones have been tried. In the first, the division depended on whether vectors could infect healthy plants immediately after they acquired virus or whether there was a delay (latent period) before they became infective. With most of the viruses studied till then that showed a latent period, this seemed, in constant conditions, to be reasonably constant in length and characteristic of individual viruses. The longer latent periods were comparable to the time between inoculation of plants and the development of systemic symptoms. However, some of the shorter ones were not only much briefer than the time taken for virus multiplication to become detectable in infected leaves, but they also differed considerably in length between individual insects. For example, although most workers reported a latent period of at least six hours before *Eutettix tenellus* transmitted beet curly top virus, Severin (1931) got some transmissions with leafhoppers fed for only 10 minutes successively on infected and healthy plants. Similarly, Watson (1946) found that the minimum period in which individual *Myzus persicae* transmitted beet yellows virus differed considerably. Occasional aphids infected when given only 30 minutes in total on the infected and test plant, but the numbers that transmitted increased steadily as the time spent on either the infected or test plant was increased. Watson concluded that, with such viruses, there is no fixed, minimum latent period in the vectors, but instead a maximum period during which the chances of transmission by insects that have acquired virus increase until all will do so.

In the second and third editions of this book, viruses were divided according to whether or not their vectors usually remained infective for a day after leaving an infected plant. This change from the criterion of a latent period seemed desirable from the work of Watson and Roberts (1939, 1940) and was an attempt to combine their basis for division with suggestions by Storey (1939). Watson and Roberts divided viruses into two groups, which they called "persistent" and "non-persistent," depending on whether the period for which vectors remain infective is prolonged or brief, but they did not specify any minimum period for qualifying as a "persistent" virus. Storey combined the concept of a latent period with that of different retentions of infectivity by defining two groups as (1) "Transmission negative on the first hosts, positive on succeeding hosts" and (2) "Transmission positive on first hosts, negative on succeeding hosts." This division has the obvious value of relying on observed results, but it has the serious drawback that its satisfactory use depends on choosing suitable time intervals for the vectors of

different viruses to spend on each of a series of test plants. Fo
instance, by using short enough intervals, several successive plan
have been infected by viruses that Storey puts in group 2 (Watso
and Roberts, 1940; Kassanis, 1941). Similarly, the first plants in
series will be infected by some of the viruses in group 1 unless th
time on them is less than a few hours.

The words persistent and non-persistent have come into genera
use, even though Watson later (1946) concluded that the tim
taken for vectors to lose infectivity, like the time taken to becom
infective, was unsuitable as a criterion for dividing viruses: she wa
led to this conclusion by the fact that persistence of infectivity wit
many viruses depended largely on how long the vectors fed on th
infected plants. All the non-persistent viruses Watson studied wer
transmitted more readily by aphids that, after having been faste
fed only briefly on infected plants, than by aphids given protracte
infection feeds. This contrasts strikingly with the behaviour of pe
sistent viruses, with which the chances of transmission increase a
the length of the infection feed is increased. This distinction
readily demonstrated experimentally, and so can be used objectivel
to separate viruses into two major types, but it gives unsatisfactor
groupings because not all viruses that fail to persist in their vecto
are acquired by their vectors in brief infection feeds; for exampl
although the vectors of dandelion mosaic (Kassanis, 1947), straw
berry crinkle (Prentice and Harris, 1946) and cocoa swollen shoo
(Posnette, 1947) viruses soon cease to be infective, the longer the
feed on infected plants the more likely they are to become infectiv
and their chances of transmitting are not increased by being faste
before they have their infection feed.

Hence, there seems no simple way in which all the anima
transmitted viruses can be fitted neatly and unequivocally into on
or other of two major types. That there are two extremes of be
haviour is obvious enough, but the simple dichotomy suggested b
these extremes is false, for there are many intermediate types o
behaviour and viruses with these can be grouped with one or othe
of the extremes only by making arbitrary or subjective decision
More information may change this position and allow a division o
the basis of whether or not viruses multiply in their vectors, but thi
is still remote; meanwhile the only objective way of grouping seem
to be by the type of vector rather than by any single feature o
behaviour during transmission, and in the rest of this chapter trans
mission will be considered under the headings of the common grou
names of the main kinds of vector.

Leafhoppers. In terms of the distinctions between viruses discussed in the previous section, the behaviour of leafhopper-transmitted viruses can be briefly summarised as (1) ability to transmit not increased by a period of fasting before the infection feed, (2) unable to transmit immediately after acquiring virus and (3) remaining infective for a long while. However, this simple statement carries an impression of uniformity that is belied when the detailed behaviour of individual viruses and their vectors is considered, for it is then not only obvious that the viruses fall into one or other of two distinct groups but that within a group there are also considerable differences. The main feature that distinguishes the two general groups is the length of the latent period, with one, typified by such viruses as aster yellows (Kunkel, 1926 a, b), corn stunt (Kunkel, 1946) and potato yellow dwarf (Black, 1938), whose vectors do not become infective until several days after they acquire virus, and the other, typified by beet curly top (Severin, 1921) and maize streak (Storey, 1928) viruses, whose vectors become infective within a few hours of acquiring virus. Vectors of viruses in either groups remain infective for long periods, many for their whole lives, but whereas those of the first group do so with infection feeds no longer than are needed to acquire virus, those of the second group do so only when their infection feeds are more protracted than this. It will, perhaps, be simplest to consider the two groups separately.

Several of the viruses in the first group have been shown to multiply in their vectors, which therefore serve as alternative hosts as well as vehicles for carrying virus from one plant host to another, and a protracted incubation period can be accepted as *prima facie* evidence that a virus multiplies in its vector. Multiplication of some viruses of this type in leafhoppers has long been accepted by some workers (Kunkel, 1926a and 1926b; Fukushi, 1934, 1935, 1940; Black, 1941), but the early results were open to other interpretations and proof was first provided by Black's (1950) remarkable experiment continued over 5 years with clover club leaf virus. This virus he found in *Agalliopsis novella*, in which it is transmitted through eggs to a large proportion of the progeny of infective females (Black, 1944, 1948). A single infective female was mated with a virus-free male, and allowed to lay her eggs on lucerne (alfalfa), which is immune from the virus. Some of the progeny were maintained continuously on lucerne, whereas the remainder were placed on crimson clover to see what proportion of the progeny had inherited virus. Females of the progeny kept on alfalfa were mated with virus-free males, and the process repeated through 21 generations, without the

line losing the ability to infect crimson clover. Fukushi (1940), i
a similar type of test, had earlier demonstrated the inheritance c
rice stunt virus to the sixth generation of a single *Nephotettix apicali*
but this, although strong presumptive evidence of multiplicatior
did not exclude the possibility that virus initially contained in th
original insect was diluted among the progeny. Black's extende
test, however, established beyond question that the progeny con
tained in total much more of the clover virus than could possibl
have been present in the female that initiated the line. That trans
mission through the egg need not necessarily be conclusive evidenc
that a virus multiplies in its vector is suggested by Black's (1959
estimate of the amount of wound tumour virus that can be containe
in a single insect. Vectors of this virus can contain enough to reac
visibly with virus antiserum, and from knowledge on the amoun
needed to do this and on the size of the virus particle, Black cal
culates that an adult leafhopper may contain 10^9 virus particles.

The second virus shown unequivocally to multiply in its vecto
was aster yellows. Black (1941) transmitted this mechanically fron
infective to non-infective *Macrosteles fascifrons* (earlier called *Cica
dula sexnotata* and *Macrosteles divisus*), and produced presumptiv
evidence of multiplication during the latent period by showing tha
extracts taken from insects early in the latent period were not infec
tive whereas extracts taken after it had ended were. However, th
conclusive evidence came with the inoculations made by Maramo
rosch (1952a), which showed that the virus maintained itself witl
its concentration apparently unchanged after being transmitted seri
ally through 10 lots of leafhoppers. Maramorosch (1952b) similarl
showed that corn stunt virus, which has a latent period in *Dalbulu
maidis* of about two weeks (Kunkel, 1948), maintained itself wher
three successive batches of insects were inoculated with extract
from the previous batch diluted 1/100.

In what tissues of their insect hosts such viruses multiply has ye
to be determined, but evidence about this may come from refinec
tissue-culture work, because the whole living insect seems to be un-
necessary. This is implied by Maramorosch (1956) finding that
when *M. fascifrons* were fed for two days on plants infected with
aster yellows virus and then cut into 10–12 pieces, which were left
in culture medium for 10 days, virus could be recovered from the
pieces though none was demonstrable at the time the pieces were
cut. There is perhaps a clue to the site of multiplication in the
report by Littau and Maramorosch (1956, 1958, 1960) that the fat
body cells of *M. fascifrons* infected with the eastern strain of aster
yellows virus become abnormal, with the cytoplasm less homogene-

us than usual, their nuclei stellate and their cell membranes indis-
inct. However, these cytological changes are specific and may have
o general significance, for the fat bodies of *M. fascifrons* infected
vith another strain of aster yellows virus were normal, as were those
f *Dalbulus maidis* infected with corn stunt virus. The cytological
hanges are presumably pathogenic, but if they harm the insects
here must be compensating advantages, because Severin (1946)
ound that *M. fascifrons* bred more prolifically and lived longer on
olants infected with aster yellows virus than they did on uninfected
olants. Whether this happens because the virus directly affects the
nsects, or because infection alters the nutritive value of the plants,
s uncertain. However, another phenomenon, which might also be
lescribed as beneficial and which seems to be a direct effect of the
virus, was described by Maramorosch (1958, 1959) with *Dalbulus
maidis*. Although this leafhopper is not a vector of aster yellows
virus, it acquires the virus when it feeds on infected plants. After
loing this, its dietary habits change so that its host range is enlarged,
and whereas normally it lives on maize only and soon dies when
caged on asters, it is now able to live, not only on infected asters,
out also on uninfected plants of aster, carrot and rye. This extension of host range almost certainly derives from the presence of the
virus in *D. maidis*, and not from the fact that the insect is otherwise
affected by feeding on diseased plants, because Maramorosch found
that after virus-containing insects were kept for 8 days at 30° (a
treatment Kunkel (1937, 1941) showed freed *M. fascifrons* from
aster yellows virus), they could no longer live on healthy aster
plants. Changing the dietary habits of *D. maidis,* like producing
changes in the fat body cells of *M. fascifrons,* seems specific to the
eastern strain of aster yellows virus and did not happen with a strain
obtained from Californian carrots.

For long, no plant virus was known to harm its insect vector, but
there is now evidence suggesting that two of the type we are considering are pathogenic. Jensen (1959) found that the average
length of life of *Colladonus montanus* was shortened from about 50
to 20 days by yellow leaf roll virus of peach, and Watson and Sinha
(1959) found that the number of progeny produced by *Delphacodes
pellucida* could be almost halved by infection with cereal striate
mosaic virus, because more than the usual number of embryos died
before the eggs hatched. There seems to be a critical time early
in the development of the ovaries after when eggs are not readily
infected, for the proportion of progeny born infective depends on
when the mothers acquire the virus; females that acquire virus while
they are nymphs produce many infected eggs, whereas those that

remain virus-free until they are adult produce few or none (Sinha 1960).

The knowledge that these viruses multiply in their vectors pro vides a ready explanation for vector specificity, for the ability t transmit could simply depend on the ability of the insect to act a a host for the virus. Similarly, the different transmitting abilitie of different races of the vectors of potato yellow dwarf (Black 1943), rice stripe (Yamada and Yamamoto, 1955) and cereal striat mosaic (Watson and Sinha, 1959), can be attributed to the race differing in their ability to support virus multiplication. Howeve there are suggestions that there may be other limiting factors. Fo example, individual *Delphacodes pellucida* that become infectiv while they are nymphs usually transmit cereal striate mosaic viru much more readily than those that do not acquire virus until the are adult. This could be interpreted as implying that the virus mul tiplies more readily in nymphs, but the difference seems to be i the different permeability of the gut wall of nymphs and adults t the virus, because puncturing the guts of adults after their infectio feed makes them transmit as readily as do nymphs (Sinha, 1960) Hence, if transmission depends on virus multiplication, the cells o adult insects must act as hosts, but the susceptible cells seem not t become infected unless the gut wall is punctured. To be effective the punctures must be made before or soon after the infection feed which obviously implies that the virus multiplies not in the gut bu in cells that it reaches only after passing through the gut wall int the blood.

There is also a suggestion that failure to transmit aster yellow virus may depend on something other than ability to multiply in vector. Maramorosch (1952b) found that non-vector species feed ing on infected plants not only acquire this virus, which inactivate *in vitro* within a day, but continue to contain it for some weeks afte leaving infected plants in amounts such that their pulped bodie when diluted 1/100 still infect injected aster leafhoppers; further and perhaps more significant, virus was not detectable in non-vecto species removed from diseased asters on which they had fed fo 2 days, but was detectable 17 days later. A similar result wit *M. fascifrons* (Black, 1941) has long been interpreted as convincin evidence that the virus multiplies during the latent period in the vector, and this interpretation has become generally accepted since multiplication has been established unequivocally. If this interpre tation is justified with *M. fascifrons*, then it seems reasonable t apply it to other species such as *Dalbulus maidis* and to conclude that aster yellows virus also multiplies in these. As these species d

ot transmit, however, accepting the idea that the virus multiplies
1 them necessitates seeking some other feature than virus multipli-
ation to explain vector specificity.

There is no positive evidence to the identity of this specific fea-
ure, but one obvious possibility is the ability of a virus to enter or
ɔ survive in the salivary glands. Everything that is known about
he transmission of these viruses suggests that they are sucked into
he gut from plant cells, must pass through the gut wall into the
•lood, then, after multiplying in some undetermined tissues, virus
ɔasses into the salivary glands, there to be mixed with salivary secre-
ions that are injected into plants while the insect feeds. Inability
ɔ penetrate the gut wall, to multiply in the species of insect, or to
nter or survive in the saliva, any one of these features might pre-
ᵛent an insect from acting as a vector. How viruses do penetrate
ɡut walls or invade organs like the salivary glands is unknown; they
ɪre far too large to pass through semi-permeable membranes, so
ɔenetration may be an active rather than a passive process and it
nay depend on the specific ability of individual viruses to affect
•ells of the particular tissue. Transmission of virus to progeny
hrough eggs similarly may well depend on the virus penetrating
nto the ovary, rather than on ability to multiply in eggs, for that
uch viruses as potato yellow dwarf and wound tumour can at least
urvive in eggs they reach is obvious from the fact that infective
ɔffspring are occasionally produced (Black, 1953b).

Unfortunately, too little is known about the viruses that multiply
ɔoth in plants and leafhoppers to seek an explanation of their be-
ɪaviour in a peculiar structure or composition. It is true that the
wo that have been photographed in the electron microscope are
.arger than the particles of other plant viruses that have been
₃tudied, but they have little in common with one another; wound
ːumour virus (Brakke, Vatter and Black, 1954), whether obtained
from insects or plants, has particles of a constant size and shape, quasi-
₃pheres of diameter 75 mμ, whereas potato yellow dwarf particles
ɪre not only considerably larger but their shape in any one prepara-
ion varies from near-spheres to rods (Black, 1955). Nor is there
any great uniformity in the behaviour of these viruses. Most have
not been transmitted to plants by manual inoculation, but potato
yellow dwarf is readily transmitted in this way. The failure with
the others cannot be attributed to their instability *in vitro*, because
several have been transmitted to insects by inoculation with extracts
from either infected plants or leafhoppers and inoculations to insects
show that the viruses retain infectivity for several hours *in vitro*.
The vectors feed from the vascular tissues, most from the phloem,

but the one that transmits the virus causing Pierce's grapevine dis
ease feeds from the xylem (Houston, Esau and Hewitt, 1947)
Therefore, to infect plants the viruses perhaps need to be introducec
directly into the vascular tissue, and vectors may do this withou
causing the damage inseparable from inoculating with needles o1
syringes. Alternatively, mechanical inoculation may fail simply be
cause extracts from infected plants, although rich enough in viru
to infect leafhopper hosts, contain too little to infect the host plant!
to which they have been inoculated.

Let us now compare these leafhopper-transmitted viruses witl
those that have incubation periods of a day or less, of which the
most studied are maize streak and sugar beet curly top viruses. The
first similarity is that, although they also can be injected successfull\
into their vectors, they are not transmitted to plants by usual method!
of manual inoculation, although curly top virus has occasionall\
infected plants inoculated by methods thought to have introducec
the virus directly into the phloem (Severin, 1924). However, al
though to infect plants maize streak virus may need to be placed ir
the phloem, it is not later restricted to the phloem but also occurs
in parenchyma at fairly high concentrations, for vectors can acquire
virus while feeding for less than a minute on diseased plants (Storey,
1938). These viruses move from their entry points in plants very
much sooner than do those that infect by manual inoculation; curly
top virus has been detected 36 cm from the entry point only one
hour after being introduced into plants (Severin, 1924) and maize
streak virus 20 cm (Storey, 1928). In this they resemble Pierce's
grapevine virus, which is probably placed in the xylem and can also
travel 20 cm. from its entry point in an hour (Houston et al, 1947),
but they contrast strikingly with tobacco mosaic virus, which takes
some days to move from an inoculated leaf into the petiole. It seems
that, instead of the local multiplication before tobacco mosaic virus
spreads from infection sites, virus particles introduced by leafhoppers into the vascular system may travel long distances before
becoming established in cells where they multiply.

The general behaviour of vectors of curly top and maize streak
virus closely resembles that of aster yellows and the other viruses we
have discussed, with transmission demanding that virus acquired
from plants should pass through the gut wall into the blood and then
be injected back into plants with the salivary secretions. Indeed
evidence for this sequence of events first came with these two
viruses. The importance of the character of the gut wall in determining vector specificity was indicated by Storey's (1932; 1933)
work with the two races of *Cicaculina mbila* he distinguished by

the fact that one (active) transmitted maize streak virus and the other (inactive) did not. The two are indistinguishable morphologically and interbreed freely, and activity as a vector is inherited as a simple Mendelian character linked with sex, the male being heterozygous for sex. Individuals of both races acquire the virus while feeding on infected plants, but in inactive individuals the virus is restricted to the gut whereas in active ones it also occurs in the blood. Puncturing the gut walls of inactive individuals, either before or soon after they feed on an infected plant, turns them into vectors, and virus then becomes detectable in their blood. Inactive individuals also become vectors when virus is inoculated directly into their blood with needles previously dipped in either sap from infected plants or blood from infective leafhoppers. Hence, both races of *C. mbila* can acquire virus from plants and both can inject it into plants, but the gut wall of the active race allows the virus to pass through and that of the inactive race does not. However, something other than the permeability of the gut wall is also involved in determining ability to transmit, for Storey failed to turn *Peregrinus maidis* into a vector of maize streak either by puncturing its gut wall or by injecting the virus into its blood.

The blood most likely provides the main reservoir for virus in infective vectors, from which it may pass into the saliva only occasionally or only in small amounts. Storey failed to detect maize streak virus in the salivary glands of infective *C. mbila* and, although Bennett and Wallace (1938) did detect curly top virus in the salivary glands of infective *Eutettix tenellus,* the concentration there was less than in other tissues. However, these tests were of necessity made with insects that were not feeding and the virus content of glands actively secreting saliva might well be higher. This expectation is perhaps confirmed by Smith (1941) showing that sugar solution fed on (through membranes) by infective *E. tenellus* for only 3 hours gained enough curly top virus to render infective 29 out of 40 virus-free *E. tenellus* that later fed on it.

Although the salivary glands and saliva obviously contain virus, tests in which infective leafhoppers feed on a succession of plants give results that fit with the idea that the glands are readily exhausted of virus and that virus occurs in saliva intermittently rather than as a steady secretion. In such tests, unless the feeding periods are prolonged, individual leafhoppers usually fail to infect all the plants on which they feed, and they will infect some plants on which they feed briefly and fail to infect others on which they feed for much longer. Whether a plant becomes infected will depend, primarily, on whether virus is injected into it; the probability of this happening will increase with increasing feeding periods, but precisely when it happens will be a matter of chance. The number of plants infected by different leafhoppers given set feeding periods differs greatly, and individuals that infect many plants are usually also those that remain infective for longer than the others. Such individual differences in behaviour may simply reflect different amounts of virus in the blood, which can be expected to affect the frequency with which virus will pass into the salivary glands, or they may indicate difference in the salivary glands of the insects that affects the readiness with which virus enters them or the saliva.

The main loss of virus from vectors is perhaps by secretion with the saliva. Storey (1932) failed to detect maize streak virus in naturally voided faeces of C. mbila, although he detected it in the rectal contents of individuals that had recently fed on infected plants. Similarly, Severin (1931) failed to find virus in the faeces of E. tenellus carrying curly top virus and Bennett and Wallace (1938) found only very little.

Nothing is known about the morphology or structure of maize streak or curly top viruses, but there is no doubt that curly top is among one of the most stable viruses. Bennett (1935) found that E. tenellus feeds satisfactorily on sugar solutions and becomes infective when fed on solutions containing extracts of either diseased beet or infective E. tenellus. Using this method of transmission, he determined some properties of the virus and found that it withstands drying, heating to 75°, ageing for 4 weeks at 20°, 90% ethanol for 2 hours, pH changes between 3 and 9, and that it is highly resistant to inactivation by disinfectants. It also survives active for 2 weeks or more in many non-vector insects, aphids, thrips and leafhoppers, that acquire it while feeding on infected plants (Bennett and Wallace, 1938). Hence, unless the virus also multiplies in these non-vectors, there seems no need to invoke multiplication in E. tenellus to explain the persistence of infectivity. That this and maize streak virus probably do not multiply in their vectors is further suggested by the fact that the length of time for which individual vectors remain infective depends on the length of time they fed on infected plants (Freitag, 1936; Storey, 1938; Bennett and Wallace, 1938). Vectors that feed for only a few minutes on infected plants may become infective, but they also soon cease to be infective, whereas those that feed for hours or days remain infective for long periods, some for their whole lives.

Insects that cease to transmit seem to do so because their supply of virus is exhausted and not because of some other factor, for they become able to transmit again after again feeding on diseased plants

(Freitag, 1936; Bennett and Wallace, 1938). This, and the much shorter incubation period, are the two major differences from the behaviour of aster yellows and the other leafhopper-transmitted viruses discussed earlier in this section. Neither difference is necessarily incompatible with multiplication, for although short by comparison with the latent periods of the other viruses, the latent periods of curly top and maize streak viruses are not much shorter than the time required for virus multiplication to be detected in leaves manually inoculated with some viruses. However, if they do multiply, the amount produced by multiplication seems to be less than what the insects can acquire by feeding on infected plants. There is, too, abundant evidence that they can acquire from infected plants more than enough to keep them infective for their whole lives. For example, Bennett (1935) found that E. tenellus became infective when fed on exudate from the phloem of diseased beet diluted 1/10,000, and had they been feeding on diseased beet for the same length of time it is reasonable to assume they would have imbibed 10,000 times this minimal amount. Similarly, whereas the vector efficiency of E. tenellus, measured by retention of ability to transmit and the number of plants infected, increases rapidly at first with increased feeding times on diseased plants, it reaches a maximum in two days. However, although longer feeding up to two weeks does not increase their ability to infect plants, it seems to increase their virus content, for extracts from them become increasingly efficient at rendering infective other E. tenellus to which they are fed (Bennett and Wallace, 1938). This increase contrasts with the decrease in infectivity of extracts from insects not feeding on diseased plants, and it seems unquestionably to result from virus acquired by feeding and not from multiplication within the insects.

All the evidence from work with curly top and maize streak is against the idea that these viruses multiply in their vectors, and unless someone shows that they can be maintained indefinitely by transmission from leafhopper to leafhopper, it must be accepted that the vectors contain no more virus than they acquire while feeding on infected plants. It is odd that the possibility of multiplication has not been thoroughly tested by such transmission tests; the only report is by Black (1959), who states that Maramorosch made E. tenellus infective by injecting them with curly top virus but failed to maintain them infective by serial transfers. Hence, despite their many similarities with aster yellows and other viruses that do multiply in their vectors, it seems unlikely that curly top and maize streak do. They seem to circulate through the bodies of their vectors in much the same manner as those that multiply, so ability to enter the blood and saliva seem not to depend on the vector possessing tissues in which the virus can multiply. Similarly, multiplication seems not to be the answer to vector specificity, for this is as great with viruses that appear not to multiply as with those that multiply in their vectors. In this chapter, curly top virus has been treated as though it were a single virus with a single vector, but the position is less simple than that. *E. tenellus* is the only vector known of the curly top virus prevalent in North America, but it does not transmit curly top viruses prevalent in South America; one strain that occurs in Argentina is transmitted by *Agallania ensigera*, which also transmits one Brazilian strain, but not another which is transmitted by *Agallia aldibula* (Bennett and Costa, 1949; Costa, 1952). There is no adequate explanation for such vector specificity, but as this type of virus has to circulate through the bodies of the vector and emerge in the saliva, the ability of a leafhopper to transmit a given virus possibly depends on whether all its various tissues between the gut and saliva are permeable to the virus. If this is so, permeability cannot be a chance event but must depend on the virus acting specifically on the tissues to render them permeable.

Similarly, there is no certain explanation for the contrasting lengths of incubation period shown by the two groups of leafhopper-transmitted viruses. However, the differences may lie either in the different concentrations achieved in infected plants by the two, or in their different stabilities. Vectors of the aster yellows type of virus may never acquire enough virus while feeding on plants to transmit this directly; to achieve and maintain enough virus for some to be secreted in the saliva, multiplication in the vector may be necessary, and the protracted latent period is the consequence. The shorter latent periods for curly top and maize streak virus, which are stable and obviously can be acquired from infected plants in considerable quantities, possibly represent simply the time taken for virus acquired from plants to penetrate the vector's gut wall, and whatever other tissues it needs to invade before it again emerges in the saliva.

Aphids. Of the viruses whose vectors are known more are transmitted by aphids than by any other type of animal, so it is perhaps not unexpected that the range of behaviour shown by aphids in transmitting different viruses should also be greater than by any other kind of vector. This range includes the kinds of behaviour already discussed for leafhopper-transmitted viruses, but only a minority of aphid-transmitted ones behave in these ways and most differ from them in two outstanding respects: (1) vectors can transmit immediately they acquire virus from infected plants or do so after a latent period so brief that its occurrence is difficult to establish with certainty; (2) vectors soon lose their ability to infect plants, remaining infective for only minutes with some viruses and for hours with others. In contrast to viruses that have latent periods and persist in their vectors for days, the non-persistent ones are mostly readily transmitted to plants by manual inoculation with plant sap. They are also usually transmitted by more different species of aphids than are viruses with latent periods, but even so there is considerable vector specificity, for an aphid that transmits one non-persistent virus may not transmit another, and one that transmits one strain of a virus may not transmit another. There seems to be no uniformity in the stability, properties or particle shapes of the non-persistent viruses. Many inactivate *in vitro* within 10 minutes at about 55° and within a few days at 18°, but some are more stable. Many have long, thread-like, flexible particles, but others are spheres, and lucerne (alfalfa) mosaic virus is shaped rather like a bacterium.

Nothing is known of the morphology, composition or properties of the viruses with latent periods in their vectors, of which only groundnut rosette and carrot motley dwarf have been transmitted by manual inoculation of plant sap, and these two only with difficulty. The failure to transmit the others by manual inoculation cannot be attributed to their instability *in vitro*, for potato leaf roll (Day, 1955b; Heinze, 1955), sugar beet yellow net (Harrison, 1958a) and barley yellow dwarf viruses (Mueller and Rochow, 1961) have been transmitted by inoculation from infective to non-infective aphids, and *Macrosiphum granarium* become infective when fed through membranes on extracts from plants infected with barley yellow dwarf virus (Rochow, 1960). These transmission techniques should now allow the properties of these viruses to be determined. Most of the viruses with latent periods resemble sugar beet curly top and maize streak viruses in as much as the latent period is to be measured in hours rather than days. However, strawberry virus 3 has a latent period exceeding a week in *Pentatrichorus fragariae* (Prentice and Woollcombe, 1951); by analogy with leaf-hopper-transmitted viruses that have comparable latent periods, it is reasonable to think that strawberry virus 3 multiplies in its vector, though this remains to be proved.

Of the aphid-transmitted viruses with shorter latent periods, potato leaf roll has been most studied. A latent period of at least a day has usually been reported (Smith, 1931; Kassanis, 1952; MacCarthy, 1954) and Harrison (1958) found that aphids injected with virus seldom transmitted within 20 hours of being injected, but there are reports (Loughnane, 1943; Kirkpatrick and Ross, 1952) of trans-mission without a latent period. This suggests there may be alter-native methods of transmission, the usual one involving the viru entering the blood and circulating through the vector's body, and a rarer one in which this journey is in some way short-circuited Stegwee and Ponsen (1958) provided direct evidence that leaf rol virus multiplies in *Myzus persicae*, for they found that the virus was maintained during 15 successive aphid-to-aphid injections, which would have involved a dilution greatly exceeding the infection end-point of the starting inoculum. Nevertheless, the aphid seems to be a poor host, for multiplication is apparently less effective than feed-ing continuously on infected plants in producing a high virus con-tent. For example, Harrison (1958) found that the infectivity of extracts of aphids, measured by injection to other aphids, increased with increasing periods of infection feeding, and was greatest at the time the infection feed ended and declined thereafter; virus was detectable in extracts of aphids made immediately they had ended an infection feeding of only 20 hours, but not in extracts made a day or more later; in contrast, extracts from aphids fed for four days on infected plants continued to be infective, though decreasingly so, for several days after the end of the infection feed. Such behaviour contrasts strikingly with that of aster yellows virus, which is not detectable in leafhoppers immediately after they have fed for two days on infected plants, but becomes detectable some days later (Black, 1941), and seems to align leaf roll more with curly top. To explain such behaviour with a virus that multiplies in its vector, it seems necessary to postulate either that virus in the gut is more readily transmitted to aphids by inoculating than is virus from other tissues, or that the amount of multiplication in the aphid is related to the amount of virus acquired by the feeding aphid. Whether made infective by injection (Harrison, 1958) or by feeding on in-fected plants (MacCarthy, 1954), aphids gradually lose their ability to transmit leaf roll virus. This is unexpected with a virus that mul-tiplies in its vector, and suggests that, if the loss of infective ability does not mean that the amount of virus in the aphid is decreasing, some physiological change in the aphid as it becomes older makes it a less effective vector.

Multiplication of a virus in its vector might be expected to make ability to transmit independent of the amount of virus imbibed dur-ing the infection feeding, as it does for some leafhopper-transmitted viruses, but this seems not to be so with leaf roll, because *M. persicae* remain infective for longer and infect more plants of a series they are fed on after a long than after a short infection feed (Heinze,

1959). This is true of other aphid-transmitted viruses, such as barley yellow dwarf (Rochow, 1959), and before potato leaf roll virus was transmitted serially through aphids it would have been regarded as strong circumstantial evidence against the viruses multiplying in their vectors. However, with the direct evidence for the multiplication of leaf roll virus in *M. persicae*, it seems that such evidence has little relevance and there is the obvious possibility that these other viruses also multiply in their vectors. If they do, though, as with leaf roll virus, it seems that virus imbibed from the plant is either more readily transmitted than virus produced within the vector or the amount produced by multiplication in the vector depends on the amount imbibed during the infection feed.

Most viruses whose vectors remain infective for several days have obvious latent periods in their vectors and they are not usually either acquired or transmitted to plants in feeding periods of a few minutes. The minimum time set for acquiring and transmitting may well be that required for the aphids to penetrate with their stylets to the phloem and feed therefrom, which takes 10–15 minutes and often much longer (Roberts, 1940; Day and Irzykiewicz, 1954), and many of these viruses may be primarily phloem inhabitants. However, these various features seem not always to be linked, for Stoner (1952) found that the virus causing leaf fleck of maize can persist in its various aphid vectors for more than 9 days, but may be acquired from infected plants and transmitted to healthy ones in feeding periods shorter than 5 minutes and the whole process of acquiring and transmitting can be achieved in fewer than 20 minutes.

Even 20 minutes seems protracted compared with the feeding times of only seconds that are needed to acquire and transmit many of the non-persistent viruses. With these, there is clearly no question of their transmission demanding virus multiplication, or even circulation of the virus through the vector's body. Indeed, Bradley and Ganong (1955a, 1955b, 1957) showed that treatments that inactivate virus on or in the terminal 15 μ of the vector's stylets prevent transmission. Hence, if any virus is taken into the aphid's gut, it is irrelevant to the process of transmission, and infection of healthy plants seems to depend on the amount retained at the stylet tips. This can be only a minute amount, so there is a ready explanation for the vector soon ceasing to be infective, but it is less easy to explain vector specificity or differences in the relative efficiency with which different aphid species transmit different viruses. How viruses are held by the stylets, and whether inside or out, is unknown, but suggestions that they are caught on scales, grooves or bristles on the chitinous surfaces (van Hoof, 1958) seem inadequate to explain that different aphids transmit different viruses, and even different strains of one virus, or that they fail to transmit such a readily transmissible virus as potato X, which morphologically resembles some of the aphid-transmitted viruses. Potato X and tobacco mosaic viruses have been reported in the mid gut of aphids that have fed on infected plants (Kikumoto and Matseu, 1962), so they are acquired but not transmitted, perhaps because they are not held at the stylet tips. More than a simple mechanical holding of virus particles seems called for, but on present knowledge it is impossible even to guess at the nature of the specific process determining whether or not the stylets of an aphid feeding on a plant infected with a given virus will retain the virus and then release it when they penetrate another plant.

TABLE 6–2

The Transmission of Cabbage Blackring Virus by Fasted and Unfasted
Aphids from Irradiated and Unirradiated Turnip Leaves *

Infection-Feeding Times	Unirradiated Leaves		Irradiated Leaves	
	Fasted Aphids	Unfasted Aphids	Fasted Aphids	Unfasted Aphids
2 min.	146	35	14	4
1 hr.	8	12	11	10
24 hr.	23	26	14	23

* Results are the total number of lesions produced on twenty-four tobacco leaves.

The ability of aphids to transmit many of these non-persistent viruses, such as henbane mosaic, potato Y, cucumber mosaic, tobacco etch, lettuce mosaic, pea mosaic, and beet mosaic, is much increased by fasting the aphids immediately before their infection feeding (Watson, 1936; 1938a, 1938b; Watson and Roberts, 1939, 1940). A fasting period as brief as 15 minutes greatly increases the proportion of aphids that transmits, and there is little gain from fasting periods longer than 1 hour, but this may increase the proportion that transmits by a factor of seven or more over the proportion of unfasted aphids. This remarkable effect of fasting is obtained only when aphids are given brief infection feeds; as the time they spend feeding on infected plants increases beyond a few minutes, the proportion of aphids that transmits decreases and after an hour the previously fasted aphids give no more infections than do unfasted ones (Table 6–2).

Various explanations for these phenomena have been advanced, but none is wholly satisfactory. Watson (1936) suggested that short infection feeds might be more effective than long ones because the tissues first penetrated by the aphids' stylets were richer in virus than the deeper tissues. However, as only fasted aphids did better with short than long infection feeds, and their stylets would be in the same tissues as those of unfasted aphids, she did not favour this explanation and suggested instead that feeding aphids produce substances that inactivate these viruses (Watson, 1938a). This second suggestion also adequately explains the fact that infective aphids remain infective longer when fasting than when feeding and it has been supported by Day and Irzykiewicz (1954), who state that the saliva contains materials that inhibit infection by some viruses. However, the more rapid loss of infectivity by feeding insects is also simply explained by postulating that their stylets are freed from virus by the act of feeding, and the fact that more aphids usually transmit after an infection feed of a day than after one of an hour (Table 6–2) is not easily reconciled with the idea that continuous feeding is necessarily deleterious.

Bradley (1952) drew attention to the fact that, when *Myzus persicae* newly colonise a leaf, they usually probe with their stylets several times before settling to feed continuously at one site, and he concluded that fasted ones not only probed sooner but made more preliminary punctures before settling to feed continuously. He suggested that aphids acquire such viruses as henbane mosaic only from the epidermis and that they cannot acquire them from deeper tissues because of the salivary sheath that surrounds their stylets when they are feeding continuously. However, aphids do acquire other viruses from deeper tissues; for example, sugar beet yellows virus is not acquired in feeding periods shorter than 10–15 minutes and the longer aphids feed the greater are their chances of becoming infective (Watson, 1946). Hence, although the salivary sheath may be impermeable to viruses and so prevent their acquisition from the mesophyll, it probably does not affect acquisition from the phloem. There is no question that fasted aphids acquire viruses such as henbane mosaic mainly from the epidermis, for most become infective too soon for their stylets to have penetrated deeper. Also, exposing infected leaves to ultraviolet radiation, so as to inactivate virus in most of the epidermal cells, abolishes the beneficial action of short feeding periods in increasing transmissions by fasted aphids (Bawden, Hamlyn and Watson, 1954). Table 6–2 shows, not only this effect with *M. persicae* transmitting cabbage blackring virus, but also the increased transmissions when aphids are fasted before being given a brief infection feed. An effect from fasting still shows with aphids fed on these irradiated leaves, but it did not with irradiated tobacco leaves infected with henbane mosaic virus, so presumably the crinkled turnip leaves were not completely exposed to the radiation and virus survived in the epidermal cells of some shielded parts. Irradiating leaves infected with some other non-persistent viruses similarly affected transmission by aphids, but it did not affect the transmission of beet yellows virus, which is not acquired during brief infection feeds.

Although the peculiarities in the transmission of these non-persistent viruses cannot be explained with certainty, a plausible explanation can be advanced based on the different feeding behaviour of fasted and unfasted aphids and on the tissues from which they feed at different times. That these viruses occur in epidermal cells is known and there is some evidence that they may be more concentrated there than in deeper tissues. Hence, if the stylets of fasted aphids are empty and they probe into the epidermis more often than unfasted aphids, they may imbibe more epidermal sap and so contain more virus than the stylets of aphids that have been feeding continuously. The loss of infectivity by many of the fasted aphids as their infection feeding is continued beyond the time their stylets are in the epidermis may mean that while penetrating through the mesophyll they acquire no virus, possibly because the salivary sheath produced there is impermeable, or because the stylets move intercellularly and imbibe no sap. When the epidermis is removed from leaves infected with cucumber mosaic virus, aphids readily become infected by feeding on the exposed mesophyll (Namba, 1962), presumably because they then behave towards the upper layers of the mesophyll as they normally do towards the epidermis. Most aphids have their stylets in the phloem within an hour and it is from here the aphids draw most of their food (Fig. 6–1) (Day and Irzykiewicz, 1953; Watson and Nixon, 1953).

The fact that aphids feeding from the phloem become infective less readily than when imbibing from the epidermis could have various explanations, of which the more obvious are that sap from the epidermis contains more virus or that some other properties of the epidermal sap increase the chances of virus being retained on the stylet tips. Bradley (1953) concluded that, of *M. persicae* that had been for many hours on tobacco leaves infected with potato virus Y, only those that had moved their feeding position and recently reinserted their stylets into the epidermis transmitted. Results with aphids fed on irradiated leaves do not support this conclusion with cabbage blackring virus in turnip, from which there seems little doubt that most aphids that are infective after long infection feedings are so because of virus acquired from deeper tissues, but they suggest that rather more than half the transmissions of henbane mosaic virus by aphids given long infection feedings on tobacco may occur because of virus acquired from the epidermis (Bawden,

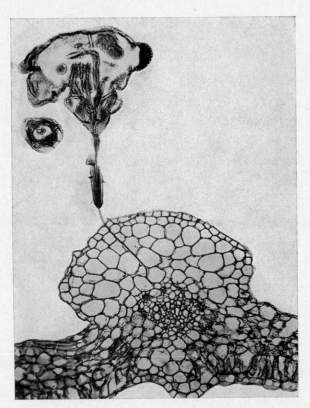

Fig. 6–1. Section of potato leaf showing the path of the stylet of *Myzus pseudosolani*. Note the path is intercellular through the cortex and that the aphid is feeding in the phloem. × 80. (T. P. Dykstra and W. C. Whitaker, 1938, J. agr. Res. 57: 319).

Hamlyn and Watson, 1954). This apparent difference between the behaviour of the viruses does not necessarily mean they are distributed differently in the tissues of infected leaves, but may simply reflect differences in the feeding behaviour of the aphid on the two plants. Turnip is a usual host plant for *M. persicae*, whereas tobacco is not, and the aphids used in the radiation experiments were bred on turnip. The transfer from one turnip plant to another

is a minor change, whereas transfer to tobacco could well alter the
aphid's behaviour considerably, make continuous feeding from the
phloem less likely and increase the chances of changing the feeding
site, with consequent repeated probing of the epidermis. Indeed
change of host may well affect the aphids in much the same way
as does a fasting period. The conditions in most transmission ex
periments differ so much from those of transmission in crops tha
it is dangerous to extrapolate from one to the other. However, wing
less aphids bred on a crop are probably rarely in the condition to
be optimal vectors of these non-persistent viruses, and only winged
forms are often likely after a period without feeding to feed briefly
on an infected plant and then move to another plant.

Although many of the non-persistent viruses are transmitted
most readily when fasted aphids are given only brief infection feed
ings, not all are. Of two that infect lettuce, for example, lettuce
mosaic is, but dandelion mosaic virus is not (Kassanis, 1947)
Fasted aphids transmit dandelion mosaic virus no more readily than
unfasted ones and the chances of either transmitting increase with
increasing duration of infection feeding; the different behaviour of
the two viruses may mean that they are differently distributed in
infected plants, with lettuce mosaic readily acquired from the epidermis and dandelion mosaic virus only from deeper tissues, probably the phloem.

Different viruses behave so differently that, using one species of
aphid as a vector, it is often possible to separate viruses simultaneously infecting the same plant. For example, fasted *M. persicae*
fed for a minute or so on sugar beet infected with beet mosaic and
yellows viruses will transmit only mosaic virus to healthy plants;
after an infection feed of an hour or more, aphids may transmit both
viruses to plants they feed on immediately, but they will transmit
only yellows virus to other plants to which they are transferred after
a few hours (Watson, 1946). Sugar beet yellows virus differs in
some respects from any already discussed. It shows none of the
characters of non-persistent viruses, and also differs from such viruses
as potato leaf roll. There is no clear latent period, for some aphids
given infection feeds of only 15 minutes will infect healthy plants
during the next 15 minutes, and these periods are not much above
the minimum required for the stylets to reach the phloem. The
proportions of aphids that transmit increase with increased feeding
times on both infected and healthy plants; increases in length of
the infection feeds also increase the length of time aphids remain
infective and the number of individual plants they will infect when
fed on a succession. Prolonging the infection feed, however, does

not make aphids remain infective for more than a few days. Some transmissions may happen from virus retained at the stylet tips, but it seems unlikely that all do. Whether this virus does circulate through the body of the aphid is unknown, but Harrison (1958) could not transmit it by inoculation to aphids. This failure is not because the virus is unstable *in vitro*, for it is transmissible to plants by manual inoculation, though not readily (Kassanis, 1949).

The range of behaviour of aphids in transmitting different viruses can be briefly summarised; acquisition feeding periods ranging from seconds to hours; periods between acquiring virus and becoming able to transmit ranging from nothing to latent periods of a few hours only with some viruses to many days with others; persistence of infectivity by vector ranging from less than an hour, to many days. Some of these differences, particularly in length of acquisition time, no doubt reflect differences between the concentrations reached by different viruses in infected plant cells or differences between the tissues from which they are most readily acquired. Other differences in behaviour, however, are clearly independent of the host plant and determined by interactions between the viruses and their vectors. Some viruses are transmitted simply because they are briefly retained at the stylet tips. Others are carried internally in their vector and circulate through its body; some at least of these probably multiply in their aphid vectors. Kennedy, Day and Eastop (1962) have summarised transmission tests by aphids with more than 250 viruses, list species that failed to transmit as well as vectors, and show whether the viruses are stylet borne or circulate in the bodies of vectors.

The transmission of some viruses in crops may be aided by effects infection has on the physiological state of the host plants. For example, Kennedy (1951) reported that the average number of young born to adult *Aphis fabae* was more on sugar beet plants with mosaic than on healthy plants. Similarly, Baker (1960) found that four aphid species not only preferentially selected beet infected with yellows to feed on rather than healthy beet, but bred more rapidly and lived longer than when on green leaves. There has been no report of any plant virus harming its aphid vector, but Ehrhardt (1960) reported that *Myzus persicae* infective with potato leaf roll virus respire much less than normal and Moericke (1961) reported that the salivary glands of such aphids contained rod-shaped inclusions that have not been seen in virus-free aphids.

Thrips. Thrips at present occupy an unique position among vectors of plant viruses in that there is only one, tomato spotted wilt

virus, that they are known to transmit. It may be significant that
this also is an unusual virus, readily transmitted by manual inocula
tion of plant sap, but extremely unstable *in vitro*, possibly because
it is very readily oxidised (Bald and Samuel, 1934; Best, 1937)
Since Bald and Samuel (1931) described its transmission by *Frank
liniella insularis* other species of thrips have been found to be vec
tors, but little has been added to knowledge about the mechanism
of transmission. Several days elapse between the vector acquiring
the virus and becoming able to transmit, but once the latent period
is over vectors remain infective indefinitely. An exceptional fea
ture is that, to become infective, insects must feed during their larva
stages on an infected plant. Both larvae and adults can transmit
but insects that do not feed on an infected plant until they are adults
do not transmit however long they live. There is no certain explana
tion for this, but transmission obviously involves the virus circulating
through the vector's body and may involve virus multiplication, and
one possibility is that some tissue changes and loses its permeability
to the virus as the insect becomes adult. An obvious suspect tissue
is the gut wall, more so since Sinha (1960) showed that adults of
the leafhopper vector of cereal striate mosaic virus are less able than
nymphs to become infective but become equally able after their guts
are punctured. However, if tomato spotted wilt virus multiplies in
its vectors, an equally likely explanation is that the tissue where it
multiplies is readily susceptible to infection only in its immature
stages.

   White-flies. Since Kirkpatrick (1930) first found that cotton leaf
curl virus was transmitted by *Bemisia tabaci*, tobacco leaf curl
(Storey, 1931), cassava mosaic (Storey and Nichols, 1938), *Abutilon*
variegation (Orlando and Silberschmidt, 1946), yellow vein mosaic
of ochra (Capoor and Varma, 1950), *Euphorbia* mosaic (Costa and
Bennett, 1950) and some other viruses have been transmitted by
this or other species of white-fly. Nothing is known of the prop
erties or constitution of any of these viruses, most of which have not
been transmitted between plants by manual inoculation of sap,
although *Euphorbia* mosaic virus has with difficulty. All the viruses
seem to behave in much the same way in their vectors, with a latent
period of from a few hours to a day or more between acquiring
virus and becoming able to transmit. White-fly can acquire virus
in infection feedings of 30 minutes, but the proportion of insects
that becomes infective increases with increasing time on infected
plants; similarly, although fully infective white-flies can infect
healthy plants in feeding periods of only 10 minutes, most require

longer (Costa and Bennett, 1950; Varma, 1955). Virus can be acquired by either nymphs or adults, and insects that feed while nymphs on infected plants continue to transmit when adults. However, the persistence of infectivity depends on the duration of the infection feeding; with yellow vein mosaic virus of ochra, no insect remained infective for more than 3 days after an infection feed of 30 minutes, whereas many remained infective for the remainder of their lives (3 weeks or more) after an infection feed lasting 6 hours (Varma, 1955).

These viruses are obviously contained in and circulate through the bodies of their vectors. There is no evidence that they multiply in their vectors and, if they do, the amount of virus produced by multiplication is either much less than can be derived by feeding on infected plants or depends directly on the amount acquired from infected plants. There is no record of transmission through the eggs laid by infective females and the only attempt reported to make white-flies infective by feeding them on extracts from infected plants failed (Costa and Bennett, 1950). The ability of different individual *Bemisia tabaci* to transmit *Euphorbia* mosaic virus differed considerably and, on average, males transmitted twice as often as females. A limiting factor in the transmission of cassava mosaic virus is that mature leaves resist infection and white-flies transmit only to leaves less than about one-quarter of their full length (Storey and Nichols, 1938).

Mealybugs. Pineapple wilt was for long thought to be caused by a toxin secreted by *Pseudococcus brevipes* which had been conditioned to produce it by feeding on pineapple plants (Carter, 1932), but later work suggests it is probably a virus disease (Carter, 1951; Carter and Ito, 1956). If it is, then the virus ranks as the first found to be transmitted by a mealybug, a distinction that otherwise falls to the cocoa swollen shoot viruses (Box, 1945). Many symptomatologically distinct viruses of cocoa are transmitted by mealybugs and there are many species of mealybugs that can transmit them. However, there is indication of some vector specificity, for although *Pseudococcus njalensis* and *Ps. citri* transmit all such viruses, *Ps. longispinus* does not and transmits none that is transmitted by *Ferrisia virgata* (Posnette, 1950).

Few insects acquire virus in feeding periods shorter than 2 hours and the proportion that becomes infective increases with increasing times up to a day. Fasting before the infection feed increases the proportion that transmits when the infection feed is shorter than 12 hours but not when it is longer. The proportion of insects that transmits is increased by increased feeding times on test plants up to one hour but not beyond. Feeding insects lose infectivity within an hour of leaving infected plants, but fasting ones may remain infective for more than a day (Posnette and Robertson, 1950). The transmission behaviour closely resembles that of dandelion mosaic virus by aphids (Kassanis, 1947), and it seems likely that the cocoa viruses are acquired from tissues below the epidermis and that they occur at smaller concentrations than most of the aphid-transmitted viruses. Virus is more readily acquired by vectors from young leaves showing red vein-banding symptoms than from old infected leaves, and infections are more readily achieved in the cotyledons of cocoa beans than in growing plants (Posnette, 1947). The viruses are presumably carried on the stylets of the mealybugs as are the non-persistent aphid-transmitted viruses, but this has not been established. They can be transmitted between plants by manual inoculation, but only with difficulty (Brunt and Kenten, 1960). Little or nothing is known about their properties, so it is impossible even to guess at what distinguishes them from aphid-transmitted viruses and makes them specifically transmitted by mealybugs.

Possibly because the virus content of infected plants is small, few infections are obtained when cotyledons are infested with single mealybugs from infected plants. Increasing the number of mealybugs increases the proportion that become infected and 95% may become infected with 25 insects per cocoa bean. Similar results have often been described with other kinds of vectors and viruses and have sometimes led to the suggestion that vectors inject leaves with amounts of virus too small to infect individually but which act accumulatively and together establish infection though none would alone. Whenever this suggestion has been tested critically, whether with aphids (Watson, 1936), leafhoppers (Storey, 1938) or mealybugs (Posnette and Robertson, 1950), it has proved to be unfounded; each inoculation is a local event independent of any other and the probability that a group of insects will infect is no greater than the probability that one or other members of the group would alone cause infection.

Mealybugs are much more sedentary than aphids, leafhoppers or thrips, and their habits fortunately make them extremely inefficient vectors of viruses. Viruses rarely spread between cocoa trees unless these are in contact and this spread is probably by crawling nymphs, which are not only rather more mobile than adults but also more efficient vectors, or by mealybugs moved from tree to tree by the ants which tend them. The occasional spread over long distances presumably happens because mealybugs are blown by the wind or because infected and infested cocoa pods or other parts of trees are carried over long distances (Thresh, 1958).

Biting insects. There are reports of what are probably unspecific transmissions by biting insects of several viruses that are readily transmitted mechanically. These transmissions presumably occur because of infective sap contaminating the insect's mouth and such insects soon cease to transmit. The transmission of these viruses will not be discussed further and here attention will be given only to those whose vectors remain able to transmit for at least a day after leaving infected plants. The first of these to be discovered was a virus causing mosaic of cowpea in the U.S.A. which Smith (1924) found to be transmitted by the beetle *Ceratoma trifurcata*. Other viruses since found to be beetle-transmitted include squash mosaic (Freitag, 1941), turnip yellow mosaic (Markham and Smith, 1949), turnip crinkle and turnip rosette (Broadbent, 1957). In addition to beetles, turnip yellow mosaic virus was transmitted by two species of grasshoppers and an earwig, but not by caterpillars (*Pieris* sp.) or any sucking insects (Markham and Smith, 1949), and turnip crinkle virus by hoppers of *Locusta migratoria* and the leaf-mining larvae of the fly *Phytomyza rufides* (Martini, 1958).

These viruses all have similar properties; they have approximately spherical particles, thermal inactivation points between 80 and 90°, are easily transmitted between plants by manual inoculation with sap, in which they occur at high concentrations and remain infective for many days. Markham and Smith (1949) suggested that larvae of the mustard beetle could not transmit turnip yellow mosaic virus until a day after their infection feed, but other workers have found that this and the other viruses can be transmitted without any latent period (Martini, 1958; Dale, 1953). Beetles can infect readily after infection feeding of only a few minutes, but longer infection feeds increase their ability to infect a series of healthy plants and the length of time they remain infective. Ability to transmit decreases with increasing time after feeding on an infected plant, but it is usually retained for some days and can be retained for two or more weeks (Dale, 1953; Freitag, 1956). None of the beetle vectors has an oesophageal valve or functional salivary glands and they all regurgitate from the foregut while feeding. Regurgitated juice and the abdominal contents of *Ceratoma trifurcata* that have fed on plants infected with cowpea mosaic virus are infective (Smith, 1924). Transmissions immediately after the infection feed may be by virus simply contaminating the mouths, but those later on probably depend on virus coming from the stomach,

and persistence of infectivity presumably depends on how much
virus is contained in the stomach at the end of their infection feed
and on how rapidly it is lost by regurgitation.

Most workers have failed to transmit these viruses by insects
that feed by sucking plant juices, but Freitag (1941) reported that
aphids occasionally transmitted squash mosaic virus and Martini
(1958) transmitted turnip crinkle virus with four species of aphids,
although more than 100 individual aphids were needed to give an
infection. Whether this means that individual aphids differ in their
ability to transmit, and that occasional ones are vectors whereas the
great majority are not, or only that aphids sometimes transmit because their stylets are by chance contaminated with virus, is unknown. The few aphids that became infective soon lost the ability
to transmit. Some aphid-transmitted viruses show a comparable
phenomenon, in as much as they are readily transmitted by some
aphid species, but by others only when very many individuals are
used (Bawden and Kassanis, 1947).

Animals other than insects. The two main groups of animals
other than insects till now identified as containing vectors of plant
viruses are the Eriophyid mites and the nematodes. It is odd that
mites have been neglected for so long, because the "big bud" mite,
Phytoptus ribis, was suspected many years ago to transmit currant
reversion (Amos, Hatton, Knight and Massee, 1927), but now they
are being increasingly studied and are known to transmit at least
five other viruses, peach mosaic (Wilson, Jones and Cochran, 1955),
fig mosaic (Flock and Wallace, 1955), wheat streak mosaic (Slykhuis, 1955), wheat spot mosaic (Slykhuis, 1956) and ryegrass
mosaic (Mulligan, 1960). Too little is known about the properties
of these viruses to seek for any common feature. None has been
transmitted by any other kind of animal while feeding, but wheat
streak mosaic and ryegrass mosaic have been transmitted to plants
by manual inoculation with sap. Ryegrass mosaic virus probably
has flexible, elongated particles, about 400 x 20 mμ, and sap from
infected plants contains enough virus to be infective when diluted
1/1000 and to give a visible precipitate with its antiserum when
diluted 1/32 (Mulligan, 1960). It seems that the different viruses
may behave differently in their vectors, for whereas *Aceria tulipae*
remains infective for many days with wheat streak mosaic virus
(Slykhuis, 1953), *Abacarus hystrix* lose their infectivity within 12
hours of leaving plants infected with ryegrass mosaic virus (Mulligan, 1960). Also, *A. tulipae* that did not feed on infected plants
until they were adults failed to transmit wheat streak mosaic virus,

whereas all stages of *A. hystrix* were equally able to acquire and transmit ryegrass mosaic virus. These differences carry the obvious implication that wheat streak virus is maintained in and circulates through the body of its vector, whereas ryegrass mosaic virus is not. Wheat streak mosaic virus is not transmitted through the eggs of *A. tulipae*, which are produced parthenogenetically. In the open, spread between cereal crops seems to depend on wind-blown mites (Slykhuis, 1953; Pady, 1955; Staples and Allington, 1956).

Since Hewitt, Raski and Goheen (1958) discovered that *Xiphinema index* transmits grapevine fanleaf virus, later shown to be a strain of arabis mosaic virus (Cadman, Dias and Harrison, 1960), five other nematodes have been identified as vectors of plant viruses: *X. diversicaudatum* for the type strain of arabis mosaic virus (Jha and Posnette, 1959; Harrison and Cadman, 1959); *X. americanum* for the peach yellow bud mosaic strain of tomato ringspot virus (Breece and Hart, 1959) and for tobacco ringspot virus (Fulton, 1962); *Longidorus elongatus* and *L. attenuatus*, respectively, for the beet ringspot and lettuce ringspot strains of tomato black ring virus (Harrison, Mowat and Taylor, 1961); and *Trichodorus pachydermus* and *T. primitivus*, respectively for Dutch and English isolates of tobacco rattle virus (Sol, van Heuven and Seinhorst, 1960; Harrison, Mowat and Taylor, 1961). This list suggests a high degree of vector specificity, for different strains of some viruses are shown as being transmitted by different nematode species, but too few tests have yet been made to know whether the ability to transmit is as restricted as present results suggest. However, it is of some interest that the viruses so far transmitted by species of *Xiphinema* and *Longidorus*, which are closely similar genera, have many properties in common. All have polyhedral particles, are readily transmitted between plants by manual inoculation (though usually not between the fruit-crop plants in which they commonly occur), are not very stable *in vitro*, and cause ringspot lesions in many of their hosts. In contrast, tobacco rattle virus, transmitted by species of *Trichodorus*, which is placed in a different family from *Xiphinema* and *Longidorus*, has rod-shaped particles and very different properties *in vitro* from those of the polyhedral viruses.

The problems in studying the behaviour during transmission of soil-inhabiting organisms are considerable, not least because it is impossible to know when roots are fed on, and it is perhaps more surprising how much is known than that much still remains to be discovered. For example, there can be no doubt that arabis mosaic virus is contained in the bodies of the nematodes, for they remain able to transmit for a month or more when deprived of food (Raski

and Hewitt, 1960; Jha and Posnette, 1961), which is longer thar
the virus remains infective in sap at 18° (Harrison, 1958b). The
shortest infection feed in which virus has been shown to be acquirec
is a day and 3 days is the shortest time on healthy plants to giv<
infection. In tests with X. *diversicaudatum* and arabis mosaic viru:
there was a suggestion of a latent period, for individuals that failec
to infect one lot of plants during 5 to 10 days infected plants or
which they were placed later (Jha and Posnette, 1961). Adults anc
larvae of *Xiphinema* sp. acquire and transmit strains of arabis mosaic
virus (Harrison and Cadman, 1959; Raski and Hewitt, 1960), bu
when larvae and adults of *Longidorus elongatus* were compared
only larvae did (Harrison, Mowat and Taylor, 1961).

The work with mites and nematodes as vectors is only at it:
beginning, but enough has been done to suggest that, in transmitting
different viruses, they may show differences in behaviour to riva
those disclosed in the longer-studied vectors, and it is reasonabl<
to suspect that at least some of the nematodes may be alternativ<
hosts for the plant viruses they transmit.

REFERENCES

Amos, J., R. G. Hatton, R. C. Knight, and A. M. Massee. 1927. Ann. Rept. Eas
    Malling Res. Sta. 1925, 13 (pt. 2): 126.
Badami, R. S. 1958. Ann. appl. Biol. 46: 554.
Baker, P. E. 1960. Ann. appl. Biol. 48: 2.
Bald, J. G., and G. Samuel. 1931. Council Sci. Ind. Res. Aust. Bull. 54.
———, and ———. 1934. Ann. appl. Biol. 21: 179.
Bawden, F. C., B. M. G. Hamlyn, and M. A. Watson. 1954. Ann. appl. Biol. 41:
    229.
Bawden, F. C., and B. Kassanis. 1947. Ann. appl. Biol. 34: 503.
Bennett, C. W. 1935. J. agric. Res. 50: 211.
———, and A. S. Costa. 1949. J. agric. Res. 78: 675.
———, and ———. 1961. Phytopathology 51: 546.
———, and H. E. Wallace. 1938. J. agric. Res. 56: 31.
Best, R. J. 1937. Aust. Chem. Inst. J. & Proc. 4: 375.
Black, L. M. 1938. Phytopathology 28: 863.
———. 1941. *Ibid.* 31: 120.
———. 1943. Genetics 28: 200.
———. 1944. Proc. Am. phil. Soc. 88: 132.
———. 1948. Phytopathology 38: 2.
———. 1950. Nature, 166: 852.
———. 1953a. Phytopathology 43: 466.
———. 1953b. *Ibid.* 43: 9.
———. 1955. *Ibid.* 45: 208.
———. 1959. *In* The Viruses (F. M. Burnet and W. M. Stanley, Eds.) 2: 157
    Academic Press, New York.
Box, H. E. 1945. Nature 155: 608.
Bradley, R. H. E. 1952. Ann. appl. Biol. 39: 78.
———. 1953. Nature 171: 755.
——— and R. Y. Ganong. 1955a. Canad. J. Microbiol. 1: 775.

———, and ———. 1955b. *Ibid.* 1: 783.

———, and ———. 1957. *Ibid.* 3: 669.

BRAKKE, M. K., A. E. VATTER, and L. M. BLACK. 1954. Abnormal and Pathological Plant Growth, Brookhaven Symposia in Biology, No. 6, 137.

BREECE, J. R., and W. H. HART. 1959. Plant Dis. Reptr. 43: 989.

BROADBENT, L. 1950. Ann. appl. Biol. 37: 58.

———. 1957. *Investigation of Virus Diseases of Brassica Crops.* (Agricultural Research Council Report Series No. 14) Cambridge University Press.

———, and T. W. TINSLEY. 1951. Ann. appl. Biol. 38: 411.

BRUNT, A. A., and R. H. KENTEN. 1960. Virology 12: 328.

CADMAN, C. H., H. F. DIAS, and B. D. HARRISON. 1960. Nature 187: 577.

CAPOOR, S. P., and P. M. VARMA. 1950. Indian J. agric. Sci. 20: 217.

CARTER, W. 1932. Ecology 13: 296.

———. 1951. Phytopathology 41: 769.

———, and K. ITO. 1956. Phytopathology 46: 601.

CLINCH, P., J. B. LOUGHNANE, and P. A. MURPHY. 1936. Sci. Proc. R. Dublin Soc. 21: 431.

COOK, M. T. 1947. *Viruses and Virus Diseases of Plants.* Burgess Publishing Co., Minneapolis.

COSTA, A. S. 1952. Phytopathology 42: 396.

———, and C. W. BENNETT. 1950. Phytopathology 40: 266.

DALE, W. T. 1953. Ann. appl. Biol. 40: 384.

DAY, M. F. 1955a. Exp. Parasitol. 4: 387.

———. 1955b. Aust. J. biol. Sci. 8: 498.

———, and F. FENNER. 1953. Intern. Congr. Microbiol. Rept. Proc. 6th Congr. 2: 586.

———, and H. IRZYKIEWICZ. 1953. Aust. J. biol. Sci. 6: 98.

———, and ———. 1954. *Ibid.* 7: 251.

DONCASTER, J. P., and B. KASSANIS. 1946. Ann. appl. Biol. 33: 66.

DOOLITTLE, S. P., and M. N. WALKER. 1928. Phytopathology 18: 143.

DRAKE, C. J., H. HARRIS, and H. G. TATE. 1933. J. econ. Ent. 26: 841.

EHRHARDT, P. 1960. Ent. exp. & appl. 3: 114.

FLOCK, R. A., and J. M. WALLACE. 1955. Phytopathology 45: 52.

FREITAG, J. H. 1936. Hilgardia 10: 305.

———. 1941. Phytopathology 31: 8.

———. 1956. *Ibid.* 46: 73.

FUKUSHI, T. 1934. J. Fac. Agric. Hokkaido Univ. 37: 41.

———. 1935. Proc. Imp. Acad. Japan. 11: 301.

———. 1940. J. Fac. Agric. Hokkaido Univ. 45: 83.

FULTON, J. P. 1962. Phytopathology 52: 375.

GOSS, R. W. 1931. Res. Bull. Neb. agric. Exp. Sta. 53.

HARRISON, B. D. 1958a. Virology 6: 265.

———. 1958b. Ann. appl. Biol. 46: 221.

———, and C. H. CADMAN. 1959. Nature 184: 1624.

HARRISON, B. D., W. P. MOWAT, and C. E. TAYLOR. 1961. Virology 14: 480.

HEINZE, K. 1955. Phytopath. Z. 25: 103.

———. 1959. Archiv. Virusforsch. 9: 396.

HEWITT, W. B., D. J. RASKI, and A. C. GOHEEN. 1958. Phytopathology 48: 586.

HOGGAN, I. A. 1931. Phytopathology 21: 199.

———. 1933. *Ibid.* 23: 446.

HOUSTON, B. R., K. ESAU, and W. B. HEWITT. 1947. Phytopathology 37: 247.

HUFF, C. G. 1931. Science 74: 456.

JENSEN, D. D. 1959. Pan-Pacific Entomologist 35: 65.

JHA, A., and A. F. POSNETTE. 1959. Nature 184: 962.

———, and ———. 1961. Virology 13: 119.

KASSANIS, B. 1941. Ann. appl. Biol. 28: 238.

———. 1947. Ann. appl. Biol. 34: 412.

KASSANIS, B. 1949. *Ibid.* 36: 270.
———. 1952. *Ibid.* 39: 157.
———. 1961. Virology 13: 93.
KENNEDY, J. S. 1951. Nature, 168: 825.
———, M. F. DAY, and V. F. EASTOP. 1962. A conspectus of aphids as vectors of plant viruses. Commonwealth Institute of Entomology, London.
KIKUMOTO, T., and C. MATSEU. 1962. Virology 16: 509.
KIRKPATRICK, H. C., and A. F. ROSS. 1952. Phytopathology 42: 540.
KIRKPATRICK, T. W. 1930. Bull. ent. Res. 22: 323.
KUNKEL, L. O. 1926a. Amer. J. Bot. 13: 646.
———. 1926b. Phytopathology 16: 67.
———. 1933. Contr. Boyce Thompson Inst. 5: 19.
———. 1937. Amer. J. Bot. 24: 316.
———. 1938. J. Econ. Ent. 31: 20.
———. 1941. Amer. J. Bot. 28: 761.
———. 1946. *Ibid.* 39: 831.
———. 1948. Arch. ges. Virusforsch. 4: 24.
LEACH, G. L. 1940. Insect Transmission of Plant Diseases. McGraw-Hill, New York
LITTAU, V. C., and K. MARAMOROSCH. 1956. Virology 2: 128.
———, and ———. 1958. Phytopathology 48: 263.
———, and ———. 1960. Virology 10: 483.
LOUGHNANE, J. B. 1943. J. Dep. Agric. Irish Free State 40: 291.
MACCARTHY, H. R. 1954. Phytopathology 44: 167.
MARAMOROSCH, K. 1952a. Phytopathology 42: 59.
———. 1952b. *Ibid.* 42: 663.
———. 1956. Virology 2: 369.
———. 1958. Tijdschr. PlZiekt. 64: 383.
———. 1959. Phytopathology 49: 545.
MARKHAM, R., and K. M. SMITH. 1949. Parasitology 39: 330.
MARTINI, Ch. 1958. Proc. 3rd Conf. Potato Virus Diseases, Lisse-Wageningen p. 106.
MOERICKE, V. 1961. Proc. 4th Conf. Potato Virus Diseases, Braunschweig, p. 117
MUELLER, W. C., and W. F. ROCHOW. 1961. Virology 14: 253.
MULLIGAN, T. E. 1960. Ann. appl. Biol. 48: 575.
NAMBA, R. 1962. Virology 16: 267.
NEWTON, W. 1953. F. A. O. Plant Prot. Bull. 2: 40.
ORLANDO, A., and K. SILBERSCHMIDT. 1946. Arq. Inst. biol. S. Paulo 17: 1.
PADY, S. M. 1955. Plant Dis. Reptr. 39: 296.
POSNETTE, A F. 1947. Ann. appl. Biol. 34: 388.
———. 1950. Ann. appl. Biol. 37: 378.
———, and N. F. ROBERTSON. 1950. Ann. appl. Biol. 37: 363.
PRENTICE, I. W., and R. V. HARRIS. 1946. Ann. appl. Biol. 33: 50.
———, and T. M. WOOLLCOMBE. 1951. Ann. appl. Biol. 38: 389.
RASKI, D. J., and W. B. HEWITT. 1960. Nematologica 5: 166.
ROBERTS, F. M. 1940. Ann. appl. Biol. 27: 348.
ROCHOW, W. F. 1959. Phytopathology 49: 744.
———. 1960. Virology 12: 223.
SCHULTZ, E. S., and D. FOLSOM. 1925. J. agric. Res. 30: 493.
SEVERIN, H. H. P. 1921. Phytopathology 11: 424.
———. 1924. *Ibid.* 14: 80.
———. 1931. Hilgardia 6: 253.
———. 1946. Phytopathology 17: 121.
SINHA, R. C. 1960. Virology 10: 344.
SLYKHUIS, J. T. 1953. Phytopathology 43: 537.
———. 1955. *Ibid.* 45: 116.
———. 1956. *Ibid.* 46: 682.
SMITH, C. E. 1924. Science, N. S. 60: 268.

SMITH, K. M. 1931. Ann. appl. Biol. 18: 141.
———. 1941. Parasitology 33: 110.
———. 1946. *Ibid.* 37: 131.
SOL, H. H., J. C. VAN HEUVEN, and J. W. SEINHORST. 1960. Tijdschr. PlZiekt. 66: 228.
STAPLES, R., and W. B. ALLINGTON. 1956. Res. Bull. Neb. agric. Exp. Sta. 178.
STEGWEE, D., and M. B. PONSEN. 1958. Ent. exp. & appl. 1: 291.
STONER, W. N. 1952. Phytopathology 42: 683.
STOREY, H. H. 1928. Ann. appl. Biol. 15: 1.
———. 1931. Nature 128: 187.
———. 1932. Proc. Roy Soc. B. 112: 46.
———. 1933. Proc. Roy. Soc. B. 113: 463.
———. 1938. *Ibid.* 125: 455.
———. 1939. Bot. Rev. 5: 240.
———, and R. F. W. NICHOLS. 1938. Ann. appl. Biol. 25: 790.
THRESH, J. M. 1958. Technical Bulletin No. 5, West African Cocoa Research Institute.
VAN HOOF, H. A. 1958. Doctoral Dissertation, Wageningen.
VAN VELSEN, R. J., and N. C. CROWLEY. 1961. Nature 189: 858.
VARMA, P. M. 1955. Indian J. agric. Sci. 25: 293.
WALTERS, H. J. 1952. Phytopathology 42: 355.
WATSON, M. A. 1936. Phil. Trans. Roy. Soc. B. 226: 457.
———. 1938a. Proc. Roy. Soc. B. 125: 144.
———. 1938b. *Ibid.* 125: 305.
———. 1946. Proc. Roy. Soc. B. 133: 200.
———. 1956. Ann. appl. Biol. 44: 599.
———. 1960. Virology 10: 211.
WATSON, M. A., and H. L. NIXON. 1953. Ann. appl. Biol. 40: 537.
———, and F. M. ROBERTS. 1939. Proc. Roy. Soc. B. 127: 544.
———, and ———. 1940. Ann. appl. Biol. 27: 227.
———, and R. C. SINHA. 1959. Virology 8: 139.
WILSON, N. S., L. S. JONES, and L. C. COCHRAN. 1955. Plant Dis. Reptr. 39: 889.
YAMADA, M., and H. YAMAMOTO. 1955. Okayama Agr. Expt. Sta. Spec. Bull. 52: 93.

Methods of Assay

For many kinds of work, but especially for studies of virus multiplication or inactivation, the need to estimate the amounts of virus, or at least the relative amounts, in different preparations will be only too obvious. However, if the value of quantitative measurements needs any argument, this is amply provided by the wealth of information there is about viruses such as tobacco mosaic, which can be assayed readily, compared with the poverty about those which cannot.

Assay methods can be based on any property that can be measured quantatively. The property of viruses most widely used is infectivity, which has two great merits; it is the most specific property of viruses and it detects smaller amounts than can be measured by other assay methods. However, infectivity assays also have considerable limitations. Infection depends on interactions between virus and host cell, the outcome of which is not determined solely by the amount of virus in an inoculum. Consequently, the results of infectivity tests cannot be translated directly into absolute amounts of virus; at best they can indicate only relative amounts in inocula compared simultaneously, and to do even this accurately requires carefully planned tests and a knowledge of what the inocula contain other than virus. Some of the components of inocula that increase or decrease the number of infections produced in inoculated leaves are described in Chapter 5 and need not be discussed again here.

An obvious way to find the absolute amount of virus is to isolate it and weigh it, but this is too laborious to be used as a routine assay method and can be applied only to the viruses that occur at high concentrations and are reasonably stable *in vitro*. As an alternative to weighing, provided the constitution of virus is known, the amount of some component, such as nitrogen, phosphorus or carbohydrate, can be determined, or the nucleic acid content can be determined by measuring the absorption of ultraviolet radiation, and the result multiplied by the necessary factor to translate it into the amount of virus. Such methods give precise results, but their safe use demands the knowledge that the preparations assayed contain nothing except virus with the property being measured, and the precision of such methods may be largely illusory because of uncertainties about either the purity of the product analysed or the extent of the losses encountered during its preparation to the state where the necessary measurements can safely be made.

Methods that have wider use, because they are applicable to less stable viruses and more dilute solutions, and are less affected by unknown contaminants, are to count the virus particles using an electron microscope or to measure the amount of material that is precipitated by antiserum to the virus. The first demands that the shape of the virus particle is known and distinctive enough to be recognised with certainty, the second only that there should be an antiserum specific to the virus and enough virus in the test fluid to give a visible reaction. These two methods can be regarded as alternatives in the sense that they usually measure the same things, for most of the material that reacts with antiserum to a virus consists of particles morphologically resembling the virus, although there are exceptions to this. However, not all the particles recognisable morphologically or by their serological behaviour are infective and these assay methods will not always give results that agree with infectivity assays. There is, indeed, no way of finding what proportion of the virus particles contained in any preparation is infective, but combining particle counts or serological assays with infectivity tests will show whether the relative proportions of infective and non-infective particles differ in different preparations. Serological tests give less precise results than counting particles, but they are easily made, entail no expensive apparatus, and give results rapidly. They are ideally suited for routine assays and it is odd that they have been so little used. Even when they only supplement infectivity tests, they give results in hours instead of days and measure differences smaller than those measurable by any except complicated infectivity tests entailing many inoculations. But the use of both serological and infectivity tests can give information that neither test alone can give; the two are not simply alternative assays, for although infectivity and antigen content are often closely related, they are not always, and when the results of the two kinds of assay disagree there is usually a phenomenon worth investigating.

Infectivity tests. The knowledge that an inoculum led to systemic infection of a plant carries no quantitative information beyond the fact that there was enough virus to infect; the final result would be the same whether the inoculum contained the minimal infecting amount or many thousand times as much. Systemic infections can provide a basis for an assay, but only when preparations are inoculated at a range of dilutions to find either the dilution at which they no longer infect or, better, at which half the inoculated plants become infected. Comparing the infectivities of different preparations by such a method entails using many plants to get even a small degree of accuracy, and then waiting at least a week to get the inaccurate results. Had this remained the only assay method, knowledge about viruses could have accrued only slowly, but assays were revolutionised after Holmes (1929) observed that some species of *Nicotiana*, especially *N. glutinosa,* produced countable necrotic lesions on leaves inoculated with tobacco mosaic virus. Since then analogous local lesions have been described in various hosts inoculated with many different viruses, and local-lesion counts provide the basis for most quantitative infectivity tests. However, for viruses such as potato leaf roll, which are not manually transmitted by inoculation to plants but can be injected into their insect vectors, the only current assay method is to inject insects with known volumes of differently diluted preparations and find what proportion of the injected insects becomes infective. To be able to do this represents a great advance from having no assay method for such viruses, but it is not a method that promises to yield reliable results quickly. Injecting a total of 40 aphids, 20 with each of two virus preparations appropriately diluted, and using 40 plants for the aphids to feed on, may show in a month that one preparation made 4 aphids infective and the other made 14, information that is no more reliable than could be got within three days by inoculating one leaf of *N. glutinosa* on its opposite halves with two preparations of tobacco mosaic virus, and finding that one produced 4 lesions and the other 14.

Holmes (1929) showed that the number of local lesions depended on the virus content of the inoculum (Fig. 7–1), and he compared local-lesion counts with Koch's plate method for counting bacteria. Many workers since have drawn analogies between the production of bacterial colonies on agar plates and the multiplication of viruses at infection sites, but although the two may be similar in some respects, the differences are very great. Identical agar plates can be produced in unlimited numbers, but no two leaves are identical, and differences between leaves greatly affect the number of lesions produced by a given inoculum. Also, any part of an agar plate is as suitable as any other for starting a bacterial colony, whereas virus infects a leaf only where it alights on an appropriate entry place.

Holmes noted that individual plants and individual leaves of one plant produced different numbers of lesions with one inoculum, and that the number also depended on the method of inoculation. Much later work has been aimed at overcoming such variations and at finding techniques and experimental designs that will decrease the standard error of measurements. Samuel and Bald (1933)

Fig. 7–1. The effect of dilution on the number of local lesions caused by tobacco mosaic virus in leaves of *Nicotiana glutinosa*. (Undiluted sap, 1:3.1, 1:10, 1:100, 1:1000). (F. O. Holmes, 1929, Bot. Gaz. 87: 39).

showed that adjacent *N. glutinosa* leaves usually differ in susceptibility more than opposite halves of the same leaf, so accuracy of comparison can be increased by inoculating half instead of whole leaves, while halving the number of plants needed to give the same number of replications. The half-leaf method is now generally used, with experimental designs that allow more than two samples to be compared. To avoid any systematic bias, each sample should be inoculated to an equal number of left-hand and right-hand halves. When comparing several samples, one can serve as a standard and be inoculated to one half of every leaf, while the others are apportioned between the other halves. Each preparation can then be related directly to the standard and indirectly through it to the others. However, this type of comparison is wasteful, for half the total inoculations are with the standard; other designs compare all samples directly with one another and can allow for variations that arise from differences between plants or leaf positions to be assessed and eliminated (Youden and Beale, 1934). When the number of preparations to be compared equals the number of leaves on a plant, the Latin square is appropriate; an example for six inocula using three plants is shown below, in which each double column repre-

sents a plant and each row half leaves occupying the same positions
on the stems:

L.	R.	L.	R.	L.	R.
1	6	2	5	4	3
4	3	6	1	2	5
5	1	4	2	3	6
2	4	3	6	5	1
3	5	1	4	6	2
6	2	5	3	1	4

When the number of inocula exceeds the number of leaves per
plant, the incomplete block (Youden, 1937a) can be used, or some
other arrangement that distributes the preparations equally over the
test plants to avoid as many sources of variation as possible. Table
7–1 shows two such arrangements for comparing eight inocula, one
(Part 1) for plants such as *N. glutinosa* that have six inoculable
leaves and the other (Part 2) for plants like French bean with only
two (the first-formed) leaves that are suitable for assays (Kleczkowski, 1950). The arrangement for plants with six leaves gives 12
replications and each inoculum occurs three times in each of the
four blocks of two plants. The arrangement for plants with two
leaves gives seven replications, with each inoculum occurring with
every other once on one leaf and twice on the same plant but on
the opposite leaf. This arrangement can readily provide for 14 replications simply by repeating it but with the order L.-R. (Left-hand
half, Right-hand half) reversed. Such arrangements allow differences between blocks and leaf positions to be assessed and eliminated during statistical analysis of results.

The number of replications needed depends on the accuracy
sought, but fewer than six are usually undesirable. Although French
bean has only two inoculable leaves, these occupy the same position on the stem, and results usually vary less than with *N. glutinosa,*
possibly because French bean are used when much younger and all
the leaves are of the same age. However, even with beans of one
age individual leaves can differ considerably in their susceptibility
to infection, and statistically designed tests are essential. Much
could probably be done to decrease the variations by paying more
attention to the production of test plants. Genetic differences probably account for some of the variation which might be eliminated
by breeding pure lines, but growing conditions are no less important. Susceptibility to infection is affected by any check to growth,
by differences in supply of nutrients or water, and by differences in

TABLE 7–1

Experimental Designs for Comparing the Relative Infectivities of Eight Inocula

PART 1

Leaf position	L.	R.	L.	R.	L.	R.	L.	R.	L.	R.	L.	R.	L.	R.	L.	R.
I	1	4	5	8	2	5	6	1	3	6	7	2	4	7	8	3
II	2	3	6	7	3	4	7	8	4	5	8	1	5	6	1	2
III	3	2	7	6	4	3	8	7	5	4	1	8	6	5	2	1
IV	4	1	8	5	5	2	1	6	6	3	2	7	7	4	3	8
V	5	8	1	4	6	1	2	5	7	2	3	6	8	3	4	7
VI	6	7	2	3	7	8	3	4	8	1	4	5	1	2	5	6
Plant	a		b		c		d		e		f		g		h	
Block	A				B				C				D			

PART 2

Leaf position	L.	R.	L.	R.	L.	R.	L.	R.	L.	R.	L.	R.	L.	R.	L.	R.
I	1	2	3	4	3	1	7	5	1	4	3	2	5	1	2	6
II	6	5	8	7	2	4	6	8	8	5	6	7	7	3	4	8
Plant	a		b		c		d		e		f		g		h	
Block	A				B				C				D			

Leaf position	L.	R.	L.	R.	L.	R.	L.	R.	L.	R.	L.	R.
I	1	6	5	2	7	1	2	8	1	8	5	4
II	8	3	4	7	4	6	5	3	7	2	3	6
Plant	i		j		k		l		m		n	
Block	E				F				G			

the light intensity to which the plants are exposed. In any one test, only plants of the same age, raised in the same conditions and that look alike, should be used. Their uniformity can be increased by removing all leaves not to be inoculated and putting plants in darkness for a day before they are inoculated; this will also increase the number of lesions they will produce by a given inoculum (Fig. 5–3), as also will a day at 36° before inoculation (Samuel and Bald, 1933; Samuel, Best and Bald, 1935; Kassanis, 1952).

The conditions in which plants are grown are so important that they can determine whether some kinds can be used to assay a given virus. For example, in the glasshouses at Rothamsted cucumber mosaic virus can be assayed on Price or Bountiful beans only during winter, because plants grown in summer produce no local lesions;

these varieties can be used throughout the year for tobacco necrosi
and some other viruses, but whereas in winter they remain in a sus
ceptible state over many days, in summer their usable period is brie
and within a few days they become too resistant for use in assays
Chenopodium amaranticolor behaves similarly and during winte
is immediately suitable for assaying several viruses, whereas in sum
mer it is not unless grown in deep shade.

The volume of inoculum rubbed over leaves seems not to influ
ence lesion numbers, provided there is enough fluid to wet the whole
surface (Samuel, Best and Bald, 1935; Youden, 1937b), but the
degree and method of rubbing are important (Samuel, 1931). Rubbing is generally assumed to serve only to make wounds in the
epidermis through which virus particles enter, but it may have other
effects. For example, there is evidence that, in addition to opening
infection sites, it can destroy them (Bawden and Harrison, 1955).
Samuel (1931) suggested that the required uniformity of rubbing
was best achieved by spatulae with flat blades of ground glass long
enough to cover the maximum width of the half-leaves, but most
people rub with either their forefingers or a piece of cheese-cloth
wet with the inoculum. Selman and Milne (1961) report more
lesions and less variability when strips of petunia leaf are inoculated
by passing the strips under a roller than when leaves are rubbed by
customary methods.

The number of lesions produced by rubbing with a given inoculum is greatly increased when fine carborundum powder or diatomaceous earths are added to the inocula, and this often allows assays
to be made that would otherwise be impossible. However, such
aids need to be used with caution, because they not only introduce
another variable, but also another uncertainty, for how they act to
increase the numbers of lesions is still far from understood. Their
abrasive action may simply increase the number of wounds, but they
may do other things such as alter the cell metabolism in ways that
favour infection, and this seems increasingly probable since Singer
and Fraenkel-Conrat (1961) conclude that bentonite, which inhibits
the action of ribonuclease, increases the number of infections by
the nucleic acid of tobacco mosaic virus but not by intact virus. The
behaviour of carborundum in facilitating transmission is described
in Chapter 5, where other evidence is also given that the number of
wounds may not be the only important factor is establishing infection sites. Some of this is relevant to assays. For example, rubbing
N. glutinosa with preparations of tobacco mosaic or tomato bushy
stunt viruses presumably produces similar numbers of wounds, but
leaves that will produce many lesions when rubbed with the first

nay give none with the second. Although a local-lesion host for both viruses, the same batch of plants will not necessarily serve for both; plants with 6–8 large inoculable leaves serve excellently for tobacco mosaic virus, but for tomato bushy stunt virus much younger plants are needed.

Relation between lesion numbers and virus content. For accurate essays, the different samples being compared should give approximately the same numbers of lesions, because there is no direct way of relating the virus contents of samples that give many lesions with those that give few. Comparisons are most sensitive when samples are tested over a range of concentrations and the relative concentrations measured that produce a mean of 15–30 lesions per half-leaf. When studying rates of inactivation, for example, from exposure to radiations, a suitable assay method is to have eight inocula of which four are dilutions of the unirradiated preparation that extend over the range of expected inactivation from four times of irradiation. In other words, if the amount of virus surviving after four exposures of different lengths is expected to be 10, 1, 0.2 and 0.04% of the initial, the unirradiated preparation should be inoculated at 1/10, 1/50, 1/250 and 1/1,250, or, to extend the range, at 1/5, 1/50, 1/500 and 1/5,000. From the numbers of lesions produced by the four unirradiated samples, a dilution curve can be drawn from which the amount of virus inactivated by each of the four exposures to the radiation can be approximately estimated by interpolation. A dilution curve needs to be derived for every assay because, as Price and Spencer (1943a; 1943b) showed, the slope of the dilution curve is not constant and cannot be predicted. A constant factor of dilution can produce very different decreases in lesion numbers at different virus concentrations, the greatest decrease is not always at the same point in the dilution series, and the decrease is rarely proportional to the dilution.

Dilution curves with tobacco mosaic and several other viruses commonly divide into three portions: (1) a flat one at high concentrations, where changes in concentration have little effect on lesion numbers; (2) a steeply-sloping portion, where a change in concentration produces more nearly proportional changes in lesion numbers; (3) another flat portion at high dilutions. However, not all viruses behave like this. Best (1935) found that the third portion with tomato spotted wilt virus slopes more steeply than the second and that, at high dilutions, numbers of lesions decrease proportionately more than the dilution factor. Similarly, the number of lesions produced when sap containing red clover mottle virus is diluted falls much more than the factor of dilution (Sinha, 1960), whereas with tobacco rattle virus the two fall almost proportionally, whether the inoculum is intact virus or solutions of nucleic acid (Harrison and Nixon, 1959b). With N. *glutinosa* plants in which the number of lesions produced by tobacco mosaic virus falls much less than the dilution factor, the number produced by its free nucleic acid may fall proportionally (Table 5–3, Chapter 5). Lesion counts with serial dilutions have been examined by various workers to find what order of differences in virus content can be measured by assays. Beale (1934) concluded that differences of 25–50% in concentrations of tobacco mosaic virus could be measured by the half-leaf method using 50 N. *glutinosa* leaves, and Loring (1937) using 40–50 bean plants distinguished differences of 10%, provided the inocula contained about 10^{-6} g. per ml. With many replicates and suitably diluted inocula of tobacco necrosis, tobacco ringspot, alfalfa mosaic and southern bean mosaic viruses, differences of between 10 and 18% in concentration have been reported to be measurable (Price and Spencer, 1943a; Price, 1945). Despite these reported sensitivities of assay methods, it is usually vain to try and assess differences smaller than a factor of two, and in most routine assays even larger factors can pass undetected.

More important than failing to detect differences, however, is attaching significance to differences that are simply reflections of experimental error. There is little doubt that this commonly happens, for few people subject the results of their local-lesion assays to statistical analyses and these few have often used inappropriate methods. Statistical tests for significance are based on the assumption that the variate is normally distributed and that the variance is independent of the mean of the population. Neither requirement is fulfilled by lesion numbers, or by the logarithms of these numbers, the two values mostly used for statistical analyses. Kleczkowski (1949), who analysed the frequency distribution of local lesions caused by tobacco mosaic and tomato bushy stunt viruses in N. *glutinosa* and by a tobacco necrosis virus in French bean, found that the distribution with each is skew and that the standard error increases with increasing mean. Transforming the numbers of lesions into logarithms over-corrects, so that the standard error now decreases with increasing mean. A satisfactory transformation, when the mean number of lesions produced by any inoculum is not fewer than about 10, is provided by $y = \log_{10}(x + c)$, in which x is the number of lesions and c is a constant that can be assessed for each experiment or any number between 5 and 20 can be used without disturbing the transformation. For smaller mean values of x than

0, the transformation $z = \log_{10\frac{1}{2}} (x + c + \sqrt{(x^2 + 2cx)})$ is needed
nd Kleczkowski (1955) has tabulated values of z so that this trans-
ormation can be used as quickly as the more simple one applicable
o larger numbers of lesions.

The two main reasons for stressing the need for correctly de-
igned experiments, adequate replication and appropriate analysis
f results, before differences in lesion numbers are interpreted in
erms of virus content are (1) that many workers attach importance
o differences in lesion numbers when they have no idea what the
probable error of their estimates can be, and (2) that some workers
ranslate lesion numbers directly into relative virus contents. Alhough indefensible, this second practice is common and many erro-
neous conclusions have been drawn by those who do it. The local-
esion method can give valuable information without an impractical
number of replications or tiresome analysis of the results, provided
arge effects are being sought and no attempt is made to calculate
precise quantitative effects on the virus from the results. For example, a virus preparation subjected to a given treatment for five
different periods, when tested in a Latin square with six replications,
might average 100 lesions per half-leaf with the control and 90, 75,
35, 25 and 5 for the samples treated for increasing lengths of time.
This leaves no doubt that the treatment is inactivating and that the
amount of virus inactivated is increasing with increased time of
reatment, but to assume that 10% was inactivated by the shortest
and 95% by the longest exposure is wholly unwarranted. Before
such quantitative conclusions are drawn, inoculations are needed
with the control appropriately diluted and the results need statistical
analysis. The many claims that inactivation of viruses by various
treatments is a first-order reaction, may all be correct, but with one
exception they are based on subjective judgments. The exception
is the inactivation of viruses by ultraviolet radiation, and to show
compatibility with the hypothesis that inactivation is a first-order
reaction Kleczkowski (1953) had to devise a new statistical method
of testing the results.

Even after every precaution is taken to ensure the adequacy of
both the experimental design and the statistical analysis of the results, differences between lesion counts may still not be interpretable
in terms of relative virus contents. Lesion counts measure the relative infectivities of samples and these are not always correlated
with relative virus contents. Provided samples are similar in all
other respects, differences in infectivity are meaningful in terms of
relative virus contents, but they may not be if samples differ in
other respects. Differences in pH, or in the contents of salts or many

other substances, can affect the number of lesions produced by a given inoculum. Many substances decrease the number of infections but some increase them. There is no call to discuss here the action of these substances but an example will serve to stress how important it is to know what other things inocula contain before differences in infectivity are related to virus content. A concentration of tobacco mosaic virus in water that produced a mean of 20 lesions per half leaf in beans, might produce 50 if dissolved in phosphate buffer and 200 if the inoculum also contained carborundum, but it would produce none if the inoculum contained a little pancreatic ribonuclease, although none of the additives alters the amount of intrinsically infective virus in the inoculum. Assays made with variously diluted samples will often indicate the presence of substances that inhibit infection, for the ability of such substances to inhibit depends on their absolute concentration and not on the ratio of inhibitor to virus, so that the number of lesions produced can increase instead of decreasing when an inoculum is diluted.

To infect even highly susceptible leaves inocula must contain very many virus particles, usually a million or more for every local lesion, though Steere (1955) reports obtaining one lesion for every 50,000 particles of tobacco mosaic virus by using a special inoculation technique. Why these enormous numbers are needed is unknown. The inoculation process is crude and, no doubt, much of the virus in the inoculum is wasted on the outside of leaves. About 94% of the virus left on leaves rubbed with concentrated inocula can be removed by washing (Yarwood, 1952; Harrison, 1956), but even if the same proportion is superficial with more dilute inocula, the particles retained by leaves greatly exceed the numbers of lesions produced. This could be because most of the particles are not infective, an idea for which Rappaport and Siegel (1955) claim some evidence, or it could be because most become inactivated before they can establish infection.

In attempts to get information about the infection process and to improve the use of assays, various people have attempted to interpret relationships between virus concentrations and numbers of local lesions according to the theory based on analogies with the growth of bacterial colonies on agar (Youden, Beale and Guthrie, 1935; Bald, 1937a, 1937b; Lauffer and Price, 1945). This theory assumes that all infection sites are uniformly susceptible, that differences between susceptibilities directly reflect different numbers of sites, and that infection depends simply on the chance that at least one virus particle will alight on a susceptible site. Although experimental dilution curves rarely fit well to the equations derived from

the Poisson series on these assumptions, most workers unquestion-
ingly continue to assume that local lesions result from single virus
particles encountering uniform infection sites. Perhaps this is widely
accepted because Lauffer and Price (1945) concluded that the
curves were compatible with this theory and incompatible with the
theory that susceptible regions vary in their susceptibility, but their
conclusions were subjective, based only on approximate graphical
fitting of experimental curves to the curves of equations derived
from the alternative theories and not substantiated by statistical
tests. The only objective statistical examination of the relationships between lesion counts and virus concentration as yet reported
(Kleczkowski, 1950) shows, in contrast to what is generally accepted,
that experimental results are incompatible with the hypothesis that
lesions are produced by chance encounters between single virus
particles and uniform infection sites, but are compatible with the
hypothesis that individual infection sites differ in susceptibility so
that different doses of virus are needed to cause a lesion, the differences being such that the logarithms of minimal effective doses are
normally distributed. Compatibility of experimental results with a
hypothesis does not prove the hypothesis, but it makes it more likely
to be true than one which is incompatible. Because different
amounts of virus may be needed to cause infection at different sites,
there is no necessary reason to conclude that infections are usually
multiple in the sense that more than one virus particle is directly
concerned in initiating virus multiplication. This may be so, but
equally it may be that different amounts of virus are needed at
different sites to ensure that at least one particle survives inactivation processes and establishes infection.

Starch-iodine lesions. Hypersensitive hosts that react with necrotic local lesions of an easily visible colour and size but remain
discrete are the ideal for counting, but assays can be made with
hosts that react in other ways. Any local reaction that can be
counted will serve. The white necrotic rings produced in tobacco
by some strains of potato virus X, or the spreading ringspot type
of lesions produced by many viruses that cause systemic infections,
are usable provided the lesions are counted before they coalesce.
Viruses that cause only mosaic symptoms usually produce no immediately obvious local effects, although they sometimes produce faint
chlorotic spots, usually too diffuse to count. A method devised by
Holmes (1931) makes the local effects of these viruses usable in
assays. The leaves are decolourised with ethanol and stained with
iodine, when local lesions show either as lighter areas against a dark

background or as dark spots against a lighter background. Which appearance they have depends on the time of the day when the leaves are picked and on two contrasting effects infection has on the cells. One effect is to decrease photosynthesis and the other to delay the movement of starch out of cells during darkness. Hence, when leaves are picked and decolourised in the evening, the lesions will contain less starch and so stain less with iodine than the uninfected parts of the leaf, whereas when picked after an appropriate period in darkness, they will contain more starch and stain more deeply than the rest of the leaf. Holmes first used the method with tobacco mosaic virus in tobacco, but similar results have been obtained with many other viruses that cause mosaic diseases and it could probably be applied generally.

Lesions are usually easier to count when they are stained against an unstained background than when they and the rest of the leaf differ only in shades of staining. To get this effect, plants are placed in the dark for an appropriate period, their leaves are then picked, plunged in boiling water, decolourised in ethanol, after which they are washed in water and stained in a solution of iodine in potassium iodide. The method can give well-defined lesions, easy to count, but success demands careful management. Plants must be in darkness long enough to free the uninfected but not the infected cells from starch, and the time needed for this differential effect will depend on the temperature and on how much starch the leaves contain, which in turn will depend on the conditions to which the plants were exposed before they were put in the dark. Also, the leaves must be picked at the correct time, for with too short an interval between inoculation and staining, the lesions will be too small to count and with too long an interval they may coalesce.

In the fluctuating conditions of most glasshouses, the method will sometimes fail, but it can be relied on when inoculated plants are kept in less variable environments. When making an assay, it is well to inoculate a few extra plants to serve as samples and show when the leaves are ready to pick and how long they should be in darkness to get the maximum contrast in staining between the lesions and the background.

Serological assays. The union of an antigen with its antibody *in vitro* can be detected and measured by various consequences, of which the most obvious is the separation of a visible precipitate, and the precipitation reaction provides the simplest methods of assaying plant viruses. It can be used in two ways, (1) to measure the greatest dilution of the antigen solution that gives a visible precipitate after a specified time of incubation with the antiserum, or (2) to measure the ratio of antigen to antiserum at which precipitation first occurs. The first is the more accurate, the second gives results more quickly, and both measurements can often be made with one lot of titrations.

Precipitates form when soluble antigens and antibodies combine in suitable proportions in the presence of electrolytes. The rate of precipitation is increased by treatments that increase the frequency of impact between antigen and antibody particles, for example, by increasing the concentrations of the two, by heating or by continuous mixing. Precipitation occurs most rapidly at a given ratio of antigen to antibody; with a great excess of either, but especially of antigen, precipitation may not only be delayed but wholly inhibited. For assaying virus preparations by the optimal proportions method, therefore, the dilution of antiserum, which is kept constant, must be less than that needed to react optimally with the most concentrated solution of a series of antigen dilutions. A convenient way to measure either optimal proportion or end-point is to have 1 ml samples of antiserum at a constant dilution in a series of test-tubes 7 mm in diameter, to each of which is added 1 ml of antigen solution at different dilutions. Serial dilutions by a factor of two are suitable, and both antiserum and virus should be diluted in normal saline (0.85% NaCl). After mixing the antigen and antibody solutions, the tubes are placed in a water-bath, kept at a constant temperature, with their fluid columns half immersed in the water so that convection currents keep their contents continuously moving. For heat-stable antigen preparations, 50° is a convenient working temperature, but this is too high for unstable viruses, or for clarified sap, which coagulates spontaneously at this temperature. The water-bath should have transparent panels in the back and front, so that when illuminated from behind with a strip-light just below the water surface, the tubes can be observed continuously without moving them and the one in which floccules first form is easily seen. This observation measures the optimal precipitation point and the precipitation end-point is measured by recording after a pre-determined interval (3 or 24 hours) the tube with the most diluted antigen that contains a visible floccule.

Measurements of optimal proportions and of precipitation end-points usually agree closely, that is to say, if one sample precipitates optimally with constant antiserum at four times the dilution of another, it will also produce a visible precipitate when diluted four times more than the end-point of another. However, there are exceptions to this. Table 7–2 shows one (Bawden and Pirie, 1945).

TABLE 7–2

Effect of Aggregation of the Precipitin Behaviour of Tobacco Mosaic Virus

Antigen	Precipitation after	Dilution of antigens							
		1/1	2	4	8	16	32	64	128
Before aggregation	1 hour	−*	−	−	−	−	−	+†	−
	2 hours	−	−	−	−	−	+	++	+
After aggregation	3 minutes	++++	++++	+++	++	+	−	−	−
	30 minutes	++++	++++	++++	++++	++++	+++	++	+
	1 hour	++++	++++	++++	++++	++++	++++	+++	++

Antiserum used at a constant dilution of 1:400.

* − = no precipitate.
† + signs show the amount of precipitate.

Material precipitable by antibodies to tobacco mosaic virus can occur as particles of very different sizes, from some no longer than their width up to others more than 100 times as long as they are wide. Particle size and shape influence precipitation behaviour, for the small particles precipitate more slowly, need to combine with more antibody to be precipitated, and give a smaller volume of floccules than the same weight of antigen contained in long particles. Table 7–2 shows these differences; both of the antigen preparations used were initially the same, but before the test the particles in one were aggregated linearly by heating. Although both contained the same weight of antigen, the unaggregated preparation precipitated optimally at a dilution of 1/64, whereas the aggregated one showed no optimal precipitation point and precipitated first (almost immediately it was mixed with antiserum) at 1/1. Long particles produce more voluminous floccules than short particles, so aggregation also increases the precipitation end-point, but the effects are small, factors of 2–3, compared with those on optimal precipitation points. Assays by the optimal-proportions method are often inaccurate with virus preparations containing very long particles, because precipitation usually occurs rapidly over a wide ratio of antigen to antibody, and they are best restricted to viruses with near-spherical particles of a uniform size, which not only precipitate more slowly, but their precipitation is also more strongly inhibited by excess of antigen.

Serological assays have the disadvantage of being less sensitive than infectivity assays, for 10–100 times as much virus is needed to give a visible precipitate with antiserum as to infect susceptible leaves. However, they have the great advantages of giving results quicker, that results obtained in tests at different times can be directly compared (the antisera do not change greatly over long periods), and that, once the end-point of a purified preparation con-

:aining a known weight of any given virus has been determined, results can be directly translated into approximate weights of virus. As Table 7–2 shows, the minimum weight that will give a visible floccule depends on particle shape and is less with elongated than with spherical particles. Fig. 7–2 illustrates the differences between the character of the precipitate produced by spherical and rod-shaped particles, and shows the much greater volume of precipitate formed by a given weight of rod-shaped particles.

The early results from serological tests closely paralleled those of infectivity tests and it first seemed that the two provided alter-

Fig. 7–2. Precipitates of tomato bushy stunt and tobacco mosaic viruses with their homologous antisera. Three left-hand tubes, 0.1, 0.05 and 0.025 mg. of bushy stunt virus; three right-hand tubes, same weights of tobacco mosaic virus; central tube, saline control. Note dense, granular precipitate of bushy stunt and bulky, flocculent precipitate of tobacco mosaic virus. (F. C. Bawden and N. W. Pirie, 1938, Brit. J. exp. Path. 19: 251).

native assay methods (Birkeland, 1934; Beale, 1934; Bawden, 1935; Chester, 1935). However, it soon became obvious that they were not and many circumstances have since been noted in which the two give conflicting results. The first major discrepancy came from work on virus inactivation, which showed that, although infectivity and serological activity often declined equally, they sometimes did not and serological activity remained unimpaired after infectivity was lost (Bawden, Pirie and Spooner, 1936; Stanley, 1936). Loss of serological activity was clearly correlated with protein denaturation, but what changes destroyed infectivity without disturbing serological activity remained without an explanation until the discovery that virus nucleic acids alone can be infective (Gierer and Schramm, 1956; Fraenkel-Conrat, 1956). The duality of the virus particle then became evident, with infectivity being conferred by the nucleic acid, which is carried internally and plays no part in serological reactions, and serological specificity being conferred solely by the protein. Serological assays, then, measure amounts of virus protein and protein only; they do this whether or not the protein contains nucleic acid, but they measure nucleic acid only incidentally when it is contained in the protein and they never distinguish between infective and non-infective nucleoprotein. Hence all grades of agreement and disagreement are possible between infectivity and serological assays. They will agree when preparations being compared contained similar proportions of native virus protein and infective nucleic acid, but otherwise they will disagree and the disagreements may reach the two extreme forms of (1) preparations being highly infective but not reacting with virus antiserum and (2) being fully active serologically but not infective.

Although discrepancies between infectivity and serological assays are most common in work on virus inactivation, they happen in other work and are especially likely to be met in tests on virus preparations fractionated in different ways. Extracts from plants infected with any one of several viruses contain more than one type of specific particle, and not all these particles are infective. Sap from plants with tobacco mosaic, for example, contains particles of very different sizes, not all of which contain nucleic acid (Bawden and Pirie, 1945; 1956; Takahashi and Ishii, 1952, 1953). Preparations containing different proportions of these variously sized particles can be made by differential centrifugation and they will have similar serological activities but widely different infectivities. Similarly, sap from plants infected with turnip yellow mosaic contains two kinds of particles that, although the same size, can be separated by differential centrifugation because they differ in weight; both react equally with virus antiserum but only the heavier, which contain nucleic acid, are infective (Markham and Smith, 1949).

Such disagreements serve only to emphasise the desirability of making both kinds of assay, for the two together often give much more information than either gives alone. Another circumstance in which the two will give different results, and often indicate the circumstance, is in working with extracts from plants that contain inhibitors of infection. Infectivity assays on such extracts are meaningless, but the materials that inhibit infection usually do not interfere with serological assays, which will show the true content of virus antigen.

An antiserum prepared against one strain of a virus is not specific to that strain but also precipitates any other strain. This is helpful in as much as only one antiserum needs to be prepared to assay many strains, but it can also sometimes give misleading results. Precipitation end-points will usually not differ much whether a strain is titrated against its homologous or heterologous antiserum, but optimal proportions may differ greatly. For example, titrating tobacco mosaic virus against diluted antiserum to cucumber virus 3, which is only remotely related serologically to tobacco mosaic virus, gives a large zone in the region of antigen excess where there is no precipitation, in contrast to titrations against the homologous antiserum with which precipitation occurs optimally with much more concentrated solutions (Bawden and Pirie, 1937). Strains that are closely related will not be distinguished between by precipitation tests, and the similar serological behaviour shown by symptomatologically distinct strains can lead to puzzling discrepancies between the results of serological and infectivity assays, when, unknowingly, mixtures of strains are being handled. Of the many strains of potato virus X, for example, only few give necrotic local lesions in tobacco or N. *glutinosa,* but all are precipitated by antiserum to the strains that do, and mixtures of strains containing different proportions of lesion-producers will give very different lesion counts but similar precipitation end-points or optimal precipitation points (Bawden, 1935).

Serological assays have mostly been used with viruses that are readily transmitted manually, but there is no reason to think they could not be much more widely applied. There may be viruses that are not antigenic, but this seems improbable and the limits to the use of serological tests are more likely set by virus preparations being too dilute to give visible reactions *in vitro* than by inability to stimulate the production of antibodies in animals. The success achieved in serological work with such viruses as sugar beet yellows (Kleczkowski and Watson, 1944) and wound tumour virus (Black and Brakke, 1954) shows that the methods are not restricted to viruses readily transmitted between plants mechanically and encourages the hope that they will be applicable to others of these kinds with which assay methods are so greatly needed. Techniques such as ring tests, or complement fixation, may succeed where the precipitation test described in this chapter fails, for they can detect smaller amounts of antigen. Complement fixation has been little used with plant viruses, perhaps because the tests are rather complicated and require as reagents, corpuscles from sheep blood, the serum of rabbits injected with sheep corpuscles, and fresh serum to provide complement, materials unfamiliar to most plant pathologists. However, enough has been done to show that the test works well with plant viruses, that it can be 10 times as sensitive as precipitation tests, and that it is given by non-infective virus that is still precipitated by antiserum (Bawden, Pirie and Spooner, 1936; Moorhead and Price, 1953). Although laborious, complement-fixation tests are less so than injecting insects, which is now the only way of assaying some viruses, and will certainly give more accurate results. Like the precipitation test, complement fixation will measure the total antigen content, which may or may not be related to infectivity.

The prime reagent in serological assays is the antiserum, and assays will be reliable only when the antiserum is specific to the virus being assayed. Whenever possible the immunising antigen should be highly purified virus, but even then the antisera should always be thoroughly tested to ensure they are free from antibodies to other antigens, not only to normal plant components, but also to other viruses.

Counting particles. Using the electron microscope to assay virus preparations by directly counting particles is in principle similar to using a light microscope and a haemocytometer to assay blood cells or bacteria. In other words, the preparation to be assayed is diluted by a known factor and the number of particles in a known volume of this dilution is counted. For electron microscopy, however, the method poses considerable technical problems. Magnifications around $\times 10,000$ are needed to make particles of most plant viruses readily countable, and electron microscopy demands dry preparations. Hence, dry preparations of a suitable size are needed and there must be a way of finding what volume of fluid produces the dry preparation. Backus and Williams (1950) found a method for doing this. Virus preparations are diluted in water containing only volatile salts, such as ammonium carbonate or acetate, and mixed with solutions containing known weights of a polystyrene latex that has particles of a uniform size and a trace of serum albumen. The mixtures are then sprayed on to electron-microscope grids with a spray gun or atomiser that produces some drops that dry to give traces small enough to be encompassed by the field of the electron microscope. The albumen is included to make the outline of the trace easily visible. The preparation is then "shadowed" with a suitable metal to make the particles readily countable and suitable traces are photographed. The volume of each drop as it left the spray gun can be calculated from the number of polystyrene particles it contains and counts of the virus particles in the trace can then be translated into numbers per unit volume. The original method had the disadvantage that many of the traces were too large to be photographed in total at the necessary magnifications. Nixon and Fisher (1958) improved it by using a high pressure air brush to produce smaller droplets and then sorting these in a cascade impactor so that most of the drops selected on the grids were of the correct size. They also used a polystyrene latex (Dow LS040A) with smaller particles, more appropriate to small drops and more nearly resembling the size of the virus particles. Fig. 7–3 shows a droplet trace suitable for assays and containing particles of this latex and broad bean mottle virus. For assays, the preparation sprayed needs to contain about 10^{11} particles per ml.

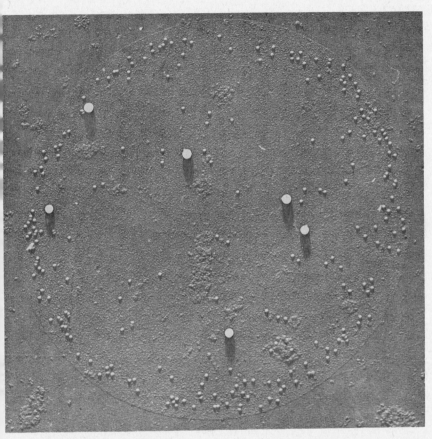

Fig. 7–3. Electron micrograph of spray droplet containing six particles of polystyrene latex and many smaller particles of broad bean mottle virus. Preparation shadowed with metal. × 25,500.

Despite the fact that the method gives results reproducible to within 5% (Backus and Williams, 1950) and so ranks as by far the most accurate assay method applicable to solutions that contain other things than virus particles, it has been little used, perhaps because for many kinds of work it is only an alternative to serological assays. However, it can have its special uses, as was shown by its application to the study of tobacco rattle virus. Sap from plants infected with this virus contains specific particles, all precipitable by virus antiserum, of a uniform width but different lengths, though most fall into two categories, one of which is about two-fifths the length of the other. Purified preparations can be fractionated by centrifuging in sucrose density-gradients to give fractions containing very different proportions of short and long particles. Infectivity assays, combined with counts of the long and short particles, showed that the relative infectivity of the fractions was directly related to the concentration of the long particles, and that the short ones are not infective (Harrison and Nixon, 1959a).

Anisotropy of flow. Solutions of many viruses with anisometric particles show the phenomenon of anisotropy of flow, that is to say, although isotropic when stationary they become anisotropic (birefringent) when subjected to a shearing force that orientates the particles along the lines of flow. Observations on this phenomenon are readily made simply by shaking solutions in narrow tubes between crossed polaroid plates illuminated from behind. The intensity of anisotropy of flow depends on the concentration of the particles and on the ratio of their length to width. It provides a crude method of assay for such viruses as tobacco mosaic and potato X, but is well worth using because of the speed with which it can be used. It can detect amounts down to about 0.1 mg/ml, and with a little practice relative concentrations can be assessed reasonably accurately, though for this preparations need to be in similar states of aggregation and at similar pH values, for anything that increases the length/width ratio of the particles will increase the intensity of anisotropy of flow. Perhaps its greatest use is to test fractions separated during the processes of purifying anisometric virus, because it immediately shows how the virus has partitioned between the fractions. It is particularly valuable with potato virus X, which is apt to go insoluble unpredictably and be lost in some discarded fraction unless preparations are checked at every stage. The method could be refined by working in prescribed conditions and using a polarising microscope, but its main use is in giving immediate answers and more detailed assays are better done serologically.

REFERENCES

BACKUS, R. C., and R. C. WILLIAMS. 1950. J. appl. Phys. 21: 11.
BALD, J. G. 1937a. Ann. appl. Biol. 24: 33.
———. 1937b. Aust. J. exp. Biol. Med. Sci. 15: 211.
BAWDEN, F. C. 1935. Brit. J. exp. Path. 16: 435.
———, and B. D. HARRISON. 1955. J. gen. Microbiol. 13: 494.
———, and N. W. PIRIE. 1937. Brit. J. exp. Path. 18: 275.

———, and ———. 1945. *Ibid.* 26: 294.

———, and ———. 1956. J. gen. Microbiol. 14: 460.

———, N. W. Pirie, and E. T. C. Spooner. 1936. Brit. J. exp. Path. 17:204.

Beale, H. Purdy. 1934. Contr. Boyce Thompson Inst. 6: 407.

Best, R. J. 1935. J. Aust. Inst. agric. Sci. 1: 159.

Birkeland, J. M. 1934. Bot. Gaz. 95: 419.

Black, L. M., and M. K. Brakke. 1954. Phytopathology 44: 482.

Chester, K. S. 1935. Phytopathology 25: 702.

Fraenkel-Conrat, H. 1956. J. Amer. chem. Soc. 78: 882.

Gierer, A., and G. Schramm. 1956. Nature 177: 702.

Harrison, B. D. 1956. J. gen. Microbiol. 15: 210.

———, and H. L. Nixon. 1959a. J. gen. Microbiol. 21: 569.

———, and ———. 1959b. *Ibid.* 21: 591.

Holmes, F. O. 1929. Bot. Gaz. 87: 39.

———. 1931. Contr. Boyce Thompson Inst. 3: 163.

Kassanis, B. 1952. Ann. appl. Biol. 39: 358.

Kleczkowski, A. 1949. Ann. appl. Biol. 36: 139.

———. 1950. J. gen. Microbiol. 4: 53.

———. 1953. *Ibid.* 8: 295.

———. 1955. *Ibid.* 13: 91.

———, and M. A. Watson. 1944. Ann. appl. Biol. 31: 116.

Lauffer, M. A., and W. C. Price. 1945. Arch. Biochem. 8: 449.

Loring, H. S. 1937. J. biol. Chem. 121: 637.

Markham, R. H., and K. M. Smith. 1949. Parasitology 39: 330.

Moorhead, E. L., and W. C. Price. 1953. Phytopathology 43: 73.

Nixon, H. L., and H. L. Fisher. 1958. Brit. J. appl. Phys. 9: 66.

Price, W. C. 1945. Amer. J. Bot. 32: 613.

———, and E. L. Spencer. 1943a. Amer. J. Bot. 30: 340.

———, and ———. 1943b. *Ibid.* 30: 720.

Rappaport, I., and A. Siegel. 1955. J. Immunol. 74: 112.

Samuel, G. 1931. Ann. appl. Biol. 18: 494.

———, and J. G. Bald. 1933. Ann. appl. Biol. 20: 70.

———, and ———. 1935. *Ibid.* 22: 508.

Selman, I. W., and R. G. Milne. 1961. Plant. Path. 10: 100.

Singer, B., and H. Fraenkel-Conrat. 1961. Virology 14: 59.

Sinha, R. C. 1960. Ann. appl. Biol. 48: 742.

Stanley, W. M. 1936. Science 83: 626.

Steere, R. L. 1955. Phytopathology 45: 196.

Takahashi, W. N., and M. Ishii. 1952. Phytopathology 42: 696.

———, and ———. 1953. Amer. J. Bot. 40: 85.

Yarwood, C. E. 1952. Nature 169: 502.

Youden, W. J. 1937a. Contr. Boyce Thompson Inst. 9: 41.

———. 1937b. *Ibid.* 9: 49.

———, and H. Purdy Beale. 1934. *Ibid.* 6: 437.

———, ———, and J. D. Guthrie. 1935. *Ibid.* 7: 37.

The Composition
of Virus Particles

Conclusions about the general chemical composition of viruses can sometimes be drawn from studying their behaviour in crude preparations. For example, the fact that potato virus X was inactivated by various proteolytic enzymes only in conditions in which the enzymes are proteolytically active provided early evidence that a virus contained protein (Bawden and Pirie, 1936). However, direct and detailed evidence demands chemical analyses on preparations whose freedom from contamination with materials other than virus particles is beyond doubt. Much work on plant viruses since the middle 1930s has been devoted to obtaining such preparations and many methods have been described for solving the problem of separating virus particles from host-plant components without losing or inactivating the virus particles during the process.

The success has been considerable, but much still remains to be achieved, for fewer than 10% of the known plant viruses have yet been obtained in conditions or quantities in which meaningful analyses can be made. Success depends on fulfilling three requirements. First, extracts of infected plants must contain enough virus for its isolation to be practical, and with current methods that seems to require not less than about 2 mg. per litre. Table 8–1 shows how greatly the different viruses that have been isolated differ in the amounts they achieve in plant extracts, and there is every reason to think that many others occur in much smaller amounts than those shown at the bottom of the table. Secondly, the virus particles must differ enough from host-plant components to be separable from them.

170

Thirdly, the virus must be stable enough to survive the fractionating procedures. Some of those that occur in small amounts are also extremely unstable *in vitro;* some may not be and these could probably be obtained in the quantities needed for analysis by working with large volumes of plant extracts and pooling yields from different extracts, but a first requirement towards doing this with the unstable ones will be to find methods that increase their stability.

TABLE 8–1

Approximate Weights of Different Viruses in a Litre of Infective Sap

Virus	Host Plant	Weight of Virus
Tobacco Mosaic		
Type strain	Tobacco	2.0 g.
" "	Tomato	1.3
" "	Spinach	0.15
Enation strain	Tomato	1.5
Masked strain	Tobacco	1.0
Cucumber 3 strain	Cucumber	0.3
Potato X		
Strain S	Tomato	0.7
" "	Tobacco	0.3
Strain Y	Tomato	1.5
" "	Tobacco	0.7
Tomato bushy stunt	Tomato (winter)	0.15
" " "	Tomato (summer)	0.01
Tobacco necrosis	Tobacco (winter)	0.2
" "	Tobacco (summer)	0.01
Alfalfa mosaic	Tobacco	0.2
Turnip yellow mosaic	Chinese cabbage	0.17
Southern bean mosaic	French bean	0.4
Tobacco rattle	Tobacco	0.05
Tobacco ringspot	Tobacco with symptoms	0.012
" "	Tobacco recovered	0.002
Severe etch	*Nicotiana glutinosa*	0.004
" "	Tobacco	0.007
Potato Y	Tobacco	0.002
Henbane mosaic	Tobacco	0.002

During the course of work that is usually called virus purification, not only have new techniques been constantly introduced, usually to supersede drastic treatments that obviously affected the virus particles, but the objects have also changed considerably. Much of the early work aimed to identify a given virus, especially tobacco mosaic virus, with a specific particle, and to this end preparations were sought that combined the maximum activity, usually infectivity, with the minimum solid content and the fewest components detectable by physico-chemical tests for heterogeneity. Although

homogeneity was often claimed, there is no reason to consider that
any preparation has yet been made of any virus that is ideally pure
in the sense that it contains particles all of which are identical in
activity, composition and every other respect. *A priori* it is perhaps improbable that such preparations are obtainable, for there is
much evidence, not only that many viruses undergo changes during
the course of fractionation, but also that extracts of infected plants
often already contain more than one type of specific particle before
they are fractionated. Further, as Pirie (1940; 1952; 1957) has
stressed, even if such preparations were obtained, their homogeneity
could not be established, for differences that could be all important
biologically and would be readily detectable in small molecules
would pass undetected in particles as large as viruses. He points
out that concepts applicable to substances with molecular weights
smaller than 10,000, in which the introduction or removal of a group
such as —CH_2CH_2— would have an observable quantitative effect,
are wholly inappropriate to particles the size of tobacco mosaic
virus in which the introduction or removal of a group with a weight
equivalent to a molecular weight of 100,000 might well pass unnoticed. Even when it is undetectable, therefore, heterogeneity or
pleomorphism should be expected, but it is often detectable. Earlier
editions of this book contained the remark that, were the same rea-
soning as has been applied to purifying viruses applied to animals,
and the ability to multiply taken as the only criterion of activity,
it would be possible to conclude that a rabbit had been purified
by cutting off its ears and tail. When this was written, there was
already no doubt that the fractionations being used to purify some
viruses were eliminating, in addition to components of normal plants,
components specific to infected plants, which are as reasonably regarded to be parts of the virus as to be parts of the host. Many
more such components have since been recognised and extracts from
infected plants are now increasingly fractionated to obtain all the
anomalous components they contain, to separate these into distinct
types and to find possible similarities and differences between them.
Heterogeneity in some physico-chemical test is now welcomed rather
than frowned upon, for it is no longer assumed necessarily to show
contamination with impurities, but to be a sign of pleomorphism and
to offer the chance of separating another anomalous particle that
may throw light on the processes involved in virus multiplication.
It long ago became evident that virus multiplication differs from the
synthesis of simple molecules and does not lead to a uniform end-
product of identical particles, but the idea that infective particles
must all have exactly the same composition was still widely held

until Harris and Knight (1955) showed the enzyme carboxypeptidase removes threonine from purified preparations of tobacco mosaic virus without affecting their infectivity. This was too obviously like cutting the tail off a rabbit and further searches to find minimal infective units, which have culminated in obtaining infective preparations of nucleic acids, have been regarded as examples of virus disruption rather than purification, even though removing the protein from one tobacco necrosis virus has increased infectivity per unit weight of preparation by five times (Kassanis, 1960).

When considering the purification of viruses, therefore, more questions need to be asked than does a given method produce consistent preparations free from contaminating host components? These are prime questions, but others are almost equally important. Does the method isolate all the kinds of particles specific to extracts from infected plants? If not, what kinds are likely to be selected and what rejected? Is the method likely to change the state of any of the particles? If so, how? By inactivation? By aggregation? By disruption? What is the significance of heterogeneity in the final product? Is the method likely to increase or decrease heterogeneity? Often many of these questions will have to go unanswered, but this is no reason for not asking them. On the contrary, only by asking them is the work likely to be done that will make them answerable and provide evidence of the extent to which particles with one or other character of virus particles can differ. Meanwhile, information on the composition of viruses must be gained by analysing such purified preparations as can be made, but when considering the significance of analytical results, the uncertainties about the precise character of the preparation being analysed need to be fully appreciated.

Preparation of starting material. The first need when attempting to purify a virus is to use a suitable host plant, which means one that provides extracts containing much virus but few such things as phenolic compounds, gums or other substances that complicate its separation. Even with such plants as tobacco, which have been used successfully for many viruses, their age and condition of growth can greatly affect the ease with which a virus can be purified. In general, rapidly growing young plants with the succulent leaves characteristic of growth in low light intensities are to be preferred, for their sap is easier to extract and contains fewer troublesome pigments than older plants kept at high light intensities. Leaves should be picked when showing their most severe symptoms. The concentration of many viruses remains unchanged for many days or even weeks after systemic symptoms reach their maximum severity, but the concentration of some, especially tobacco ringspot (Stanley, 1939) and alfalfa mosaic (Ross, 1941), decreases considerably and rapidly after reaching a maximum. With viruses like those causing tobacco necrosis, which produce only necrotic local lesions, the inoculated leaves should be picked when the lesions have fully developed but before the leaves shrivel. Putting infected plants in darkness for a day or two before the leaves are harvested sometimes helps virus purification by decreasing the amount of total material extracted in the sap.

Many viruses occur much more concentrated in the leaf blades than in the main veins or petioles, which therefore can with advantage be removed and avoid unnecessarily diluting the virus when the leaves are macerated. The simplest way to extract the sap is to grind the leaves in a domestic meat mincer and then squeeze the macerated leaves in muslin. Some virus will remain in the leaf fibre. Part of this can be extracted by simply soaking the fibre in water or M/15 pH 7 phosphate buffer and squeezing again, but to release the rest requires fine grinding in a roller mill (Bawden and Pirie, 1944, 1945a, 1945b) or incubating the fibre with enzymes that dissolve it, of which a suitable mixture occur in the alimentary tract of snails (Bawden and Pirie, 1946; Bawden and Crook, 1947). The way in which this tightly bound virus is held in the leaf fibre is unknown, and most workers have neglected it, although it may amount to almost half the total virus content of the leaves. In most conditions the amount seems to be proportional to the amount that occurs in the sap, so using the amount in sap as a guide to the relative virus contents of different lots of leaves will often be accurate enough, although it underestimates the total content.

As many workers seem to consider sap a normal environment for viruses, it is necessary to stress that it is a wholly abnormal fluid bearing no relation to conditions that obtain inside host cells. Extracting sap may mean exposing the virus particles to changes in pH and osmotic conditions and certainly exposes them to a range of enzymes, interacting with their substrates, and to disintegrating cell components. That these conditions are inimical to some viruses is obvious enough from the speed with which they inactivate in sap but because others survive is no reason to assume they are wholly unaffected or that every kind of particle with virus-like attributes survives exposure to sap. For example, by avoiding the conditions usually encountered in sap, various workers (Cochran and Chidester 1957; Engler and Schramm, 1959; Diener, 1962) have advanced evidence for the idea that cells in which tobacco mosaic virus is rapidly

ultiplying contain free infective nucleic acid. Any such would in-
ctivate in sap as normally made, for even at 0° sap diluted 1/50
activates nucleic acid preparations in a few minutes (Bawden and
'irie, 1959).

Exposing sap to air starts the phenolic compounds oxidising to
uinones, which combine with proteins. This can be prevented by
dding either a reducing agent such as sodium sulphite or ascorbic
cid, or ethylenediamine tetra-acetate (Versene) which binds the
etal needed to catalyse the oxidation. For some viruses such as
omato spotted wilt, which are inactivated by oxidation, some such
tabilising treatment is essential, but for most it is useful mainly
ɔ simplify the making of colourless virus preparations. The extent
ɔ which different viruses, and even different strains of one virus,
ombine with components of plant sap differs considerably. Thus,
;inoza, Atkinson and Wildman (1954) found that their strain U2
ɔf tobacco mosaic virus is readily obtained colourless, whereas the
ype strain combines with a brown substance that is removed only
ɔy some such treatment as incubation with citrate. That the sub-
tance is contracted from sap and is not a part of the virus particles
s shown by the fact that preparations of the type strain that have
ɔeen freed from it contract it again when added to sap from unin-
ected plants. Pirie (1957) also reports normal plant proteins and
ibonuclease associating with tobacco mosaic virus and accompany-
ɪg it through many procedures widely used to make purified virus
ɔreparations. In addition to the possibility of inactivation in sap
nd combining with sap components, anisometric viruses also tend
ɔ aggregate linearly in the conditions obtaining in sap.

Fractionating leaf extracts. As virus particles can suffer changes
ɔf various kinds in sap, it seems reasonable to expect that removing
hem from this environment as soon as possible will help to retain
hem near to their original state. This expectation may be realised
vith many viruses, but it is not with all. Other components of sap
han virus particles also suffer in the environment of sap and these
nclude systems that inactivate some viruses. For instance, ultracen-
rifugation of freshly expressed sap gives preparations of a tobacco
ecrosis virus that soon lose their infectivity, whereas virus sedi-
nented from sap that has stood for a day at 18° before centrifuga-
ion is much more stable. This is because, along with the virus
ɔarticles, centrifugation also sediments and concentrates a virus-
nactivating system, which occurs too dilute in sap to have much
effect on the virus and where it is soon destroyed, whereas it is
table in pellets resuspended in water. This system does not inacti-

vate tobacco mosaic virus, but does tobacco ringspot virus (Bawde and Pirie, 1957a).

The first preliminary towards purifying a virus is to clarify th sap. Low-speed centrifugation removes only the largest particle and is usually unsatisfactory without some additional treatmen Many such treatments have been used, and the most appropriat will depend on the identity of the virus and the host plant in whic it was propagated. Freezing the leaves or the expressed sap, allow ing the sap to age for a day at 18°, heating it to about 55°, addin Na$_2$HPO$_4$ or an appropriate amount of ethanol, any of these trea ments produces a copious coagulum readily removed by low-spee centrifugation and leaving a clear supernatant fluid. The choice be tween them will rest on the different extents to which a given viru is lost on the different coagula or inactivated by any of the trea ments. Heating will probably destroy some infectivity of viruse that have isometric particles without necessarily denaturing ther or affecting their serological behaviour. A method of clarificatio that has proved particularly successful with some unstable viruse such as tobacco ringspot and alfalfa mosaic is to mix sap with tw volumes of a mixture of equal parts of n-butanol and chlorofor and then separate the aqueous phase by centrifuging; the residu butanol and chloroform in the aqueous phase denatures contamina ing protein but seems to stabilise the viruses (Steere, 1956).

Steere (1958) detailed 40 procedures that have been used t purify different plant viruses and there is no call here to do more tha discuss the various types of fractionations. In the early method fractionation was almost exclusively by treatments that selectivel precipitate either the virus particles or normal plant components, o that selectively denature normal host components. The main trea ments were precipitation with ethanol or, more often, ammoniur sulphate, acidification, and incubation with proteolytic enzymes the procedures usually ended in crystallising isometric viruses an in the making of liquid crystals with anisometric ones. Since th development of high-speed centrifuges made it possible to sedimen virus particles from neutral solutions, differential centrifugation ha increasingly supplanted the earlier precipitation techniques, ofte perhaps to the detriment of the purity of the final preparation. Th usual method is to centrifuge clarified sap for an hour or more a 40–60,000 g., dissolve the pellet in water, centrifuge the solution a 5–10,000 g. for a few minutes to get rid of insoluble material, an then repeat the cycle of alternate high- and low-speed centrifuga tion once or twice. Preparations of tobacco mosaic virus made i this way become contaminated with bacteria that do not grow i reparations made by precipitations with salt and acid, and such reparations seem never to have been tested to see whether they ail to give an anaphylactic response in the uterus of guinea pigs sensitised against normal plant protein, as have preparations prepared y precipitation methods and incubation with trypsin (Bawden and 'irie, 1937b). Also, preparations made solely by centrifugation arely become liquid crystalline unless they are more concentrated han 5%, whereas preparations made by precipitation with salt and cid, particularly after heating the sap to 60° and incubating the reparation with trypsin, may deposit a liquid crystalline layer from olutions less concentrated than 1%. This implies great differences etween the average length to width ratio of the particles in the two ypes of preparation, and there is more than a suggestion that length f particles to some extent depends on freedom from contaminants. 'or example, partially purified preparations made by precipitation ften do not deposit a liquid crystalline layer unless they are more oncentrated than 4%. In such preparations, residual contaminants re more plentiful in the upper isotropic fluid than in the lower liquid rystalline layer, where average particle length is greater (Bawden nd Pirie, 1937a). Hence, the extent to which particles aggregate inearly may depend on their freedom from contaminants at their nds and only when such contaminants are removed, by exposure o salts, incubation with trypsin, heating or long ageing *in vitro*, do hey readily join together end-to-end.

In addition to possible differences in amount of contaminants, reparations of tobacco mosaic virus made by precipitation methods robably also differ from those made by ultracentrifugation in containing a more representative sample of the total material specific o infective sap. High-speed centrifugation will sediment only the arger of the particles that are serologically related to the virus, vhereas ammonium sulphate and acid not only precipitate all of hese but also aggregate the smaller particles into rods, which will hen sediment along with the larger particles that occur in sap Bawden and Pirie, 1945b; Takahashi and Ishii, 1952, 1953). Unless eeking a specific type of particle, it seems desirable when making reparations of tobacco mosaic virus for analysis that sedimentation hould always be supplemented by precipitation procedures.

The ease with which different viruses can be purified differs reatly and also depends on the method that can be used to clarify he sap. Turnip yellow mosaic virus is perhaps the easiest, for after ap from infected Chinese cabbage leaves has been clarified by dding 0.3 volumes of 90% ethanol and centrifuging, it can be immeiately crystallised by adding half a volume of saturated ammonium

sulphate solution. The first crop of crystals contains other crystal
line material, possibly calcium sulphate, but this is insoluble and ca
be removed by dissolving the virus in water and centrifuging, whe
the virus can be recrystallised from the supernatant fluid (Mark
ham, 1959). This method gives preparations that contain particle
all of one size and that show only one component when examine
electrophoretically, but they show two components when ultracen
trifuged (Markham and Smith, 1949). These two component
which occur approximately in the ratio of one of the lighter to tw
of the heavier (Matthews, 1958), can be separated by differenti
ultracentrifugation. The two differ in that the lighter consist c
protein only, whereas the heavier contain nucleic acid (Markhan
Matthews and Smith, 1948; Fraser and Cosentino, 1957).

Most other viruses that crystallise do so less readily than turni
yellow mosaic, although the satellite virus that accompanies tobacc
necrosis viruses produces a crystalline pellet when clarified tobacc
sap is ultracentrifuged (Fig. 8–1) (Bawden and Pirie, 1945a). Be
fore others crystallise when precipitated by salts, they need to b
concentrated and freed from some contaminants. When ammoniur
sulphate is added to sap containing tomato bushy stunt or som
other viruses (Bawden and Pirie, 1938b, 1942; Pirie, Smith, Spoone
and McClement, 1938), the precipitates produced are amorphou
but crystals can then be obtained by dissolving these precipitates i
water and adding ammonium sulphate until the solutions becom
opalescent at 18°. Left at this temperature, amorphous precipitate
will soon separate but when put at 0° the fluids first become clea
and then deposit crystals. This method fails to give crystals of th
small virus that seems to multiply only together with necrosi
viruses: it crystallises when sedimented by ultracentrifugation an
concentrated solutions in water crystallise (Fig. 8–1), but all pre
cipitates produced by salting the virus out of solutions are amor
phous. Crystallisation can provide a valuable fractionation, but, a
is evident from the behaviour of turnip yellow mosaic virus, it serve
only to select particles of a uniform size and is no criterion of uni
formity of composition, biological activity or of other properties.

Precipitation of virus from clarified sap by ammonium sulphat
is widely used as a first step in purification and to concentrate th
virus before ultracentrifugation or some other procedure. Most c
the viruses that have been studied precipitate at concentrations o
the salt between 20 and 40% saturation, a range in which many nor
mal plant proteins also precipitate. Broad bean mottle virus, whic
has isometric particles, is unusual in that it does not precipitate unt
the ammonium sulphate concentration exceeds 75% saturation, a fac

hat can be adapted to purifying the virus. Most of the proteins contained in sap from uninfected broad bean (*Vicia faba*) are precipitated at 50% saturation, so after centrifuging off the precipitate produced at this salt content, the virus can then be precipitated at 30% saturation. The precipitate obtained contains little except virus,

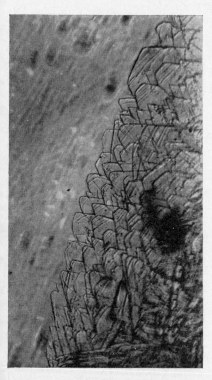 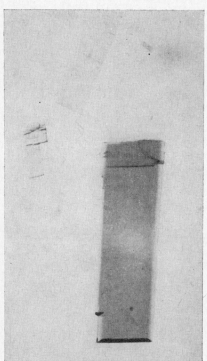

Fig. 8–1. Crystals of the satellite virus contained in the Rothamsted culture of tobacco necrosis virus. *Left:* the serrated edge of a crystalline pellet sedimented by ultracentrifugation. × 45. *Right:* large crystals produced after crystal growth had proceeded in a salt-free solution for three months. × 9. (F. C. Bawden and N. W. Pirie, 1945, Brit. J. exp. Path. 26: 277).

and is at first white, but soon blackens and the pigment can be removed only with difficulty by treating the preparation early on with activated charcoal (Bawden, Chaudhuri and Kassanis, 1951). Some components of many kinds of sap are denatured or precipitated by acid, and exposure to pH values between 3 and 5 is a useful fractionation for viruses that withstand this. The treatment will precipitate most of the viruses that have anisometric particles, for these are insoluble at their isoelectric points, which usually fall within this range. Potato virus X is unusual in that the whole of preparation often fails to precipitate at any given pH value, and th part that has precipitated once at, say, pH 4.5 may fail to precipitat again at this pH, and some may precipitate at pH 4 and some a pH 5. Purified or partially purified preparations of virus X some times go insoluble even at neutrality because the particles not onl aggregate end-to-end but also associate laterally to produce er tangled masses (Kleczkowski and Nixon, 1950). This presumabl is a consequence of the particles of virus X having an unusuall small surface potential, shown by the fact that they barely move a pH 7 in an electrophoretic cell (Bawden and Kleczkowski, 1959 In contrast to the anisometric virus, the isometric ones are mostl soluble at their isoelectric points, so acidification is a method of pr cipitating host components while leaving the viruses in solution.

Density gradient centrifugation, which was developed by Brakk (1953, 1956), is a method of fractionation that has already prove its value in purifying some of the large unstable viruses such a wound tumour, potato yellow dwarf and tomato spotted wilt, an in separating the specific particles of different weights, sizes an shapes that occur in extracts from plants infected with turnip yellov mosaic, alfalfa mosaic or tobacco rattle viruses. The principles an practice of density gradient centrifugation have been fully describe by Brakke (1960) and here there is no need to do more than briefl describe the method of "rate zonal centrifugation," which is mostl used in work with plant viruses. In this, the virus solution is floate as a layer on the top of a preformed gradient column in a centrifug tube and centrifuged long enough at high speed for particles of di ferent kinds to form distinct zones that can readily be separate from one another. The gradient column is usually formed by pu ting layers of sucrose solutions decreasing in concentration from 6C in the bottom layer to 5% in the top, which then gives a change i density from 1.23 at the bottom to 1.02 at the top. Machines hav been described for producing a smooth gradient rapidly, but th discontinuities in columns produced when solutions of different cor centrations are layered above one another smooth by diffusion an most workers are content to make the columns one day and do tf centrifugation the next. Gradient columns should be centrifuge immediately after the virus solution has been floated on them, the should be handled carefully before and after centrifuging, and acce eration and deceleration should both be gradual to avoid unnece sary mixing. The rate at which particles sediment down the densit gradient column depends on their density, size and shape; all pa ticles of one type will occur in a narrow zone and the zone contair

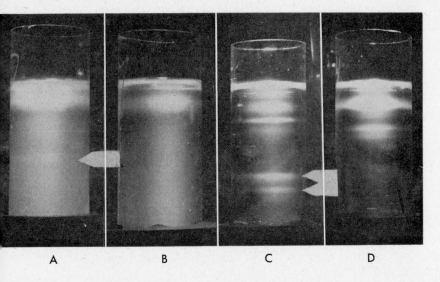

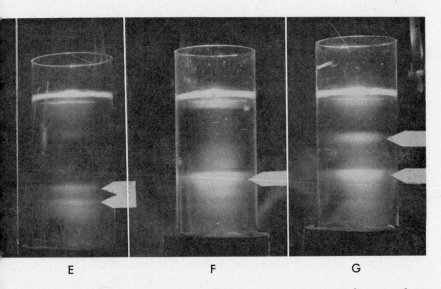

Fig 8–2. Gradient columns after centrifugation. A. Untreated extract from barley infected with barley stripe mosaic virus. B. Extract from uninfected plants. C and D. Extracts from infected and uninfected plants heated 1 hour at 40° before centrifuging. E. Extract from infected plants shaken with *n*-butanol. C, D and E contain 0.1% Igepon T-73. F. Tobacco mosaic virus. G. Tobacco mosaic virus plus brome mosaic virus, both previously sedimented by ultracentrifugation. Arrows show zones containing virus. (M. K. Brakke, 1960, Advanc. Virus Res. 7: 193).

ing particles of different types will become increasingly separated a
centrifugation continues. When the centrifuged columns are illum
nated with a narrow band of light shone into them from above o
below, the zones containing particles are often easy to see, parti
ularly when purified virus preparations are being used, but they ma
be indistinct when preparations contain much other material (Fi
8–2) (Brakke, 1960). Rate zonal centrifugation is not adaptable t
purifying a large bulk of virus, but it efficiently separates sma
amounts when other fractionating methods fail and it is especiall
valuable for separating different types of particles that are specif
to infected plants.

Another advantage of the density gradient method is that th
zones provide an immediately obvious way of following the cours
of fractionations. With other methods additional checks are needed
Any of the assay methods discussed in Chapter 7 can be used, bu
although infectivity tests are needed to assess the activity of the fin
product, these give results too slowly to be used at each major step
Serological tests probably provide the most generally applicabl
method, but with anisometric viruses observations on anisotropy o
flow give results even more quickly. With strains of tobacco mosai
virus, there is no need even to examine the fluids in polarised ligh
for the intense satin-like sheen shown by solutions, especially thos
that are below pH 7 or contain much salt, when shaken and observe
by reflected light is usually guide enough to show how the virus ha
partitioned between different fractions. Measurements with a qual
itative ultracentrifuge, an electrophoresis apparatus or a spectro
photometer, can all be used to follow the course of virus purification
and will also provide information about virus concentration an
about other materials in the preparation. Before preparations ar
analysed chemically to gain information about virus composition
their sedimentation and electrophoretic behaviour and their absorb
ency should be examined to see how many components can b
detected, and whether there are signs of contaminants, but im
provements in density gradient centrifugation may well lead to thi
method supplanting the use of the expensive types of apparatu
previously needed to show heterogeneity.

Elementary analyses. Table 8–2 gives elementary analyses o
purified preparations of five strains of tobacco mosaic virus and o
eight other viruses. The values for carbon, hydrogen and nitrogen
are in the range usual for proteins and so provide no guide to th
purity of a preparation. Differences between strains of tobacc
mosaic virus show only in the figures for sulphur, which, as will be

TABLE 8–2

Analyses of Purified Virus Preparations

Virus	Carbon %	Hydro- gen %	Nitro- gen %	Sulphur %	Phos- phorus %	Ash %	Carbohy- drate %
'obacco mosaic							
type	50	7	16.6	0.2	0.53	1.5	2.5
aucuba	50	7	16.7	0.2	0.52	1.5	2.5
enation	50	7	16.7	0.3	0.53	1.0	2.5
Rib-grass	50	7	15.7	0.6	0.54	2.27	2.3
Cucumber 3	50	7	15.4	0.0	0.54	2.28	2.3
'otato X	49	7	16.4	—	0.45	2.2	2.7
'otato Y	50	—	16.0	—	0.4	—	3.0
'obacco rattle	—	7	16.5	—	0.42	—	2.8
lfalfa mosaic	53	6.7	16.2	0.6	1.4	—	9.0
'omato bushy stunt	49	7.5	16.1	0.6	1.5	3.0	6.0
'obacco necrosis	45	6.5	16.3	1.6	1.65	7.0	6.5
'obacco ringspot	51	7.6	14.6	0.4	4.1	—	18.0
'outhern bean mosaic	46	6.5	17.0	1.3	1.9	5.7	—

shown later, reflect the presence or absence of sulphur-containing aminoacids in the individual strains. Differences between viruses show most in their contents of phosphorus and carbohydrate, differences that are associated with differences in particle shape, for those with rod- or thread-like particles, such as tobacco mosaic and potato viruses X and Y, contain only a third or less as much of these components as do viruses with isometric particles. The viruses yet examined all contain nucleic acid and there is no evidence to suggest that phosphorus or carbohydrate occur in any form other than as nucleic acid. Indeed, enough nucleic acid has been isolated from some to account for all the phosphorus and carbohydrate, and ultraviolet absorption spectra of others show that their content of nucleic acid is related to the amount of phosphorus. Solutions of the purified viruses are colourless and absorb little visible light, but in the ultraviolet range absorption increases to a maximum at 260 mμ, followed by a minimum at 250 mμ and then general absorption at shorter wavelengths. Absorption in the region of 260 mμ is characteristic of the purines and pyrimidines contained in the nucleic acid, and as Fig. 8–3 shows, tomato bushy stunt virus which contains 1.5% phosphorus absorbs more strongly at this wavelength than does tobacco mosaic virus which contains 0.5% phosphorus. Carbohydrate is a common contaminant of preparations of some viruses and when the ratio of phosphorus is less than 1 to 4 or 5, the preparations can usually be further fractionated. Similarly, after the absorption spectrum of a given virus has been accurately determined, absorp-

tion spectra are useful checks on purity, though of course they wil
not necessarily show contamination with nucleoproteins containin
the same relative proportion of nucleic acid to protein as there is i
the virus under study.

Indeed, no such tests can be taken alone as guarantee that puri
fied virus preparations are chemically homogeneous. For instance
crystallised preparations of turnip yellow mosaic virus will giv
ratios of phosphorus to carbohydrate appropriate for nucleic acid
and will give consistent absorption spectra with high absorption a

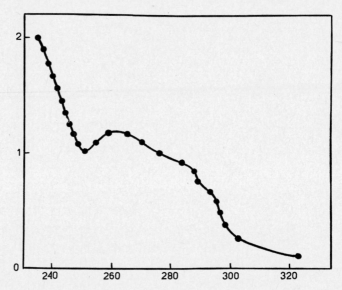

Fig. 8–3. Ultra-violet absorption spectra of purified virus preparations. In
each of the curves the abscissa is the wavelength of light in $m\mu$ and the ordinate
is the $\log_{10}$ of the amount of light of that wavelength that is incident on a 2 cm
deep layer of solution to the amount of light that is transmitted through the

260 $m\mu$, but they contain two kinds of particles that can be separated
by differential centrifugation. Approximately two thirds of the particles as obtained by only crystallisation contain 3.7% phosphorus,
whereas the other one third are phosphorus-free (Markham, 1959).
For this reason, analytical figures for preparations of this virus are
excluded from Table 8–2, which includes only viruses that have the
great majority of their particles, however variable they may be in
other characters, with similar chemical compositions.

The values in Table 8–2 for the ash remaining after purified virus
preparations are burnt are unusually large for proteins. The values
given are for residues from neutral preparations, and part of the ash

will come from alkali used to neutralise the viruses, which all have isoelectric points below pH 7. However, even after prolonged dialysis or electro-dialysis at their isoelectric points, the viruses still leave a large percentage of ash. Only a small part of this is probably the actual metal content of the protein, and most of it will be derived from the phosphorus of the nucleic acid, which will be converted to

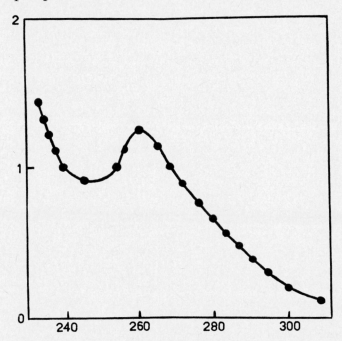

solution. *Opposite:* 0.02% solution of tobacco mosaic virus (F. C. Bawden and N. W. Pirie, 1937, Proc. Roy. Soc. B. 123: 274). *Above:* 0.012% solution of tomato bushy stunt virus (F. C. Bawden and N. W. Pirie, 1938, Brit. J. exp. Path. 19: 2151).

metaphosphate by burning. The ash from most viruses has still to be examined in detail, but that from tomato bushy stunt virus contains mainly calcium and sodium with traces of twelve other metals (Pirie, 1945).

With the introduction of new techniques, especially chromatography, knowledge on the composition of viruses has increased rapidly and the detail now being revealed is quite beyond any expectations of the late 1940s. It was then a feat to have shown that a virus consisted largely of protein and nucleic acid; now it is becoming commonplace, not only to have quantitative analyses for the aminoacids composing the proteins and the nucleotides of the nucleic

acid, but to have the sequence of aminoacids in the proteins deter
mined. It is difficult to know how to present all this detail, but
particularly so without creating the impression that knowledge is
more complete than it may actually be. For instance, by adding the
amount of nucleic acid in tobacco mosaic virus to the amounts of
the individual aminoacids that have been determined, almost 100%
of the virus is accounted for. Clearly there can be little else except
protein and nucleic acid, but one other component has been reported
and it would be rash to assume there may not be others. It must be
stressed that even as little as 0.5% of tobacco mosaic virus is equivalent to a molecular weight of more than 100,000, which is ample
to contain many molecules that may be biologically very important
though quantitatively very minor. Of the two major components,
protein provides the bulk of the particles of all viruses yet studied;
it ranges from about 95% of tobacco mosaic and other anisometric
viruses to about 65% of turnip yellow mosaic and tobacco ringspot
viruses.

Virus proteins. There is nothing in the composition of any virus
proteins yet analysed to distinguish them from any other proteins.
In other words, like other proteins, they consist of the usual kinds
of aminoacids joined by peptide links. The general structure of the
aminoacid can be represented as $R—CH(NH_2)—COOH$, in which R
is the group or side chain determining the character of the aminoacid; it is a hydrogen atom in the simplest one, glycine or aminoacetic
acid, but in others is a carbon chain or ring. Although the number
of possible R-groups is enormous, only about 25 aminoacids occur
as constituents of proteins, most of which make do with about 20
and some with fewer. The aminoacids contain basic (NH_2) and
acidic $(COOH)$ groups, and join with one another to form peptide
chains with the general structure

$$-NH-\underset{\underset{R}{|}}{C}H-CO-NH-\underset{\underset{R}{|}}{C}H-CO-NH-\underset{\underset{R}{|}}{C}H-CO-NH-\underset{\underset{R}{|}}{C}H-COO$$

A peptide chain has a free amino group at one end and a carboxyl
group at the other, so it has both acidic and basic properties, regardless of the nature of the R-groups. The peptide linkages give all
proteins a similar basic structure and the specific properties of individual proteins derive primarily from the nature and arrangement
of the R-groups, but probably equally important is the way in which
the peptide chains coil and fold.

What makes viruses unusual, is their size; tobacco mosaic virus,
for instance contains something like half a million total aminoacid

esidues. However, all these are not joined to give a single polypeptide chain, for the virus particle consists of more than 2,000 regu-
arly arranged sub-units, each of which can be regarded as equivalent to the more usual kind of protein molecule and contains 158
aminoacid residues. It is this fact that makes it possible to identify
not only the total aminoacid composition, that is, to find which
aminoacids occur and in what amounts in different viruses or virus
strains, but also the sequence in which aminoacids occur in the
polypeptide chains.

Over the twenty years during which the aminoacid composition
of tobacco mosaic virus has now been studied, the values reported
for the contents of some individual aminoacids have differed considerably from time to time. Table 8–3 gives what now seems to
be the agreed composition and compares it with the reported compositions of cucumber virus 4, which not only resembles tobacco
mosaic virus morphologically but shares some antigens with it, of
potato virus X, also an anisometric virus, and of three other viruses
that have isometric particles. Many other strains of tobacco mosaic
virus have been analysed, and the results can be summarised by saying that, whereas some closely resemble the type strain, others differ
from it considerably; in general, the similarity in aminoacid constitution accurately reflects the closeness of serological relationships,
and strains that produce similar antisera give similar analyses for
aminoacids whereas the fewer antibodies their antisera have in common the more their aminoacid compositions differ. There is little
else of biological significance that comes from the analyses, except
perhaps that strains such as cucumber virus 4, which have been
found infecting plants in families other than the Solanaceae, are
likely to differ more from the type strain than do symptomatologically distinct strains found infecting the Solanaceae, and differences may be qualitative as well as quantitative. Holmes' ribgrass
(plantain) strain and the cowpea strain in its leguminous form, for
instance, both contain histidine, which does not occur in either type
tobacco mosaic virus or cucumber virus 4, and cucumber virus 4
has no cysteine though the type strain has. In contrast, strains that
differ pathogenically in the type of symptom they cause in solanaceous plants usually differ only in the relative amounts of individual
aminoacids they contain and some, such as the masked and type
strain, have the same compositions. Similarly, three strains of
tomato bushy stunt virus that differ greatly in their virulence towards *Datura stramonium* give the same analytical results for
aminoacid composition (de Fremery and Knight, 1955). About the
only conclusion relevant to pathogenicity that can be drawn from

TABLE 8–3

Aminoacid Composition of Purified Virus Preparations

Aminoacid	Virus					
	Tobacco Mosaic	Cucumber 4	Tomato Bushy Stunt	Turnip Yellow Mosaic	Wild Cucumber Mosaic *	Potato X
	(Gm. aminoacid residue 100 gm. virus)					
Alanine	5.6	4.9	4.7	2.8	5.3	12.1
Arginine	8.9	8.3	5.7	1.3	3.8	4.7
Aspartic acid	11.6	11.3	9.2	3.6	7.8	10.6
Cysteine	0.5	0.0	0.6	–	0.9	–
Glutamic acid	11.2	5.7	5.0	4.6	6.6	8.4
Glycine	1.8	1.1	4.0	1.9	2.6	3.4
Histidine	0.0	0.0	1.2	0.9	2.0	0.9
Isoleucine	5.3	4.0	2.7	4.2	7.2	4.6
Leucine	7.7	8.1	8.9	4.8	13.0	4.2
Lysine	1.35	2.1	3.1	2.9	5.8	4.4
Methionine	0.0	0.0	0.7	1.2	0.7	3.3
Phenylalanine	6.2	8.7	3.7	2.1	6.0	6.5
Proline	4.0	4.8	2.8	6.4	9.2	6.1
Serine	8.3	7.8	5.6	3.6	9.9	4.4
Threonine	9.0	5.9	8.1	7.4	5.8	8.7
Tryptophan	2.4	0.5	0.6	–	1.7	2.0
Tyrosine	3.3	3.3	3.1	0.8	3.1	1.3
Valine	7.3	7.5	7.3	3.4	6.6	4.4
Total	94.45	84.0	77.0	51.9	98.0	90.0
% Nucleic acid	5	5	17	35		5

Results from Knight (1947, 1959), de Fremery and Knight (1955), Fraser and Cosentino (1957), Ramachandran (1958), Yamazaki and Kaesberg (1961) and Shaw and Larson (1962).

* Values for wild cucumber mosaic virus are for protein particles only. Infected plants contain three kinds of specific particles, all with similar protein constitutions, but one contains no nucleic acid, another is about 6% nucleic acid and the third, the only infective kind, is about 34% nucleic acid (Yamazaki and Kaesberg, 1961).

aminoacid analyses is that symptoms seem not to be governed by the sequestration of individual aminoacids by virus strains.

The aminoacid composition of a virus is presumably a constant feature independent of the environment in which the virus was produced, but the only reported work on this point is by Aach (1961a, b), who analysed three strains of tobacco mosaic virus propagated in tobacco and two non-solanaceous hosts, *Phacelia tanacetifolia* and *Phlox drummondii*, with some plants kept continuously at 35° and others at ordinary glasshouse conditions. The different strains multiplied to different extents in the different hosts and the two temperatures, but each kept its characteristic aminoacid composition. Changes in composition, such as happen when the cowpea strain is transferred between leguminous and solanaceous plants (Bawden, 1959), presumably reflect the fact that occasional variants with different aminoacid compositions are selected because they become systemic in the new host, whereas the other cannot.

Quantitative information about aminoacid constitution can be applied to estimate the size of the sub-units composing the virus particles, on the assumption that individual aminoacids are represented equally in each sub-unit. Cysteine is the aminoacid present in least amount in the type strain of tobacco mosaic virus, and assuming there is one residue per sub-unit, an equivalent molecular weight can be calculated for the sub-unit of 18,000; a similar value is given from the content of tryptophan, assuming two of its residues per sub-unit. More convincing evidence for polypeptide chains of about this size comes from the effect of carboxypeptidase, which liberates threonine and only threonine from several strains of tobacco mosaic virus (Harris and Knight, 1955). Carboxypeptidase attacks only the C-terminal end of polypeptide chains and its action stops after releasing threonine because the next linkage (prolyl) resists its action. The number of threonine molecules liberated is one for about every 17,000 molecular weight equivalent. There seems only one discordant fact in these kinds of calculations based on the assumption that all the sub-units have similar aminoacid compositions. The tryptophan content of cucumber virus 4 allows only one residue per unit of 35,000 molecular weight, so if the sub-units of this strain are uniform, they are presumably twice as large as those of the type strain. There is no other evidence suggesting a larger sub-unit, so possibly only every other sub-unit contains tryptophan, or most sub-units contain none and a few many residues. From the amounts of tryptophan, cysteine, methionine and histidine reported in tomato bushy stunt virus, assuming that these are distributed equally in the proportions of 1:2:3:3 per sub-unit, the sub-unit would have an equivalent molecular weight of between 25 and 28,000 (Caspar, 1956). Similarly, the tryptophan content of turnip yellow mosaic virus suggests a molecular weight of about 20,000 for the protein sub-unit, which could contain some 280 aminoacids (Markham, 1959).

The sequence of aminoacids in protein sub-units, or polypeptide chains, has so far been reported on only with strains of tobacco mosaic virus (Gish, 1959; Anderer et al, 1960; Wittmann, 1960; Tsugita and Fraenkel-Conrat, 1960; Tsugita et al, 1960). Work on sequence entails different procedures from quantitative determinations of individual aminoacids, in which every peptide link is hydrolysed to liberate all the aminoacids. Instead, the protein is subjected to treatments that break specific linkages, first to produce peptide chains that can be separated from one another, after which the sequence of aminoacids in each chain is determined by subjecting it to a succession of specific treatments. The relative positions in the original protein of the peptide chains are determined by breaking the protein at different points to get a range of peptides with aminoacid sequences that overlap one another. For instance, in the sequence of 158 aminoacids published by Tsugita et al (1960) for the type strain (Fig. 8–4), twelve peptide chains were produced by incubating the protein with trypsin, which attacks arginine and lysine linkages, and the relative positions of these chains were found by incubating the protein with chymotrypsin and subtilisin, which attack other linkages and produce other peptide chains whose constitution overlaps that of the chains produced by trypsin. (None of these enzymes hydrolyses intact tobacco mosaic virus, but they attack the protein after the virus has been disrupted and the protein separated from the nucleic acid.) Fig. 8–4 shows the positions where trypsin splits the protein and also gives the position of 19 of the 21 amide groups thought to be present. This sequence contains one more aminoacid than the one reported by Anderer et al (1960) and also differs from it in a few other ways. The C-terminal aminoacid was readily identified as threonine by the action of carboxypeptidase (Harris and Knight, 1955), but identifying the N-terminal one (serine) was unexpectedly difficult because it is acetylated, a type of end group for a polypeptide not previously encountered (Narita, 1958). The technical achievement in producing the sequence of 158 aminoacids shown in Fig. 8–4 cannot but be admired, even though whether it represents the actual sequence in every sub-unit will remain in doubt until there is conclusive evidence that they are all identical. Most must have the same structure for otherwise the analysis could not be made, but a minority may differ from the majority. For any understanding of the behaviour of viruses, it probably matters little whether the sequence shown is wholly correct, for at the present state of knowledge there is no biological significance that can be attributed to aminoacids occurring in any given sequence. However, should the sequence of nucleotides in the nucleic acid also be determined, the correctness of animoacid sequence will be essential for attempts to relate one to the other.

Strains of tobacco mosaic virus that have different gross aminoacid compositions obviously must also differ in the way their aminoacids are arranged in sequence. (To take the simplest example:

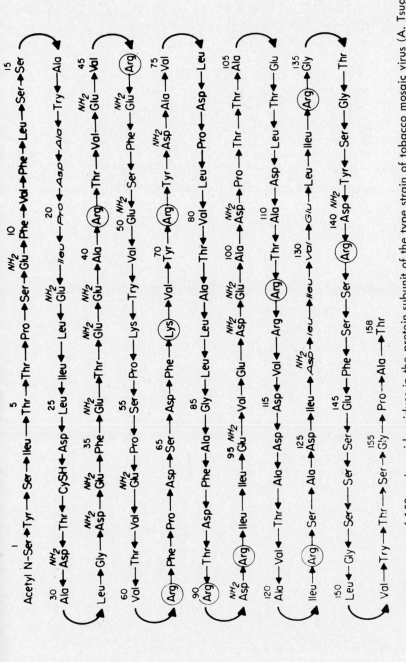

Fig. 8–4. Sequence of 158 aminoacid residues in the protein subunit of the type strain of tobacco mosaic virus (A. Tsugita et al, 1960, Proc. nat. Acad. Sci. Wash. 46: 1463).

histidine will occur somewhere in the sequence for the rib-grass and cowpea strains, but is not represented in the type strain). What biologically is more interesting than establishing differences is to know whether virus strains that differ pathogenically can have the same sequence. Apparently they can, for Wittmann (1959) reports that a variant isolated from a preparation of the type strain exposed to nitrous acid has the same aminoacid sequence as the type strain. This suggests that differences in pathogenicity reflect differences in the nucleic acid or in the manner in which the polypeptide chains are folded and linked together. Another variant obtained from a similarly treated preparation of the type strain has been reported to have a different composition (Tsugita and Fraenkel-Conrat, 1960); this strain, and others that differ greatly from the type strain in gross aminoacid compositions, all seem to have the same number of amino-acids in their polypeptide chains (Wittmann, 1960).

Virus nucleic acids. Probably the main reason for determining the aminoacid sequence in different virus strains lies in the hope that differences will be able to be correlated with differences in the structure of the nucleic acids. Nucleic acids have long been thought to be directly concerned in protein synthesis, and their dominant role has become increasingly evident since the discovery that virus nucleic acids freed from protein can initiate infection and cause the production of complete virus particles, indistinguishable from those produced in infections initiated by intact virus. In other words, the nucleic acid seems not only to reproduce itself but is also able to direct the synthesis of a specific protein. How it achieves either of these activities is still unknown, but the current idea about protein synthesis is that the order in which the constituents of the nucleic acid are arranged specifies a code that is translatable in terms of aminoacid sequences. An analogy often used is the Morse code, in which the whole alphabet is represented and any message can be written by the correct arrangement of three symbols (dot, dash and space); nucleic acids have the equivalent of four symbols and as the number of aminoacids in proteins is about the same as the number of letters in the alphabet, they seem more generously equipped than the Morse code for conveying messages, but it is also obvious that they do other things than determine the arrangement of aminoacids. Strains of plant viruses currently provide the most favourable material for testing the coding hypothesis, but even with them progress is likely to be slow. Not only are the nucleic acids very large, equivalent molecular weight about 2,000,000, but the fewness of their components also makes sequential analysis incomparably more difficult than with proteins. The coding hypothesis, therefore, is unlikely to be anything but a hypothesis for some time to come, but ignorance about mechanisms does not make any less important the knowledge that the nucleic acids and not the proteins primarily determine the biological specificity. With that, let us turn to consider what is known about virus nucleic acids.

Since tobacco mosaic virus was shown to contain a nucleic acid of the ribose type (Bawden *et al*, 1936), this has been about the only feature shared by all other plant viruses that have been studied. It would be premature yet to assume this is generally true, because most viruses that infect bacteria, and some that infect animals, contain deoxy nucleic acid, and there seems no *a priori* reason why viruses containing deoxy nucleic acid should not infect flowering plants. However, if there are any, they await discovery. The two nucleic acids derive their names from the different sugars they contain, one, D-ribofuranose and the other D-2-deoxyribofuranose, but they also differ in another respect. Both characteristically contain four nitrogenous compounds (bases), of which two are the purines adenine and guanine, common to both types, and two are pyrimidines, cytosine and uracil in ribose nucleic acids and, usually, cytosine and thymine in deoxy nucleic acids. The structural part, or back-bone, is similar in all nucleic acids and is a chain of sugar residues joined by an equivalent number of phosphoric acid residues; the specificity of different nucleic acid chains is presumably conferred by the arrangement and identity of the bases along this chain. There is no reason to suspect that the pentose sugar in any of the plant viruses is other than ribose, but this has been rigorously established only with tobacco mosaic (Schwerdt and Loring, 1947; Knight, 1954), turnip yellow mosaic (Markham and Smith, 1951), and tomato bushy stunt (de Fremery and Knight, 1955) viruses.

Many methods for separating virus nucleic acids from their proteins have long been known. These include disrupting the particles by heat, by alkali, by sodium dodecyl sulphate, phenol, glacial acetic acid, urea and various other simple organic substances (Bawden and Pirie, 1937a; 1938a; 1938b; 1940a; 1940b: Sreenivasaya and Pirie, 1938). Many of these treatments produce a coagulum of insoluble protein, and the extent to which the nucleic acid remains associated with this coagulum differs greatly with different viruses; for example, the nucleic acid separates from the protein almost completely when tobacco mosaic virus is denatured by heat, but only partially with potato virus X, and the coagulum produced by denatured tomato bushy stunt or tobacco necrosis viruses carries with it all the nucleic acid. The nucleic acid of turnip yellow mosaic virus can be obtained

by the unusually mild method of simply treating the virus with 34%
ethanol in the cold at pH 7 (Markham and Smith, 1949).

The most widely applicable methods are probably exposure to
alkali, to surface active agents, such as sodium dodecyl sulphate, to
phenol or to acetic acid. Alkali and acetic acid disrupt the protein
of tobacco mosaic and some other viruses into fragments that are
still soluble and still able to react specifically with virus antisera

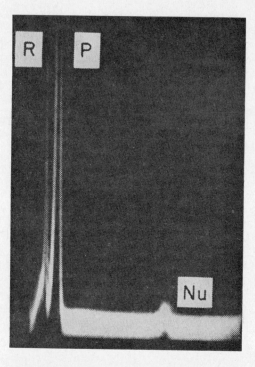

Fig. 8–5. Ascending electro
phoretic pattern of a 1.3% solu
tion of potato virus X partially
split into protein and nucleic acid
by incubation at pH 10 for 20
hours at 20°. R. Almost station
ary, residual virus; P. Virus pro
tein; Nu. Nucleic acid. (F. C
Bawden and A. Kleczkowski,
1959, Virology 7: 375).

when acidified, the fragments of protein from tobacco mosaic virus
reassemble into rods morphologically resembling virus particles
(Schramm, 1947; Schramm, Schumacher and Zillig, 1955; Fraenkel-
Conrat, 1957). Acetic acid splits the bonds between the nucleic
acid and protein and precipitates the nucleic acid, which can be
removed by centrifuging, leaving the protein in the supernatant
fluid, from which it precipitates when the acetic acid is removed by
dialysis. From virus dissociated around pH 10, the protein can be
precipitated by ammonium sulphate, leaving the nucleic acid in solution, or the two components can be separated by electrophoresis
(Schramm and Zillig, 1955). Potato virus X behaves rather similarly, except that the protein fragments produced by alkali do not
reaggregate when acidified into threads resembling the original virus

particles. This virus is unusual in barely moving in an electric field at pH 7; as Fig. 8–5 shows, the disrupted protein is a little more mobile, and the nucleic acid much more than the intact virus, so the components are readily separable electrophoretically. This greater mobility of the protein contrasts with tobacco mosaic virus, of which the disaggregated protein moves more slowly than the intact virus or the reaggregated protein (Schramm *et al*, 1955; Kleczkowski,

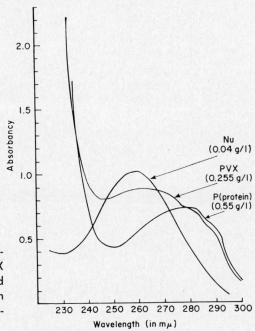

Fig. 8–6. Ultraviolet absorption spectra of potato virus X (PVX), its nucleic acid (Nu) and its protein (P). (F. C. Bawden and A. Kleczkowski, 1959, Virology 7: 375).

1959). Fig. 8–6 shows the ultraviolet absorption spectra of intact potato virus X and of its two components separated electrophoretically after the virus was disrupted by alkali (Bawden and Kleczkowski, 1959).

When virus preparations are treated in ways that disrupt the particles into protein and nucleic acid, their infectivity usually falls greatly and this fact, together with the lability of the separated nucleic acid, for long made it seem that infection could be initiated only by whole virus particles. The important discovery that fragments of tobacco mosaic consisting largely, and possibly exclusively, of nucleic acid can be infective was made almost simultaneously by Gierer and Schramm (1956), who used phenol to disrupt the virus, and Fraenkel-Conrat (1956) who used sodium dodecyl sulphate.

Since then nucleic acid prepared from tobacco mosaic virus disrupted by heating has also been found to be infective (Knight, 1956) though other methods such as disruption by alkali, urea or strontium nitrate gave non-infective nucleic acid (Bawden and Pirie, 1957b). Disruption by phenol has also produced infective nucleic acid preparations from a dozen or so other viruses, with widely differing shapes and ratios of nucleic acid to protein, and because of its simplicity has become the method of choice for making nucleic acid preparations. Exposure to phenol denatures the protein, and essentially the method involves the partition of denatured protein and sodium nucleate between layers of phenol and water. The ratio of water to phenol and the salt concentration are both important. With tobacco mosaic virus, the method works well when equal volumes of virus in 0.017M sodium citrate, or pH 7 phosphate buffer, and of 900 g./l. aqueous phenol are mixed at $0°$, shaken briskly by hand for a few minutes and then centrifuged for 15 minutes at 3,000 rev./min. The upper layer is siphoned off, shaken with a quarter of its volume of the aqueous phenol, and centrifuged again. The supernatant fluid is now shaken for a few minutes with 10 volumes of ether to remove most of the phenol, and then, still at $0°$, the ether is removed by exhaustion with a filter pump. The final solution contains about one half the nucleic acid of the original virus and more can be separated by shaking the combined phenol layers with their own volume of water and repeating the centrifugation and extraction with ether.

That the infectivity of such nucleic acid preparations, from tobacco mosaic or other viruses, is not conferred by residual virus particles is shown by the failure of electron microscopy to show such particles, the failure of the preparations to be affected by virus antisera, the lability of infectivity and, especially, inactivation by ribonuclease preparations that do not affect intact virus particles. The calculated weight of nucleic acid contained in one particle of tobacco mosaic virus is equivalent to a molecular weight of about 2,000,000 and measurements of sedimentation, diffusion, viscosity and light-scattering on freshly-made preparations suggest the presence of particles of this size in nucleic acid preparations (Hopkins and Sinsheimer, 1955; Schuster, Schramm and Zillig, 1956; Gierer, 1957). It seems, then, that the whole nucleic acid is contained in a single polynucleotide chain containing more than 6,000 mononucleotides, and Gierer (1957) states that a single break in the chain destroys infectivity. The nucleic acid readily depolymerises, though it is reported to be more stable in 0.1M pH 7 pyrophosphate than other solutions (Fraenkel-Conrat, 1959), and most preparations are molecularly inhomogeneous. Preparations soon lose infectivity at room temperature, but remain infective for many months at −20°. Preparations of nucleic acid contain some metals, not all of which are removed by chelating agents (Loring and Waritz, 1957), but their significance is unknown.

After hydrolysing the nucleic acids, usually by alkali or acid, the constituent nucleotides can be separated chromatographically and their amounts estimated from their absorption of ultraviolet radiation. Table 8–4 gives the compositions of nucleic acids reported for

TABLE 8–4

Nucleotide Composition of Nucleic Acids

Virus	Relative Proportion of Nucleotides			
	Adenylic Acid	Guanylic Acid	Cytidylic Acid	Uridylic Acid
Tobacco mosaic	1.13	1.00	0.77	1.11
Cucumber 3 and 4	0.97	1.02	0.78	1.25
Potato X	1.29	0.87	0.95	0.89
Tomato bushy stunt	1.02	1.12	0.82	1.03
Southern bean mosaic	0.97	1.03	0.96	1.05
Turnip yellow mosaic	0.91	0.69	1.53	0.89
Turnip crinkle	1.10	1.02	0.98	0.89
Wild cucumber mosaic	0.72	0.66	1.59	1.02
Tobacco ringspot	0.96	0.99	0.93	1.13
Alfalfa mosaic	0.94	0.67	0.98	1.42

Figures from Knight (1954, 1959), Dorner and Knight (1953), de Fremery and Knight (1955), Markham (1959), Markham and Smith (1951), Kaper and Steere (1959), Yamazaki and Kaesberg (1961), Frisch-Niggemeyer and Steere (1961).

several viruses and shows considerable differences between different ones. Turnip yellow mosaic and wild cucumber mosaic viruses, which resemble one another in several respects, and may be remotely related, have the most distinctive compositions in that the base ratios depart from unity to an unusual amount. Cucumber virus 3 has a slightly different composition from type tobacco mosaic virus, to which it is related serologically, but 15 symptomatologically distinct strains all have the same composition as the type strain, although some have distinctive aminoacid compositions. Similarly, three symptomatologically distinct strains of tomato bushy stunt contained their four bases in the same ratio. Obviously, if analyses are going to explain biological specificity, they will need to be taken further than for total amounts of nucleotides and extend to determining nucleotide sequences. The sequences of the some 6,400 nucleotides in tobacco mosaic virus will not be known for a long time to come, but if strains differ greatly in the way different nucleotides are distributed in different parts of their nucleic acid chains, this fact may soon be established by analyses on fragmented nucleic acid (oligonucleotides). Reddi (1957) reported that the acid-soluble fraction after incubating nucleic acid from the masked strain contained much more cytidylic acid and uridylic acid than the comparable fraction from the type strain, which would imply great differences in distribution of nucleotides between strains with similar aminoacid compositions. However, Rushizky and Knight (1960) not only failed to confirm these differences, but found that twenty different fractions from the nucleic acids of these two strains had indistinguishable compositions; in contrast to the similarity between the type and masked strains, they report 10 points of differences between fractions obtained from the type and the rib-grass (plantain) strain, which also have different aminoacid compositions.

Polyamine. Johnson and Markham (1962) report that turnip yellow mosaic virus contains a polyamine, bis(3-aminopropyl)amine, in an amount equal to 0.7% of the weight of the virus particles. It seems mostly to be associated with the virus nucleic acid and is enough to neutralise about 1/7th of its phosphoric acid groups. They also found the polyamine in turnip crinkle, broad bean mottle and tobacco mosaic viruses, but it amounted to only 0.003% of the weight of tobacco mosaic virus. They could not find this polyamine in uninfected plants of Chinese cabbage, so infection of the host by turnip yellow mosaic virus presumably stimulates its synthesis.

REFERENCES

AACH, H. G.   1961a.   Biol. Zbl. 80: 453.
———.   1961b.   Arch. Mikrobiol. 39: 253.
ANDERER, F. A., H. UHLIG, E. WEBER, and G. SCHRAMM.   1960.   Nature 186: 922.
BAWDEN, F. C., R. P. CHAUDHURI, and B. KASSANIS.   1951.   Ann. appl. Biol. 38: 774.
———, and E. M. CROOK.   1947.   Brit. J. exp. Path. 28: 403.
———, and A. KLECZKOWSKI.   1959.   Virology 7: 375.
———, and N. W. PIRIE.   1936.   Brit. J. exp. Path. 17: 64.
———, and ———.   1937a.   Proc. Roy. Soc. B. 123: 274.
———, and ———.   1937b.   Brit. J. exp. Path. 18: 290.
———, and ———.   1938a.   Brit. J. exp. Path. 19: 66.
———, and ———.   1938b.   Brit. J. exp. Path. 19: 251.
———, and ———.   1940a.   Biochem. J. 34: 1258.
———, and ———.   1940b.   Biochem. J. 34: 1278.
———, and ———.   1942.   Brit. J. exp. Path. 23: 314.
———, and ———.   1944.   Brit. J. exp. Path. 25: 68.
———, and ———.   1945a.   Brit. J. exp. Path. 26: 277.
———, and ———.   1945b.   Brit. J. exp. Path. 26: 294.
———, and ———.   1946.   Brit. J. exp. Path. 27: 81.

——, and ——. 1957a. J. gen. Microbiol. 16: 696.
——, and ——. 1957b. J. gen. Microbiol. 17: 80.
——, and ——. 1959. J. gen. Microbiol. 21: 438.
——, ——, J. D., BERNAL, and I. FANKUCHEN. 1936. Nature 138: 1051.
BRAKKE, M. K. 1953. Arch. Biochem. 45: 275.
——. 1956. Virology 2: 463.
——. 1960. Advanc. Virus Res. 7: 193.
CASPAR, D. L. D. 1956. Nature 177: 475.
COCHRAN, G. W., and J. L. CHIDESTER. 1957. Virology 4: 390.
DIENER, T. O. 1962. Virology 16: 140.
DORNER, R. W., and C. A. KNIGHT. 1953. J. biol. Chem. 205: 959.
ENGLER, R., and G. SCHRAMM. 1959. Nature 183: 1277.
FRAENKEL-CONRAT, H. 1956. J. Amer. chem. Soc. 78: 882.
——. 1957. Virology 4: 1.
——. 1959. The Viruses, 1, 429. Academic Press, New York.
FRASER, D., and V. COSENTINO. 1957. Virology 4: 126.
FREMERY, DE D., and C. A. KNIGHT. 1955. J. biol. Chem. 214: 559.
FRISCH-NIGGEMEYER, W., and R. L. STEERE. 1961. Virology 14: 83.
GIERER, A. 1957. Nature 179: 1297.
GIERER, A., and G. SCHRAMM. 1956. Nature 177: 702.
GINOZA, W., D. E. ATKINSON, and S. G. WILDMAN. 1954. Science 119: 269.
GISH, D. T. 1959. Biochim. biophys. Acta. 35: 557.
HARRIS, J. I., and C. A. KNIGHT. 1955. J. biol. Chem. 214: 215.
HOPKINS, G. R., and R. L. SINSHEIMER, 1955. Biochem. biophys. Acta 17: 476.
JOHNSON, M. W., and R. MARKHAM. 1962. Virology 17: 276.
KAPER, J. M., and R. L. STEERE. 1959. Virology 7: 127.
KASSANIS, B. 1960. Virology 10: 353.
KASSANIS, B., and H. L. NIXON. 1961. J. gen. Microbiol. 25: 459.
KLECZKOWSKI, A. 1959. Virology 7: 385.
——, and H. L. NIXON. 1950. J. gen. Microbiol. 4: 220.
KNIGHT, C. A. 1947. J. biol. Chem. 171: 297.
——. 1954. Advanc. Virus Res. 2: 153.
——. 1956. Methods in Enzymology, 3, 684. Academic Press, New York.
——. 1959. The Viruses, 2, 127. Academic Press, New York.
LORING, H. S., and R. S. WARITZ. 1957. Science 125: 646.
MARKHAM, R. 1959. The Viruses, 2, 33. Academic Press, New York.
MARKHAM, R., R. E. F. MATTHEWS, and K. M. SMITH. 1948. Nature 162: 88.
——, and K. M. SMITH. 1949. Parasitology 39: 330.
——, and ——. 1951. Biochem. J. 49: 401.
MATTHEWS, R. E. F. 1958. Virology 5: 192.
NARITA, K. 1958. Biochem. biophys. Acta. 28: 184.
PIRIE, N. W. 1940. Biol. Rev. 15: 377.
——. 1945. Advanc. Enzymol. 5: 1.
——. 1952. Brit. J. Phil. Sci. 2: 269.
——. 1957. Advanc. Virus Res. 4: 159.
——, K. M. SMITH, E. T. SPOONER, and W. D. McCLEMENT. 1938. Parasitology 30: 543.
RAMACHANDRAN, L. K. 1958. Virology 5: 244.
REDDI, K. K. 1957. Biochim. biophys. Acta 25: 528.
ROSS, A. F. 1941. Phytopathology 31: 394.
RUSHIZKY, G. W., and C. A. KNIGHT. 1960. Proc. nat. Acad. Sci., Wash. 46: 945.
SCHRAMM, G. 1947. Z. Naturforsch 2b: 112, 249.
——, G. SCHUMACHER, and W. ZILLIG. 1955. Z. Naturforsch 10b: 481.
——, and W. ZILLIG. 1955. Z. Naturforsch 10b: 493.
SCHUSTER, H., G. SCHRAMM, and W. ZILLIG. 1956. Z. Naturforsch 11b: 330.
SCHWERDT, C. E., and H. S. LORING. 1947. J. biol. Chem. 167: 593.
SHAW, J. G., and R. H. LARSON. 1962. Phytopathology 52: 170.

Sreenivasaya, M., and N. W. Pirie. 1938. Biochem. J. 32: 1707.
Stanley, W. M. 1939. J. biol. Chem. 129: 429.
Steere, R. L. 1956. Phytopathology 46: 60.
———. 1958. Advanc. Virus Res. 6: 3.
Takahashi, W. N., and M. Ishii. 1952. Phytopathology 42: 690.
———, and ———. 1953. Amer. J. Bot. 40: 85.
Tsugita, A., and H. Fraenkel-Conrat. 1960. Proc. nat. Acad. Sci., Wash. 46: 636.
———, D. T. Gish, J. Young, H. Fraenkel-Conrat, C. A. Knight, and W. M. Stanley. 1960. Proc. nat. Acad. Sci., Wash. 46: 1463.
Wittmann, H. G. 1959. Vererbungslehre 90: 463.
———. 1960. Virology 11: 505.
Yamazaki, H., and P. Kaesberg. 1961. Nature 191: 96.

chapter 9

The Morphology
of Viruses

To use the phrase "morphology of viruses" would until recently have been little more than pretentious synonymity for the study of particle sizes and shapes, but its use is now more than justified by the much new information that has been gained about the internal structure of a few viruses. That different viruses have particles of characteristic shapes and sizes has been obvious since the middle 1930's when work on their purification led to the isolation of some as liquid crystals and others as true crystals. It was also apparent from the early X-ray diffraction studies with these purified virus preparations (Bawden et al, 1936; Wyckoff and Corey, 1936; Bernal and Fankuchen, 1941), not only that particles of some viruses were uniform enough in size to fit into crystal lattices, but also that the individual virus particles were in a sense themselves equivalent to crystals, in as much as they are built up from repeating units of a uniform size regularly arranged. The major recent developments have been to interpret these crystallographic patterns in terms of protein sub-units, to determine the number and arrangement of these sub-units, and to identify the relative positions in the particles occupied by the protein and nucleic acid.

X-ray diffraction and electron microscopy have recently provided so much information about the morphology of a few viruses that it is perhaps salutary to stress how little is still known about the great majority. For many, knowledge is limited to the size and shape of their particles as shown by electron microscopy; for others, there is not even this, and nothing is known about their particles except that they have not been resolved by microscopes using visible light. The structural similarities between the few that have been studied intensively make it almost certain that many others will also resemble them, particularly as these few differ widely from one another in many properties, but it would be premature to assume that all necessarily fall into one or other of the categories described in this chapter.

Particle sizes and shapes. Few problems have received more attention in the study of plant viruses than the size and shapes of their particles, especially of tobacco mosaic virus. Certainly no other single problem has entailed so many mathematical formulae, so many ingenious and diverse techniques, or so much costly apparatus. There is, therefore, perhaps nothing to be surprised about that the problem has also probably received more different answers than any other. Indeed, the very nature of the problem made this almost inevitable and, although it is worth explaining the reasons, there is no call now to report the many changes in ideas about the weight and size of tobacco mosaic virus. The early estimates, like most of the methods used to make them, have little more than historic interest since it became possible to resolve viruses by electron microscopy and measure their sizes directly. Until this happened, size could be estimated only indirectly from measurements of such properties as filterability through membranes of different average pore sizes (Elford, 1931), or sedimentation or diffusion. In estimating sizes from such measurements, assumptions were made about the particles that were later found to be wholly unwarranted. For instance, until tobacco mosaic virus was obtained in the form of liquid crystalline solutions, anomalous in most of their physical properties (Bawden and Pirie, 1937), it was assumed that all viruses had particles resembling billiard balls and that their solutions had usual physical properties. Formulae that apply to anhydrous smooth spheres are wholly inapplicable to hydrated hollow tubes with uneven surfaces, and it is a testimonial to physical-chemical theory that formulae were produced by which particle weight and size were estimated from measurements of sedimentation velocity and viscosity to give values not far removed from those currently accepted for tobacco mosaic virus (Lauffer, 1938).

Schachman and Williams (1959) recently described the various physical techniques that can be used to estimate particle sizes and shapes and discussed the physical properties of plant viruses in detail. There is therefore no need to consider this subject further here, but one comment needs making now that sizes of viruses are determined almost exclusively by electron microscopy. This means that measurements are made on dry particles, and viruses do not normally exist dry but in solution, where they may well be associated with, at least, their own weight of water. When considering sizes and shapes, therefore, it is essential to remember that the words have no generally agreed meaning and may mean different things in different environments. As Schachman and Williams (1959) point out, the words "are always circumscribed in their meaning by consideration of the ways in which they are measured. Thus, the X-ray crystallographer determines the size of a virus as it exists in a unit cell of a crystal; the hydrodynamicist determines the effective size of the particle as it plows its way through a solution; the electron microscopist finds its shape and size, when dry, by direct photography. If virus particles were hard objects, like marbles, these distinctions among methods would be irrelevant, but a virus particle may be more like a sponge with water bound both internally and externally. It has amphoteric properties which may confer upon it different effective diameters, depending upon concentration and the ionic environment. We should not be surprised if we find that the same virus particles apparently have different sizes and shapes in the hands of different experimenters, all of whom have performed their work correctly."

Electron micrographs of virus particles, particularly of shadowed preparations, which are the ones most used to determine size and shape, carry an impression of solidity and of smooth surfaces that is entirely false. For example, Fig. 3–2 shows tobacco mosaic virus particles looking like solid smooth rods, which indeed they were long assumed to be, though as will be shown later in this chapter they are hollow tubes with deeply grooved surfaces. In solution, not only will the centre and the interstices contain water and ions, but the outside will also be surrounded by a volume of associated water and ions, which will differ at different parts of the particle depending on the type and nature of the locally charged groups. Electron micrographs of preparations made by the "negative" staining technique of Brenner and Horne (1959) probably give a more realistic impression of virus particles than do shadowed preparations, for they indicate a loose structure readily penetrated by such materials as phosphotungstic acid. Measurements of such stained preparations also often suggest slightly smaller particle sizes from those given by measurements on shadowed preparations, perhaps because the stain penetrates the outer parts, whereas the evaporated metal rests on them.

Unfortunately viruses have little power to scatter electrons and when simply dried on a collodion grid and examined in an electron microscope the contrast between the virus particles and the background is rarely good enough for size to be measured accurately, because the virus particles show only as darker grey areas on an already grey background. Contrast is enormously enhanced when the specimen is coated with a thin film of some heavy metal, by placing it in a vacuum at an oblique angle to a heated wire of the metal (Williams and Wyckoff, 1944, 1946; Müller, 1942). Depositing the metal obliquely causes the higher elevations of the specimen to cast "shadows," regions free from the metal, on the sides away from the wire. In the electron microscope, the scattering of electrons by different parts of the specimen is proportional to the thickness of the deposited metal, and great contrast is obtained between the particles covered with metal and the shadows they cast. Measuring the length of the shadows can also provide information about the heights or thickness of the particles, and the outlines of the shadows sometimes indicate that apparently spherical particles are polyhedrons. The technique most used is to shadow the specimens and examine them directly in the electron microscope, but for this they must be thin enough to be penetrated by electrons. Specimens too thick for this can be examined by making replicates of their surfaces in strippings of Formvar or polystyrene-silica, which are then shadowed. Wyckoff (1956) has used the replica technique with great success to show the arrangements of virus particles in crystals (Fig. 9–1).

To measure the size of a virus, particularly one with a distinctive shape, it is not always necessary to purify it carefully. When viruses occur reasonably concentrated, simply diluting clarified sap will produce preparations suitable for electron microscopy. Drops of the fluid that exudes from leaves of infected plants when pressure is applied to their cut stems or petioles (Johnson, 1951), give excellent preparations of many viruses, and simply touching a wet specimen grid with the freshly cut surface of an infected leaf suffices with some. Viruses that occur too dilute in sap to be prepared in these ways for electron microscopy may be obtained in a suitable state by layering clarified infective sap on a density gradient, centrifuging and then taking a droplet from the appropriate zone in the centrifuge tube.

The shapes of viruses from higher plants yet examined range from near spheres to rods or threads fifty or more times as long as they are wide, but all are relatively simple compared with some

acteriophages, which have polyhedral heads and complex tails
earing flagellum-like appendages (Fig. 1–6). The isometric ones
sually appear spherical in shadowed preparations, but many, and
erhaps all, are polyhedral. Each isometric one usually occurs in
articles of only one size; different ones range in diameter from

Fig. 9–1. Electron micrograph of a crystal of the "satellite" virus that mul-
iplies when accompanied by a tobacco necrosis virus. (Photograph supplied
by Dr. R. W. G. Wyckoff).

about 17 mμ for the smallest which depends on tobacco necrosis
viruses for its multiplication, between 20 and 30 mμ for tobacco
necrosis, arabis mosaic, raspberry ringspot, tomato black ring, tomato bushy stunt, turnip yellow mosaic and southern bean mosaic
viruses, to about 60 mμ for wound tumour virus.

The anisometric ones fall into three readily distinguishable categories: (1) bacillus-like bodies only a few times as long as they are
wide; (2) rigid rods and (3) flexible threads. About the only common feature to all the anisometric viruses is that each occurs in
extracts from infected plants in particles of different lengths, though
uniform widths. Category (1) as yet contains only one virus, alfalfa
(lucerne) mosaic, from higher plants, but bacillus-like particles have

also been reported in mushrooms suffering from die-back disease (Hollings, 1962). Lucerne (alfalfa) mosaic virus has particles about 18 mμ wide and various lengths up to about 60 mμ, though most fall into three groups, one about 36 mμ long, the other 48 and the third 58 mμ. The 58 mμ group contains the most and the 48 mμ one the fewest particles. These three sizes correspond with the three sedimentation constants (73s, 89s and 99s) reported for preparations of alfalfa mosaic virus, and work with fractionated preparations suggests that only the largest particles are infective (Bancroft and Kaesberg, 1960).

The three viruses known with apparently rigid, rod-like particles, are tobacco mosaic, tobacco rattle and barley stripe mosaic. Early X-ray measurements (Bernal and Fankuchen, 1941) suggested that tobacco mosaic virus particles were 15.2 mμ wide, a value that has long been accepted, for it is also given by measurements across several closely packed parallel particles in electron micrographs However, shadowed individual particles often seem thicker, and later X-ray measurements show that they have a maximum diameter of about 18 mμ; the particles are grooved and 15.2 mμ is their mean diameter as measured by the distance between the centres of particles that become intermeshed when in a close-packed hexagonal array (Franklin and Klug, 1956). Values reported by different workers for the widths of tobacco rattle and barley stripe mosaic viruses have also differed, but there is agreement that both are wider than tobacco mosaic and recent measurements are respectively, 25 mμ (Harrison and Nixon, 1959) and 20 mμ (Kassanis and Slykhuis, 1959). All three occur in particles of many and greatly differing lengths, from some little longer than their width up to those many times as long as they are wide. For each, though, there is a length that is more common than any other; for tobacco mosaic virus the length is now usually accepted as 300 $\pm$ 5 mμ; the variation possibly indicates the actual polydispersity of this type of particle rather than the experimental errors in measuring them (Hall, 1958). The commonest length for barley stripe virus is 130 mμ and for tobacco rattle virus 75 mμ, which is unusual in having a second common length of 185 mμ, with about half as many particles of this length as there are 75 mμ long (Harrison and Nixon, 1959). Plotting the particle-length distribution of other anisometric viruses often shows two peaks, but the second and smaller one is usually at a length twice that of the commonest, and can be explained by two particles of this length aggregating linearly. However, this cannot explain the two commonest lengths with tobacco rattle virus, for these differ by a factor of 2.5. Nor can the two lengths readily be

xplained by breaks in the longer particles, for breaks that produce
particles 75 mμ long should also produce equal numbers of particles
10 or 35 mμ long, but these do not occur.

What significance should be attached to these particles of differ-
nt lengths is unknown. Whatever their length, they seem to be
erologically identical, although very short particles precipitate with
ntibodies to give dense granular floccules, whereas long particles
give fluffy open precipitates. The small particles of tobacco mosaic
virus readily aggregate linearly when treated in various ways and
hey then give fluffy floccules and precipitate over a wider range
f antigen/antibody ratios than before (Bawden and Pirie, 1945,
1956). The smallest of all the particles that react with virus antise-
um seem to consist of protein only (Takahashi and Ishii, 1953) but
ods shorter than 300 mμ may contain the usual proportion of nucleic
cid. It is now generally assumed that only the particles of about
300 mμ or longer are infective, but Bawden and Pirie (1945) re-
orted some infectivity in preparations in which particles of this
ength could not be found by electron microscopy, and the problem
equires further study by modern techniques. The only recent crit-
cal work correlating infectivity with particle lengths is with tobacco
attle virus; only particles of about 185 mμ long seem able to initiate
nfection, which means that the great majority of particles, including
the most common length of 75 mμ, are not infective (Harrison and
Nixon, 1959).

Williams and Steere (1951) suggested that the short particles
seen in electron micrograms of tobacco mosaic virus are fragments
produced by the 300 mμ particles breaking when dried to make the
specimen but the suggestion is not acceptable. Short particles already occur in virus preparations before they are dried, and extracts
from infected plants are readily fractionated by differential centrifugation into preparations that contain particles of very different
average lengths (Bawden and Pirie, 1945). Williams and Steere
were prompted to make their suggestion because the totalled length
of the short particles in their electron micrographs was divisible by
300 mμ, but this could be a consequence of the fact that all other
lengths except the commonest seem to occur with equal frequencies
in freshly prepared extracts, not only with tobacco mosaic but also
with other rod-shaped and thread-like viruses (Brandes and Wetter,
1959). This may indicate that they are fragments of the larger particles, but if so fragmentation occurs for other reasons than drying
to make specimens for electron microscopy. It has already been
stated that breaks in the longest particles of tobacco rattle virus
cannot explain the lengths of the two commonest particles, which

are therefore presumably made as such in infected cells. This ma
also be true of the other lengths, but there is no evidence one wa
or the other. The only unequivocal knowledge about lengths o
particles in cells comes from measurements on the crystalline inclu
sions produced by tobacco mosaic virus, which contain particle
about 300 mμ long (Wilkins *et al*, 1950; Steere, 1957); howevei
this is not evidence that there are not particles of other lengths, fo
crystallisation demands particles of a uniform size and so may b
selecting 300 mμ particles and leaving other lengths dissolved in th
cell sap. Not all particles shorter than the commonest lengths neec
have the same origins. Some may come from longer particles frag
menting, perhaps *in vivo*, or perhaps when the cells are disrupted
Others may originate as such; if virus protein and nucleic acid ar
synthesised separately in infected cells and then assembled into par
ticles, the length of the resulting particles may be determined b
the length of the nucleic acid thread. Two explanations can b
offered for the threads differing in length: (1) they may actuall
be synthesised in different lengths; (2) they may be synthesised ir
uniform lengths but some get broken before they are stabilised by
an adequate covering of protein.

The many flexible, thread-like viruses, are all longer than tobacco
mosaic virus and narrower, with reported widths of 10–13 mμ (Fig
9–2). Each occurs in particles of greatly differing lengths, but the
distribution curve of particle for each shows a sharp peak around a
length that is characteristic of the individual virus (Brandes and
Wetter, 1959). The arithmetical mean length calculated from the
particles contained in this peak has been called the normal lengtl
(Wetter and Brandes, 1956; Bode and Paul, 1955). Brandes and
Wetter (1959) quote the following normal lengths: white clover
mosaic 480 mμ; potato X 515; potato aucuba mosaic 580; Wisconsin
pea streak 620; potato virus S 650; wheat streak mosaic 700; beef
mosaic, potato A, potato Y, tobacco etch and henbane mosaic 730;
bean common mosaic, soybean mosaic, turnip mosaic, cocksfoot
streak, lettuce mosaic and sorghum red stripe 750; beet yellows
1250 mμ.

The structure of anisometric viruses. The first indications that
tobacco mosaic virus particles are not solid rods of uniform nucleoprotein came from electron micrographs of preparations freeze-
dried (Rice, Kaesberg and Stahmann, 1953) or degraded by alkali
(Schramm, Schumacher and Zillig, 1955), which showed axial
threads either joining segments of rods or protruding from the ends
of partially degraded rods. Hart (1955) confirmed the suggestion

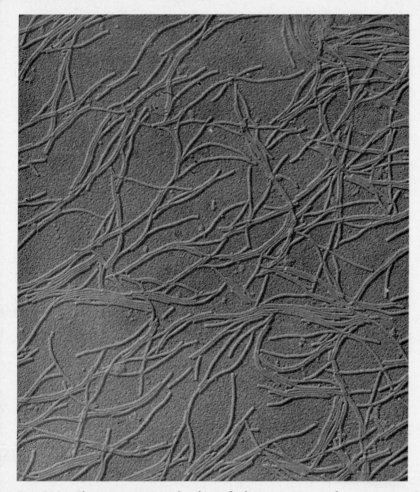

Fig. 9–2. Electron micrograph of purified preparations of potato virus X, shadowed with platinum-iridium alloy. × 45,700.

that these threads were the nucleic acid, by showing that those protruding from particles partially degraded with detergent were dissolved by ribonuclease. His observations also suggested that the two ends of the virus particles differ, for particles partly disrupted usually had nucleic acid protruding from one end only. Further evidence for structural differences between the two ends comes from studying disruption by alkali, which suggests that protein is rapidly unravelled from one end until about two-thirds of the protein units are removed, but the remaining one-third seems more resistant (Harrington and Schachman, 1956).

Electron micrographs of degraded virus often show small discs with holes in their centres; it seemed probable that these holes had originally contained nucleic acid and for a time it was assumed that tobacco mosaic virus was essentially a hollow tube of protein surrounding a central core of nucleic acid. However, the discs with holes are probably not residual pieces of a particle from which the nucleic acid has been removed, but are more likely formed as such *in vitro* by disaggregated protein units reaggregating. Electron

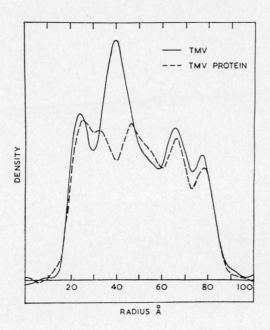

Fig. 9–3. Radial density distribution of tobacco mosaic virus (TMV) and reassembled protein showing a peak of 40Å in the virus but not in the reassembled protein and indicating the position of the nucleic acid chain (R. E. Franklin, A. Klug and K. C. Holmes, 1957, *in* The Nature of Viruses, Churchill, London).

micrographs could not show whether the nucleic acid fibres were axial or coaxial, but this point was settled by X-ray diffraction, which also gives precise information about particle width and the arrangement and number of protein sub-units.

This information required measurements not only on normal virus, but on particles made by reassembling disaggregated protein alone and on virus in which the heavy metals lead and mercury had been introduced by treating preparations with lead acetate and methyl mercuric nitrate. The treatment with lead probably substitutes lead for a proton in each of the protein sub-units (Fraenkel-Conrat and Narita, 1958) and mercury reacts with the sulphydryl group and labels the cysteine in the protein sub-unit (Fraenkel-Conrat, 1959). X-ray measurements on the lead-substituted virus showed that the rods are hollow with a hole of diameter 3.5–4.0 mμ

extending along the axis and that the maximum radius of the particles is about 9 mμ (Caspar, 1956). This is shown in Fig. 9–3, which gives the radial density distribution and shows that there are regions of high density at distances of 2.5, 4, 6.6 and 7.8 mμ from the centre. Particles made by reassembling protein only have a strikingly different radial density distribution from the virus, in that instead of a density peak at a radius of 4 mμ there is a density minimum (Franklin, 1956). This difference (Fig. 9–3) clearly indicates the position of the phosphate-sugar backbone of the nucleic acid thread, which is therefore embedded in the protein at about 2 mμ from the inward end of the sub-units and 5 mμ from their outward end.

Other X-ray measurements show that the protein sub-units and the nucleic acid thread are spirally arranged, with a pitch of 2.3 mμ, and there are 49 protein sub-units in every three turns of the spiral, i.e., every 6.9 mμ along the length of the virus particles (Franklin and Klug, 1955; Franklin and Holmes, 1956, 1958; Franklin, Klug and Holmes, 1957). The nucleic acid has 49 nucleotides per turn of the spiral, so there are three nucleotides for every protein sub-unit. Present information about the configuration of the parts of the virus is summarised by the drawing in Fig. 9–4 of a short segment of the virus in which the upper two turns of the protein spiral are omitted to show the position of the nucleic acid when held in place by the protein (Klug and Caspar, 1960). The position of the nucleic acid precludes it from attack by large molecules such as ribonucleases, but not from inactivation by readily diffusible substances such as formaldehyde and nitrous acid.

Some of the conclusions reached from X-ray diffraction analyses have been confirmed by electron microscopy. Thus the axial hole is shown by the negative-staining technique of Brenner and Horne (1959) using neutralised phosphotungstic acid. Appropriately stained preparations of reaggregated protein (Fig. 9–5) show, not only the hole very clearly, but also transverse striation with a periodicity of 2–2.5 mμ, corresponding to the pitch of the spiral; also pieces of rods standing on end show about 16 bumps, corresponding to the number of protein sub-units per turn of the spiral predicted by X-ray analysis (Nixon and Woods, 1960). Similar striations are less evident in stained preparations of normal virus; they perhaps show better in the reaggregated protein because the units are less firmly united or because the sites normally occupied by the nucleic acid can become filled with stain and make the spiral grooves more evident, but they have recently been clearly demonstrated in intact virus by Horne and Wildy (1961). Particles shadowed with metal

often have uneven outlines, but the only report of a regularly repeat
ing pattern is by Hart (1961), who found regular striations with a
periodicity of 2.3 mμ on some particles of normal virus lightly shad
owed with tungsten.

Fig. 9–4. A drawing of a short segment of tobacco mosaic virus in which
the last two turns of the protein spiral are omitted to show the configuration of
the nucleic acid when inside the framework of protein. There are 3 nucleotides
(shown as flat discs parallel to the axis) per protein sub-unit, spaced about 5Å
apart. (A. Klug and D. L. D. Caspar, 1960, Advanc. Virus Res. 7: 225).

The exact shape of the protein sub-units is unknown, but they
are possibly ellipsoids 7 mμ long and 2–2.5 mμ wide at their widest
point and they must taper down towards the outsides to give the
grooves detected by Franklin and Klug (1956). They are hexago-
nally close packed in the spiral out to a radius of about 5.5 mμ
where they are 2.1 mμ wide (Klug and Caspar, 1960). The units
are formed by the coiling of the polypeptide chain, and the position

f the cysteine residue, which is the 27th from the N-terminal end
: the chain, is given by X-ray measurements on mercury-substituted
irus; it is at a radial distance of 5.6 mμ from the axis of the particles,
'hich means it is about midway between the inner and outer surface
f the protein. As the C-terminal aminoacid, threonine, is removed
y carboxypeptidase from the intact virus, it must be near the outer
irface where the enzyme can reach it, whereas none of the several
nkages susceptible to attack by proteolytic enzymes is accessible

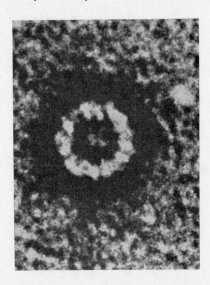

Fig. 9–5. Disc of reaggregated pro-
in of tobacco mosaic showing 16 sub-
its. Preparation stained with neutral
nosphotungstate. × 2,000,000. (H. L.
ixon and R. D. Woods, 1960, Virology
): 157).

ɔ these enzymes until the particles are disrupted and the protein
nits disaggregated. Reaggregating the protein into rods restores its
esistance to attack by proteolytic enzymes, presumably by again
1aking these linkages inaccessible to attack (Kleczkowski and van
{ammen, 1961). The orderly arrangement of protein units into rods
/hen preparations are acidified can be explained by the fact that the
ifferent surfaces of the units have different electrokinetic potentials
Kramer and Wittmann, 1958). Disaggregated protein moves more
lowly than intact virus towards the anode at pH values above 6,
/hich means that the units are less negatively charged on the parts
ɔwards the centre of the virus particle than on the outer, normally
xposed parts. When reaggregated into rods by lowering the pH to
•elow 6, or by exposure to ultraviolet radiation (Kleczkowski, 1959),
he mobility becomes the same as that of the intact virus in the same
onditions, showing that mobility is determined only by the way the
•rotein units are arranged and is independent of the nucleic acid.
'he orderly aggregation of the protein units when acidified can be

explained by the fact that the surfaces that are normally hidde
inside the virus particles become isoelectric and so cease to repel or
another before the surface that is normally towards the outsid
When protein is disaggregated by lowering the pH below pH 3.
it moves towards the cathode faster than intact virus at the san
pH, from which Kramer and Wittmann (1958) concluded that th
surfaces normally unexposed are then more positively charged tha
those normally exposed. In these conditions, the normally expose
parts will become isoelectric first when the pH is raised, so removir
the mechanism for the orderly coming together of the normally u
exposed surfaces, and the protein produces amorphous floccules i
stead of the rods.

The protein units are presumably notched at about 2 mμ fro
their inside ends to accommodate the thread of nucleic acid. Th
presence of the nucleic acid apparently stabilises the particles, f
whereas normal virus, and particles reconstituted from protein an
nucleic acid, remain whole when the pH is raised above 7, particl
consisting of reaggregated protein alone disaggregate.

Most workers assume that the protein sub-units are all identica
and this may be so, but protein preparations obtained by disruptin
tobacco mosaic virus by alkali are antigenically heterogeneous; i
gel diffusion tests they may give as many as six precipitation lin
when tested against virus antiserum, whereas virus or protein r
aggregated into rods gives only one line (Kleczkowski, 1960).
the individual units are identical, then it seems that the groups
six or so units that comprise the bulk of protein disrupted by alka
must differ from one another in the antigenic groups they expos
and many seem to expose groups that are hidden when the units a
assembled into rods.

Several strains of tobacco mosaic virus have been examined, b
all have the same basic structure, with the nucleic acid at a radi
distance of 4 mμ. Small differences suggest that, whereas the typ
strain may have 49.02 protein sub-units in three turns of the spira
strain U2 has 49.5 and cucumber virus 4 48.98, which, if all a
300 mμ long, means that U2 has one more and cucumber 4 two few
sub-units than the type strain (Klug and Caspar, 1960). The radi
density distribution of the bean form of the cowpea virus diffe
more from type tobacco mosaic virus than does any other examine
but even so its protein sub-units have the same general configur
tion and pack in the same way (Holmes and Franklin, 1958).

No other anisometric virus has been studied in anything like th
same detail as tobacco mosaic, but enough has been done to sugge

they probably have similar general structures. The best evidence comes from tobacco rattle virus, which, like tobacco mosaic virus also has rigid rod-like particles, but thicker and so more amenable to study by electron microscopy (Frontispiece). By studying shadowed mounts of partially degraded particles and unshadowed mounts stained with solutions of various heavy metals, Nixon and Harrison (1959) showed that particles are tubular, with a central hole approximately 4 mμ in diameter, and a width that varies between 17 and 25 mμ according to the treatment. Next to the central hole, which fills readily with lanthanum nitrate or uranyl acetate, is a region 1–1.5 mμ thick, which stains heavily with osmium tetroxide, phosphomolybdic and phosphotungstic acids. The rest of the particle stains only lightly but shows transverse bands 2.5 mμ apart along the length of the particles, suggesting the pitch of a spiral arrangement of protein units similar to that in tobacco mosaic virus. There is no direct evidence about the position of the nucleic acid, but it may be in that part of the particle that stains least, immediately outside the part lining the central hole; this is at a radial distance from the axis of about 5 mμ, which is, in proportion to total width, the same relative position as the nucleic acid in tobacco mosaic virus.

Of filamentous viruses, there is information about only potato X and sugar beet yellows. Early X-ray photographs (Bernal and Fankuchen, 1941) of virus X are compatible with a spiral structure, of similar pitch to tobacco mosaic virus, but with the sub-unit pattern repeating after two instead of three turns (Klug and Caspar, 1960). This virus has a very small surface potential, which probably accounts for the readiness with which it goes insoluble. It is almost stationary in an electric field at pH 7, but the disaggregated protein produced when the virus is disrupted at pH 10 is more mobile (Fig. 8–5). Hence, the parts of the protein units normally exposed seem to be less charged than those hidden inside the particles; this is the opposite from tobacco mosaic virus, and may explain why the protein precipitates as amorphous floccules instead of reaggregating into filaments when neutral solutions are acidified (Bawden and Kleczkowski, 1959). The negative staining technique applied to sugar beet yellows virus, which is about 10 mμ in total diameter, shows it to have a hollow central core 3–4 mμ in diameter, and a regular periodicity along its length of about 2.8 mμ (Horne, Russell and Trim, 1959). It seems probable therefore that it also is a spiral structure with a slightly larger pitch than tobacco mosaic virus.

Lucerne (alfalfa) mosaic virus. Lucerne mosaic virus differs strikingly from other anisometric viruses; not only is the length/width ratio of its particles much less, but it has rounded, closed ends, and its ratio of nucleic acid to protein is three times greater. Hence, a spiralling thread of nucleic acid embedded in a spiral of protein units is excluded as a possible structure; instead it seems to resemble more the isometric viruses in being essentially a protein shell containing nucleic acid, though this has not been established unequivocally. However, it is not hydrolysed by ribonucleases but is by trypsin (Ross, 1941), so clearly the protein but not the nucleic acid is accessible to enzymes. Shadowed virus preparations show no definite surface or internal structure, but it can be inferred from the lengths and widths of the shadows that the particles tend to flatten when dried. Their rigidity is increased by treating them with formaldehyde. Electron micrographs of particles mounted in sodium phosphotungstate sometimes show that the surfaces are covered with knob-like projections at right angles to the particles, and therefore most clearly shown at their edges. The projections show in two different patterns; in one they are equally spaced at a distance of 4–4.5 mμ; in the other they show at the corners of polygons, arranged in two rows parallel to the long axis of the particle, with the polygonal spaces in one row alternating with those in the next. Fig. 9–6 shows an electron micrograph of a virus preparation and a photograph of a glass model that may show how the projections are arranged on the virus particle. The points of attachment of the projections are at the corners of six interlocking hexagons, which cover the surface with the rows parallel to the long axis. At both ends of each row of hexagons there is a pentagon, with projections at each corner. The pentagons fit on the ends of the particles and conform to the general pattern that each knob-like projection is surrounded by three others and three spaces. The arrangement of the projections means that the model can stand in only two positions, which show the two patterns similar to those noted in electron micrographs of the virus. The projections on the model are longer in proportion to the width than those on the virus particle, which has a maximum diameter of about 18 mμ and the projections are probably about 2.5 mμ long (Gibbs, 1961).

Isometric viruses. The first indication that the viruses usually called spherical, which is what they seem in electron micrographs of shadowed preparations although they are polyhedrons, are shells of protein enclosing the nucleic acid came from the discovery that preparations of turnip yellow mosaic virus contained two kinds of par-

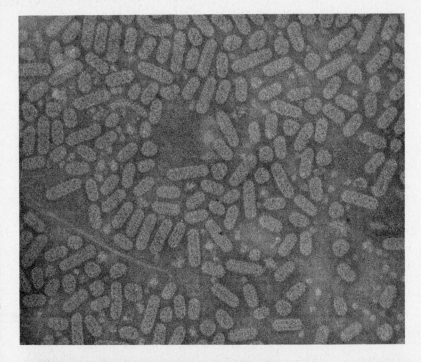

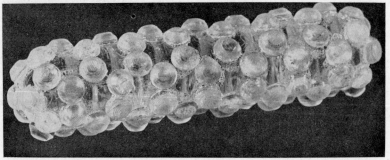

Fig. 9–6. Electron micrograph of purified preparation of alfalfa (lucerne) mosaic virus stained in phosphotungstate. × 175,000. *Below:* photograph of model showing possible arrangement of protuberances on the particles of alfalfa mosaic virus. (Photographs provided by Dr. A. Gibbs and Mr. H. L. Nixon).

ticles, of similar size and with similar properties attributable to their surface, but one of which consisted only of protein (Markham and Smith, 1949; Markham, 1951). A synthesis of results from X-ray diffraction studies and from electron microscopy of negatively stained preparations of both kinds of particles has given more information about the structure of this than of any other virus except tobacco mosaic. However, enough has been done with tomato bushy stunt (Caspar, 1956) and southern bean mosaic (Magdoff, 1960) to suggest that these have similar general structures. X-ray diffraction showed that the particles, whether containing nucleic acid or not, and whether naturally occurring particles of protein only or made from virus particles by degradation with alkali (Kaper, 1960) have icosahedral (532) symmetry (Klug and Finch, 1960a, 1960b). Hence, this symmetry is conveyed by the arrangement of protein units only. If these units were all structurally similar, there would need to be 60, as was pointed out by Crick and Watson (1956; 1957), who first suggested that a likely structure for these viruses was an arrangement of protein units packed in cubic-point symmetry. However, electron microscopy (Nixon and Gibbs, 1960; Huxley and Zubay, 1960) shows that the particles are composed of 32 protuberances, arranged so that 20 fall at the vertices of a pentagonal dodecahedron and 12 at the vertices of an icosahedron. Hence the units distinguished by electron microscopy, although they may be all chemically similar, are structurally different, for whereas 20 are arranged in twelve rings of 5, with each unit being shared between three adjacent rings, the other 12 are at the centres of these rings. Unlike tobacco mosaic virus, in which the morphological units seem identical with the chemical ones, i.e., the distinct polypeptide chains, the morphologically distinguishable units of turnip yellow mosaic virus are themselves composed of sub-units, regularly arranged, possibly six in the 20 similarly situated protuberances and five in the other twelve. The protuberances are probably not spherical, and may be ring- or disc-shaped. Differences between the X-ray diffraction patterns given by the two kinds of particles suggest that the nucleic acid has a definite structure and is not simply a randomly coiled thread. Markham (1959) suggests the thread may be cross-linked by polyvalent bases and Klug and Finch (1960a) conclude that this kind of structure, with parts of the nucleic acid in contact with the protein and with a similar symmetry to the protein, is compatible with present knowledge. The nucleic acid perhaps does something to hold the protein shell together, for the unit cell of virus particles is slightly smaller than that of particles containing protein only (Bernal and Carlisle, 1951); also it may affect their permeability to stains, for as Fig. 9–7 shows, some particles are deeply penetrated by phosphotungstate and these are presumably the ones without nucleic acid.

Negatively stained preparations of tomato black ring, raspberry ringspot and arabis mosaic viruses also all show some particles that are similarly penetrated by phosphotungstate (Harrison and Nixon,

)60); these again are probably free from nucleic acid, for infec-
vity depends on the presence of unpenetrated particles. All three
ave icosahedral particles, but nothing is yet known about the num-
er or character of the sub-units that presumably compose the pro-
ein shell of these viruses. The much larger virus, wound tumour,

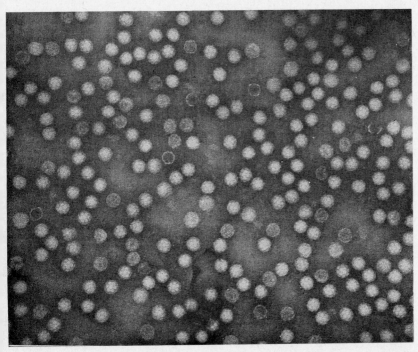

Fig. 9–7. Electron micrograph of purified preparation of turnip yellow
mosaic virus stained with phosphotungstate, showing arrangement of sub-units
and some particles penetrated by the stain, presumably because they are empty,
.e. do not contain nucleic acid. × 149,000. (Photograph provided by Mr.
H. L. Nixon).

is also an icosahedron about 60 mµ in diameter. Its surface consists
of 92 units about 7.5 mµ in diameter and its core, about 35 mµ in
diameter, stains heavily with uranyl acetate, indicating nucleic acid.
When the outside is disintegrated, strands about 3 mµ wide are released, presumably the nucleic acid coiled or folded, or combined
with some protein (Bils and Hall, 1962).

In summary, then, despite the considerable differences between
the gross sizes and shapes of different viruses, there is a general
similarity in their structure. Essentially, all seem to have their outside surfaces composed of regularly arranged protein units, with

their nucleic acid carried internally. The type of pattern in whic the protein units are arranged differs with different viruses, as als must be the position and orientation of nucleic acid relative to th protein covering. The structure suggests that virus particles forr by a process analogous to crystallisation, by the orderly aggregatio of similarly sized units into a three dimensional array. On thi analogy, the usual stimulus for crystallisation may be nucleic acic around which the protein units aggregate. The behaviour of pro tein from tobacco mosaic and turnip yellow mosaic viruses *in vitro* however, shows that it can aggregate in an orderly manner withou nucleic acid, and the natural occurrence of particles free from nuclei acid suggests that, *in vivo* also, other stimuli than virus nucleic acic may sometimes bring protein units into their set patterns.

REFERENCES

BANCROFT, J. B., and P. KAESBERG. 1960. Biochim. biophys. Acta 39: 519.
BAWDEN, F. C., and A. KLECZKOWSKI. 1959. Virology 7: 375.
——, and N. W. PIRIE. 1937. Proc. roy. Soc. B. 123: 274.
——, and ——. 1945. Br. J. exp. Path. 26: 294.
——, and ——. 1956. J. gen. Microbiol. 14: 460.
——, ——, J. D. BERNAL, and I. FANKUCHEN. 1936. Nature, Lond. 138: 1051.
BERNAL, J. D., and C. H. CARLISLE. 1951. Disc. Faraday Soc. 11: 227.
——, and I. FANKUCHEN. 1941. J. gen. Physiol. 25: 111.
BILS, R. F., and C. E. HALL. 1962. Virology 17: 123.
BODE, O., and H. L. PAUL. 1955. Biochim. biophys. Acta 16: 343.
BRANDES, J., and C. WETTER. 1959. Virology 8: 99.
BRENNER, S., and R. W. HORNE. 1959. Biochim. biophys. Acta 34: 103.
CASPAR, D. L. D. 1956. Nature, Lond. 177: 928.
CRICK, F. H. C., and J. D. WATSON. 1956. Nature, Lond. 177: 473.
——, and ——. 1957. Ciba Foundation Symposium on The Nature of Viruses p. 5. Churchill, London.
ELFORD, W. J. 1931. J. Path. Bact. 34: 505.
FRAENKEL-CONRAT, H. 1959. Symposium on Sulfur in Proteins (R. Benesch *et al.* eds.), p. 339. Academic Press, New York.
——, and K. NARITA. 1958. Symposium on Protein Structure (A. Neuberger, ed.) p. 249. Wiley, New York, and Methuen, London.
FRANKLIN, R. E. 1956. Nature, Lond. 177: 928.
——, and K. C. HOLMES. 1956. Biochim. biophys. Acta 21: 405.
——, and ——. 1958. Acta cryst., Camb. 11: 213.
——, and A. KLUG. 1955. Acta cryst., Camb. 8: 777.
——, and ——. 1956. Biochim. biophys. Acta 19: 403.
——, ——, and K. C. HOLMES. 1957. Ciba Foundation Symposium on The Nature of Viruses, p. 39. Churchill, London.
GIBBS, A. J. 1961. Properties of Lucerne Mosaic Virus and its behaviour in Lucerne Crops. Ph.D. thesis. University of London.
HALL, C. E. 1958. J. Amer. chem. Soc. 80: 2556.
HARRINGTON, W. F., and H. K. SCHACHMAN. 1956. Arch. Biochem. Biophys. 65: 278
HARRISON, B. D., and H. L. NIXON. 1959. J. gen. Microbiol. 21: 569.
——, and ——. 1960. Virology 12: 104.
HART, R. G. 1955. Proc. nat. Acad. Sci., U.S. 41: 261.
——. 1961. J. Mol. Biol. 3: 701.

OLLINGS, M. 1962. Nature, London 196: 962.

OLMES, K. C., and R. E. FRANKLIN. 1958. Virology 6: 328.

ORNE, R. W., G. E. RUSSELL, and A. R. TRIM. 1959. J. Mol. Biol. 1: 234.

——, and P. WILDY. 1961. Virology 15: 348.

UXLEY, H. E., and G. ZUBAY. 1960. J. Mol. Biol. 2: 189.

HNSON, J. 1951. Phytopathology 41: 78.

APER, J. M. 1960. J. Mol. Biol. 2: 425.

ASSANIS, B., and J. T. SLYKHUIS. 1959. Ann. appl. Biol. 47: 254.

LECZKOWSKI, A. 1959. Virology 7: 385.

——. 1960. Immunology 4: 130.

——, and A. VAN KAMMEN. 1961. Biochim. biophys. Acta 53: 181.

LUG, A., and D. L. D. CASPAR. 1960. Advanc. Virus Res. 7: 225.

——, and J. T. FINCH. 1960a. J. Mol. Biol. 2: 201.

——, and ——. 1960b. Ibid. 2: 434.

RAMER, E., and H. G. WITTMANN. 1958. Z. Naturf. 13b: 30.

AUFFER, M. A. 1938. J. biol. Chem. 126: 443.

AGDOFF, B. E. 1960. Nature, Lond. 185: 673.

ARKHAM, R. 1951. Disc. Faraday Soc. 11: 221.

——. 1959. In The Viruses (F. M. Burnet and W. M. Stanley, eds.) 2: 33. Academic Press, New York.

——, and K. M. SMITH. 1949. Parasitology 39: 330.

ÜLLER, H. O. 1942. Kolloidzschr. 99: 6.

IXON, H. L., and A. J. GIBBS. 1960. J. Mol. Biol. 2: 197.

——, and B. D. HARRISON. 1959. J. gen. Microbiol. 21: 582.

——, and R. D. WOODS. 1960. Virology 10: 157.

ICE, R. V., P. KAESBERG, and M. A. STAHMANN. 1953. Biochim. biophys. Acta 11: 337.

OSS, A. F. 1941. Phytopathology 31: 394.

CHACHMAN, H. K., and R. C. WILLIAMS. 1959. In The Viruses 1: 223. Academic Press, New York.

CHRAMM, G., G. SCHUMACHER, and W. ZILLIG. 1955. Nature, Lond. 175: 549.

TEERE, R. L. 1957. J. biophys. Biochem. Cytol. 3: 45.

AKAHASHI, W. N., and M. ISHII. 1953. Amer. J. Bot. 40: 85.

VETTER, C., and J. BRANDES. 1956. Phytopath. Z. 26: 81.

VILKINS, M. H. F., A. R. STOKES, W. E. SEEDS, and G. OSTER. 1950. Nature, Lond. 166: 127.

VILLIAMS, R. C., and R. L. STEERE. 1951. J. Amer. chem. Soc. 73: 2057.

——, and R. W. G. WYCKOFF. 1944. J. appl. Phys. 15: 712.

——, and ——. 1946. Ibid. 17: 23.

VYCKOFF, R. W. G. 1956. I. R. E. Trans. Med. Electron. PGME–6: 49.

VYCKOFF, R. W. G., and R. B. COREY. 1936. Science 84: 513.

Types of Inactivation

The inactivation of viruses *in vitro* is studied for two main rea‐
sons: one is in the hope of learning something about the kinds of
physical and chemical changes in virus particles that destroy infec‐
tivity, to understand what confers the property of infectivity; the
other is in the hope of finding specific parameters to aid diagnosis.
Many more viruses have been studied for the second than for the
first reason, and since Johnson (1927) pointed out the uncertainties
in identifying viruses from the symptoms they cause and that other
properties often have greater diagnostic value, most workers de‐
scribing what they consider to be a new sap-inoculable virus have
provided information about such properties as its thermal inactiva‐
tion point, longevity *in vitro,* and resistance to such agents as acid,
alkali or ethanol. This information is usually reported from meas‐
urements made in infective sap, for the simple reason that it is the
easiest medium in which to make them, but the relevance of such
measurements to the intrinsic properties of the virus is far from cer‐
tain. Sap is a variable and complex fluid; some of its many com‐
ponents readily coagulate and could well entrain virus particles in
their coagula; it contains enzymes of various kinds, salts and sugars,
and a wide range of complex organic substances; its constitution and
pH varies, not only between species, but within a species depend‐
ing on the age of the plants and the way they are grown. Also, the
traditional practice is to determine an end point, that is, the mini‐
mum treatment that prevents sap from infecting, and this has little
scientific meaning, for it will depend not only on intrinsic properties
of the virus but on its concentration in the sap and on the suscep‐
tibilities of the plants being inoculated. It would be far more mean‐

ingful to measure rates of inactivation and report treatments that decreased infectivity by a stated amount, say to a tenth. Despite their crudity, measurements of end-points in sap have some value for diagnosis, because viruses differ so much from one another in their stability. For instance, thermal inactivation points range from just over 40° to over 90°, and longevities *in vitro* from a few hours to many years. However, their value is limited to viruses that are unusually stable or unstable, and such tests are of little help in distinguishing between the many viruses with inactivation points between 50° and 60° and longevities of a few days.

Some of the viruses that soon inactivate in sap do so because the environment is unfavourable rather than because they are intrinsically unstable *in vitro*, for they survive much longer when purified and dissolved in water or buffer solutions. Oxidases and acidity are probably the most usual causes of viruses being more unstable in sap than when purified, but there is increasing evidence that some viruses may occur in sap as infective particles of more than one kind and that some kinds are quickly inactivated by other agents, perhaps ribonuclease. Some strains of tobacco rattle virus (Sanger and Brandenburg, 1961; Cadman, 1962) and of a tobacco necrosis virus (Babos and Kassanis, 1962) seem to occur mainly in forms susceptible to ribonuclease. Ribonucleases rapidly inactivate preparations of virus nucleic acid, but do not inactivate nucleoprotein particles, though pancreatic ribonuclease is a powerful inhibitor of infection by all viruses yet tested, particularly of infection in French bean. Most viruses are not hydrolysed by proteolytic enzymes, but potato virus X and lucerne (alfalfa) mosaic virus are, and trypsin is a moderate inhibitor of infection.

Separation of infectivity from serological specificity. Two contrasting types of inactivation have long been known. In one, loss of infectivity is accompanied by loss of serological specificity and of all other specific characters of the virus particles. In the other, infectivity is lost while the virus particles retain their characteristic morphology, gross physical properties and chemical constitution, and serological specificity. A third type has recently been recognised in which serological activity and specific physical properties are destroyed, while retaining some infectivity. The residual infectivity is ephemeral and readily lost in conditions where intact virus particles remain infective, which explains why this type of inactivation was for long not distinguished from the one in which infectivity and serological specificity are lost together. A fourth type should perhaps be added, in which the characteristic morphology and physical properties of virus preparations are destroyed, but serological specificity is retained although the character of serological reactions is changed. This fourth type is exemplified by the action on tobacco mosaic virus of alkali (Schramm, Schumacher and Zillig, 1955) and strong acetic acid (Fraenkel-Conrat, 1957); both treatments disrupt the virus particles to give small protein fragments, which still react with virus antiserum but behave like somatic instead of flagellar antigens; these fragments can be reaggregated into rods morphologically resembling virus particles, which then behave serologically like virus particles. Fraenkel-Conrat (1962) states that these treatments produce free nucleic acid that still retains some infectivity though less than possessed by nucleic acid produced by disrupting the virus at pH 7. However, exposure to pH 10.5 also produces much non-infective material that still has the morphological and serological behaviour of tobacco mosaic virus (Bawden and Pirie, 1957a). Whether these are particles in which the nucleic acid has been inactivated internally, or whether they are particles reassembled from disrupted protein and nucleic acid that has been free, is uncertain.

These different kinds of inactivation are explicable by what is known about the structure of virus particles and the role of the two main components. Whether or not preparations are infective is determined by the integrity of the nucleic acid, which is carried internally and plays little part in determining either the gross morphology of their particles or many of their physical properties, and has no part in their serological reactions. The morphology, main physical properties and serological behaviour of the viruses are determined by the integrity of the protein shells. Hence, treatments that destroy infectivity but not other specific characters are those that reach and affect the nucleic acid without greatly altering the protein shell. Treatments that destroy specific characters other than infectivity are those that denature the protein without impairing the integrity of the nucleic acid. Treatments that destroy all specific characters denature the protein and impair the nucleic acid, whereas those that inactivate and change serological behaviour, while preserving serological specificity, impair the nucleic acid and disrupt the protein shell, without denaturing the sub-units from which the protein shell is built.

Many and various treatments can destroy infectivity without impairing the integrity of virus particles, or affecting their crystallinity or gross physical and chemical properties. Some of these act generally, others with some but not all viruses. Among those that act generally are exposure to radiations of various kinds, and treatment with formaldehyde, nitrous acid, or oxidising agents. The latitude between exposures that destroy infectivity and those that affect the serological behaviour differs with different treatments and is greatest with radiations and formaldehyde, but the amount of latitude also differs with different viruses. Nitrous acid and hydrogen peroxide must be used with care, because they readily denature some viruses. Concentrations of H_2O_2 between 0.2 and 1% will inactivate potato virus without denaturing it, but concentrations above 1% denature and destroy serological activity, whereas tobacco mosaic virus is not denatured by even 5% acting for 5 hours. All these treatments do affect protein as well as nucleic acid, but their effects on protein while inactivating the nucleic acid are not such as to change its gross character.

Heating for minutes only at temperatures much below the thermal inactivation point will destroy the infectivity of some viruses while leaving their other properties unimpaired, but with others inactivation is closely correlated with the denaturation of the protein. Similarly, ageing in sap inactivates some viruses without affecting their serological behaviour. In general, it seems that viruses with isometric particles are those that can be readily inactivated by heat without being denatured. Table 10–1 shows the

TABLE 10–1

Effect of Heating Potato Virus X and Tomato Bushy Stunt Viruses for Ten Minutes at Various Temperatures and pH 6

Potato Virus X			Bushy Stunt Virus		
Temperature	Infectivity	Serological Titre	Temperature	Infectivity	Serological Titre
Unheated	108	1/256	Unheated	153	1/500
59°C.	94	1/256	50°C.	79	1/500
62°C.	29	1/128	60°C.	20	1/500
65°C.	2.5	1/8	70°C.	9	1/500
68°C.	0	No. ppt.	80°C.	2	1/500
			85°C.	0	No. ppt.

difference in behaviour between tomato bushy stunt, an isometric virus, and potato virus X, which has long thread-like particles, when heated for 10 minutes at various temperatures. Whereas bushy stunt virus loses much of its infectivity in 10 minutes at more than 30° below the temperature at which it begins to lose its serological activity, potato virus X loses infectivity only near the temperature at which its serological activity is also destroyed. Serological activity is lost when the protein is denatured, and protein denaturation has a large temperature coefficient, but loss of infectivity with tomato bushy stunt and similar isometric viruses has a small temperature coefficient. As will be shown later, the inactivation of infective nucleic acid from tobacco mosaic virus also has a small temperature coefficient. It seems, then, that the nucleic acid of isometric viruses can be affected, perhaps broken, by heating at temperatures well below those at which the protein is affected, whereas the nucleic acid is held more firmly in anisometric viruses where it is unaffected by heat until the protein framework begins to break down.

Heating of tobacco mosaic and other anisometric viruses was for long thought to be a treatment that destroyed infectivity and serological activity more or less simultaneously. However, by heating briefly above the thermal inactivation point and cooling rapidly, serological activity can be destroyed and preparations of infective nucleic acid obtained (Knight, 1956; Bawden and Pirie, 1959). Whether this is also true of other anisometric viruses has yet to be tested. Also, some other methods of denaturing viruses that were generally thought to destroy infectivity as well as serological specificity may also produce infective nucleic acid, provided precautions are taken to preserve its infectivity, and it is rather odd that this possibility has been so little studied. Disruption of tobacco mosaic virus by phenol (Gierer and Schramm, 1956) and by solutions of sodium dodecyl sulphate (Fraenkel-Conrat, 1956) are of this kind, and it was work with these reagents that first showed that the multiplying unit was not, as for long thought, the whole nucleoprotein particles.

Disruption with phenol has become the method of choice for producing infective preparations of virus nucleic acids, and a dozen or more plant viruses have been found to retain infectivity after this treatment. Indeed, as there seems to be no report of failure, the method seems to be generally applicable and its success perhaps explains the fact that other methods of disrupting viruses have been little tested. The infectivity of nucleic acid preparations usually reported is only a small fraction of that of the virus preparation before disruption, but this does not necessarily mean that much of the nucleic acid is inactivated by treatment with phenol. More likely the nucleic acid as freshly prepared has all the infectivity, but much of it becomes inactive between being applied to leaves and establishing infection.

There are several reasons for thinking that the intrinsic infectivity of the nucleic acid preparations is probably much greater than

sually evident by comparisons with intact virus. First, the relative
ifectivity of the two types of inocula depends greatly on the con-
ition of the test plants inoculated, and nucleic acid preparations
rom tobacco mosaic virus may have as much as 5% of the infectivity
f their parent virus preparations, per unit of phosphorus, when
ested on one lot of *Nicotiana glutinosa,* but have less than 0.001%
vhen tested on another lot (Bawden and Pirie, 1957a, 1959). Sec-
ndly, that much of the potential infectivity of the nucleic acid
reparations never becomes actual, is also strongly suggested by the
act that recombining the separate nucleic acid with protein can
reatly increase its infectivity (Fraenkel-Conrat and Singer, 1957).
Thirdly, Kassanis (1960) described conditions in which nucleic acid
reparations of a tobacco necrosis virus made with phenol are as
nfective as their parent virus preparations. This fact does not mean
hat this nucleic acid is intrinsically any more resistant than that
rom tobacco mosaic virus to nucleases or other inactivating sys-
ems encountered in inoculated leaves. More likely, it implies that
he tobacco necrosis virus itself is less protected against inactivation,
nd in this connection it may be relevant that mitochondrial prep-
rations from leaves inactivate the tobacco necrosis virus *in vitro,*
vithout destroying serological activity, so presumably act by affect-
ng the nucleic acid through the protein wall, but have no effect on
obacco mosaic virus (Bawden and Pirie, 1957b). Also, the tobacco
ecrosis virus depends much more than tobacco mosaic virus on the
hysiological condition of its host plants for its ability to infect, and
onditions that favour infection are similar to those that favour in-
ection by inocula of nucleic acid. Tobacco mosaic virus is rela-
ively indifferent to the physiological condition of the host cells and
urvives in cells where its nucleic acid and other viruses become
nactive. Its ability to do this presumably reflects its greater stabil-
ty, conferred by the greater protection afforded to the nucleic acid
by the way it is contained in the protein. Nucleic acids of all viruses
are probably at equal risk of inactivation when inoculated to leaves;
the risk to intact particles of different viruses will differ depending
on the extent to which their structure prevents potentially inactivating systems from affecting the nucleic acid. Hence, the smaller proportion of the initial infectivity reported in preparations of nucleic
acid from tobacco mosaic virus than from some other viruses probably reflects only the greater stability of tobacco mosaic virus rather
than the greater instability of its nucleic acid.

Few of the many other methods known of denaturing viruses and
separating the nucleic acid from the protein have yet been tested

to know whether they would yield infective nucleic acid, but nc all seem to. For instance, although nucleic acid separated fror tobacco mosaic virus by phenol retains its infectivity when expose to 8M urea, nucleic acid preparations made by disrupting the viru with 8M urea were not infective (Bawden and Pirie, 1957a). An method of separating the nucleic acid from the protein that break it probably inactivates, for there is evidence that the whole threa or particle of 2,000 nucleotides must be intact to be infective (Giere 1957; Ginoza, 1958). In addition to physical breaks, chemica changes in unbroken nucleic acid, such as deaminations or methyla tions, also destroy infectivity.

An unusual feature of virus inactivation by urea, is that the rat is minimal at 20° and is much increased by lowering the tempera ture to −10°. Different viruses differ in their resistance to inactiva tion by urea and in the way they break down; whereas the nuclei acid and protein separate from inactivated tobacco mosaic virus anc potato X virus but remain dissolved in the urea solution, inactivatec tobacco necrosis and tomato bushy stunt viruses precipitate in th urea and the precipitates contain nucleic acid (Bawden and Pirie 1940). Some other simple organic substances are more efficien inactivators than urea or commonly used solvents such as ethanc or acetone, whose precipitating and inactivating actions are mor widely known. Of 15 substances tested by Bawden and Piri (1940a), ranging from urethane, guanidine and related substances to pyridine, benzoate and salicylate, all except arginine and nicotin at 4M or less inactivated tobacco mosaic and other viruses at pH 7 Arginine or nicotine can produce reversible fibrous precipitates witl tobacco mosaic virus; without salt even 20% nicotine has no effec on the appearance of purified virus preparations, but in the presenc of a little salt opaque precipitates slowly separate which can b immediately dispersed by shaking and which again slowly reforn in solution left undisturbed. Some of the other substances whei dilute also act as precipitants without inactivating, but most have ε threshold concentration above which they produce irreversible changes. This concentration differs with different viruses and, a: with urea, is less for potato X than for tobacco mosaic and is stil larger for tomato bushy stunt; most of the substances separate the nucleic acid from the protein of potato X and tobacco mosaic, but not from tomato bushy stunt virus, whereas sodium dodecyl sulphate does from all three.

Inorganic salts, too, can inactivate, but again effects differ greatly with different viruses. Ammonium sulphate inactivates tobaccc ringspot virus, separating the nucleic acid from the protein (Stanley, 1939), but this effect seems not to have been reported with other viruses. Strontium nitrate (Pirie, 1954) at over 1M splits tobacco mosaic virus into denatured protein and free nucleic acid, which is apparently uninfective, but denatures tomato bushy stunt virus without separating the nucleic acid from the protein. Inactivation produced by mercuric chloride has been claimed to be partially reversible (Went, 1937; Manil, 1938), but the claims were not confirmed by Kassanis and Kleczkowski (1944) and may have arisen because at concentrations above 0.01% this salt acts as an inhibitor of infection. Even M/10 pH 7 phosphate buffer, the medium in which viruses are commonly suspended for use as inocula, is not necessarily always benign. For example, it can inactivate potato virus X, though whether it does so depends on the temperature and what other materials are present. At 37°, particularly with chloroform present, denaturation is rapid, and a protein coagulum separates that is free from nucleic acid. The denaturation proceeds for some hours at a uniform rate, but then almost stops and leaves a small residue of serologically active material that is only poorly infective. It does not proceed detectably at 20°, and at 37° is prevented by the presence of proteins or plant sap.

Drying, and freezing and thawing, are treatments to which viruses are often subjected and whose effects differ with different viruses and the type of preparation treated. The ability of tobacco mosaic virus to withstand drying has long been known and taken as a parameter that distinguished it from most others. However, the retention of some infectivity after drying is no evidence that drying has been without effect. Drying and redissolving purified tobacco mosaic virus approximately halves its birefringence, infectivity and serological activity, and this decrease is repeated in successive dryings. The changed material is susceptible to hydrolysis by trypsin, and incubating repeatedly dried preparations with trypsin will recover a residue of material with the birefringence and serological activity of the original virus preparation (Bawden and Pirie, 1937a). The main distinction of tobacco mosaic is that it withstands slow drying at air temperature in leaves or sap, whereas most other viruses do not. However, when dried rapidly in small leaf pieces at 1° many viruses retain some infectivity (McKinney, 1947) and most do so when dried rapidly from frozen sap. Of 39 viruses tested by Hollings and Lelliott (1960), only potato virus A was not infective after freeze-drying and most showed little further loss of infectivity when stored under vacuum for many months.

Most isometric viruses seemed to be little affected by freeze-drying, but several viruses with elongated particles lost much of their infectivity.

Although viruses retain infectivity after freeze-drying in sap, they might fail to do so in other environments, for freezing and thawing alone can denature some. Tomato bushy stunt (Bawden and Pirie, 1938b, 1943) and tomato ringspot (Stanley, 1940) viruses, for example, survive freezing and thawing in either leaves or sap, but not in salt-free purified preparations. The inactivation of bushy stunt virus increases with increasing virus concentration in the solutions frozen, with decrease in pH below 6, and with increase in the length of time the fluids are kept frozen. Inactivation can be prevented by sugars, glycerol, proteins and salts; the protection afforded by different salts depends on their salt:ice:water eutectic temperature. In sap, not only is the virus dilute and the pH well above the isoelectric point, but the salts, sugars and other components also protect against inactivation. Virus in sap dialysed and brought to pH 3 is inactivated by freezing. Loss of infectivity is usually accompanied by loss of serological activity and the precipitation of denatured protein, but effects are complex and infectivity is sometimes lost while serological activity is retained. In many conditions where freezing inactivates bushy stunt, other viruses are unaffected, but these others have not been studied over a range of conditions and there may be conditions in which they would be inactivated. Purified preparations of tobacco mosaic virus, for example, although unaffected by repeated freezing and thawing at neutrality, lose some infectivity and serological activity when frozen at pH 3.

Of the many treatments known to inactivate viruses, very few have been studied kinetically and only three with both intact virus and nucleic acid. These are heating, formaldehyde and exposure to radiations, and the remainder of this chapter will be devoted to these. All of them, like many other inactivation reactions, are reactions of the first order, that is, the fraction remaining infective decreases exponentially with increasing time of treatment. This means that plotting the logarithm of the proportion remaining unchanged against the time of treatment gives a straight line, from the slope of which can be calculated the specific reaction rate. Such curves when obtained in radiation work are often referred to as "single-hit" and are assumed to be evidence that single quanta of energy inactivate. However, this is not a necessary assumption, for denaturation of protein by heat is also a first-order reaction but it is rarely suggested that this happens from "a single hit." Approximation to a first-order reaction means simply that, in constant conditions, there is a constant probability, $p = e^{-k}$, that any given particle still active will become inactive during the next minute.

Heating. In sharp contrast to the vast numbers of virus preparations that have been heated to find thermal inactivation points, there have been very few tests on the kinetics of inactivation. Lauffer and Price (1940) found that tobacco mosaic virus denatured and became insoluble at 70° in pH 7 phosphate buffer according to first-order kinetics, and by measuring reaction rates at different temperatures calculated an energy of denaturation slightly greater than 150 kcal/mole. They showed that loss of infectivity proceeds about three times faster than protein denaturation, but probably has about the same energy of action. Lauffer (1959) gives the entropy of activation for loss of infectivity as about 2.3 entropy units higher than for denaturation, for which it is approximately 350 units. These values differ strikingly from those reported by Ginoza (1958) for the inactivation of the nucleic acid in 0.1 M phosphate buffer at pH 7.1; he calculated that inactivation has heat and entropy of activation of 19 kcal/mole and −19.5 entropy units, respectively, showing the much greater lability of infectivity when the nucleic acid is freed from its protein.

From his results Ginoza concludes that the nucleic acid is likely to be a single strand, that inactivation does not involve the disordering of secondary structure maintained by many weak bonds, and he suggests, from the first-order kinetics, that inactivation results from the hydrolysis of a single phosphodiester bond. He interprets the negative entropy of activation as indicating that a cyclic triester is made as an intermediate form in the activated state of the molecule. In intact tobacco mosaic virus, this bond is presumably protected from hydrolysis until heating affects the protein, whereas in other viruses, such as tomato bushy stunt, it may not be stabilised in the same way, but open to attack inside the protein wall. The kinetics of inactivation of such viruses and their nucleic acids have not been compared, but the little that has been done with tomato bushy stunt virus suggests that the rate at which this loses infectivity at around 55° may not differ greatly from that reported by Ginoza (1958) for free nucleic acid of tobacco mosaic virus. It is surprising that the heat inactivation of viruses and their nucleic acids has been so little studied for it might provide information on the linkages between protein and nucleic acid in different viruses; also, it would be interesting to know whether viruses that differ greatly in their resistance to heating owe this fact solely to their protein or whether their nucleic acids also differ in resistance.

It is not only comparisons of intact viruses with their free nuclei acids that are lacking, for very little has been done on the kinetic of inactivation of intact viruses. Fig. 10–1 (Price, 1940) gives re sults with four viruses heated each at a single temperature in sa

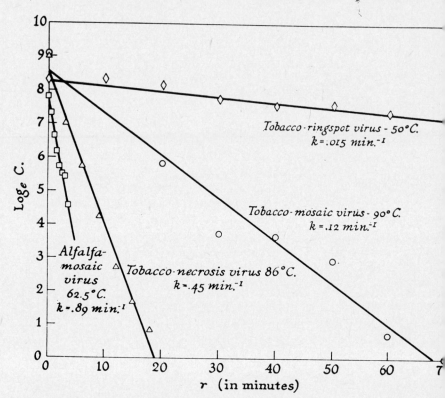

Fig. 10–1. Curves illustrating the thermal inactivation rate of tobacco ring-spot virus at 50°, tobacco mosaic virus at 90°, of tobacco necrosis virus at 86° and of alfalfa (lucerne) mosaic virus at 62.5°: all were heated in sap freshly extracted from infected plants. (W. C. Price, 1940, Arch. ges. Virusforsch. 1: 373).

for different lengths of time and shows that inactivation of each approximates to first-order kinetics. Preparations of tobacco ne-crosis viruses also inactivate according to first-order kinetics, but these contain two fractions that inactivate at greatly different rates. The ratio of the two fractions differs at different temperatures of heating; at 50°, the more slowly inactivating fraction is about one-tenth the total infectivity, but its proportion decreases with increas-ing temperature of heating (Babos, 1962).

Formaldehyde. The general ability of formaldehyde to inacti-
ate viruses and kill bacteria without destroying their antigenicity
s evident from its extensive use to produce vaccines. As the virus
roteins have many groups that can react with formaldehyde, such
groups seem not to be concerned with the antigenic specificity, for
o difference has been reported between the antigenicity of infective
irus preparations and those inactivated with formaldehyde. While
he whole nucleoprotein of tobacco mosaic virus was thought to be
eeded to infect, the claim was made that some changes in the pro-
ein were reversible and that reversing them also partially restored
nfectivity (Ross and Stanley, 1938). However, Kassanis and Klecz-
owski (1944) not only failed to confirm the reversibility of colour
hanges and failed to reactivate treated preparations, but also
howed that inactivation by formaldehyde at different pH values
ave preparations whose residual infectivity was not correlated with
he extent of colour changes in the protein. Similarly, Fischer and
auffer (1949) found that, although loss of infectivity and changes
n electrophoretic mobility both proceeded according to first-order
inetics, the first proceeded many times faster than the second.
This work, incidentally, led to the first suggestion, since confirmed,
hat the nucleic acid does not contribute to the net charge of tobacco
nosaic virus at pH 7.)

From studying the rate of inactivation in 2% formaldehyde at
lifferent temperatures, Lauffer (1959) gives the enthalpy of activa-
ion as 23 kcal/mole and the entropy of activation as 2.8 entropy
mits, suggesting that inactivation results from simple chemical re-
ctions involving a single bond. Because the rate of inactivation is
ndependent of pH changes between 2.5 and 8.5, he suggests that
ormaldehyde reacts with a group that is not ionised in this range,
f which the ribose and amino groups on the bases in the nucleic
cid are possibilities. As it does against heating, the protein of
obacco mosaic virus also protects the nucleic acid against formalde-
yde, and the nucleic acid inactivates much faster when free than
vhen contained in intact virus particles. There has been no similar
vork on the kinetics on inactivation of other plant viruses by form-
ldehyde, but some other viruses are much more readily inactivated
han tobacco mosaic virus.

Radiations. All kinds of radiation, ultrasonic, ionising or ultraviolet, have the common property of inactivating viruses without
lestroying their serological specificity. Exposure to ultrasonic ra-
liation, however, does affect the serological behaviour of tobacco
nosaic virus, for it breaks the rod-shaped particles. When liquid

crystalline preparations are exposed to the radiation, they imme diately lose their spontaneous birefringence and the extent to whic they show the phenomenon of anisotropy of flow decreases as th time of exposure is increased. The infectivity and the number of par ticles about 300 mμ long both decrease exponentially with tim (Oster, 1947), and, though there may be other changes, it is plausibl to assume that inactivation is a consequence of the nucleic aci breaking. As irradiation is extended and the average length c broken particles decreases, the preparations precipitate with ant serum more slowly, over only a narrower range of antigen/antibod ratios, and the precipitate becomes more granular; in other word: the precipitation behaviour changes from being characteristicall flagellar to more nearly resembling that of bacterial somatic ant gens. Broken particles combine with proportionally more antibod than unbroken ones, but the breaking seems not to produce any ne\ antigenic determinants (Malkiel, 1947). The effects of ultrasoni radiation on other viruses, or on the free nucleic acid of tobacc mosaic virus, have yet to be determined.

Of ionising radiations, X-rays have been the most used, and ther is evidence that they inactivate tobacco mosaic virus by breakin the nucleic acid thread inside the intact protein wall (Lauffe 1959), which seems not to protect the nucleic acid as it does agains inactivation by many other treatments, for the dose response rela tions are similar whether intact virus or free nucleic acid are irra diated (Ginoza and Norman, 1957). The intrinsic viscosity o the nucleic acid isolated from virus preparations inactivated by X rays is less than that from active preparations, and the intrinsic vis cosity of infective nucleic acid decreases when it is inactivated b X-rays (Lauffer, 1959). The intrinsic viscosity with particles o uniform width depends on their length, so inactivation probabl reflects the breaking of a chemical bond in the main chain of th nucleic acid, a bond that breaks equally readily in intact virus a in the free nucleic acid. It has long been known that, unlike en zymes, with which the volume sensitive to inactivation by X-ray and other ionising radiations is the whole volume of the particle the sensitive volume of viruses is less than this (Lea, Smith, Holme and Markham, 1944). The proportion of the volume of the whol particle comprising the sensitive volume is greater with isometri than with anisometric viruses, and is so small with tobacco mosai virus that Lea and Smith suggested in 1942 that the whole nucleo protein particle was not the smallest infective unit. It is remarkabl that their important suggestion had so little effect that it took an other 15 years to establish that the infective unit was the nucleic acid, and to appreciate that measuring target volumes from inactivation by ionising radiations was a method of estimating, not sizes of virus particles, but the volumes occupied by their nucleic aid.

The fact that target volumes of viruses, calculated on the assumption that single ionisations inactivate, agree reasonably well with the proportion of virus particles occupied by their nucleic acid, is itself an indication that inactivation does result from a single change in the nucleic acid. The idea that ultraviolet radiation also inactivates because of a single hit is widely held, but there is no evidence for it except that inactivation follows first-order kinetics. Indeed, although it does not disprove the idea that virus particles are inactivated by single quanta of radiation energy that happen to hit regions essential for infectivity, the extreme smallness of the quantum yields does throw some doubt on it; a particle of tobacco mosaic virus, for example, absorbs on the average about 25,000 quanta of radiation at 254 mμ before it is inactivated (Oster and McLaren, 1950; Kleczkowski, 1954). Kleczkowski (1960) pointed out that first-order kinetics are equally satisfied by postulating that irradiation produces a state of disequilibrium, caused by excitations in various parts of the particle, during which inactivation could occur at any time without any definite number of quanta needing to be absorbed by any one specific site. The disequilibrium hypothesis could also explain the deviations from first-order kinetics that have occasionally been noted, and does not demand, as does the single-hit hypothesis, postulating that radiation absorbed by any part other than some critical small unit, perhaps a single pyrimidine ring, does not affect infectivity.

Different viruses, and different strains of tobacco mosaic virus, differ considerably in their susceptibility to inactivation by ultraviolet radiation. Action spectra have been determined only with strains of tobacco mosaic virus. The spectrum of the type strain is unusual, and plotting inactivation efficiency against wavelength gives no peaks. The line rises as the wavelength shortens below 290 mμ, slowly at first and then rapidly below 250 mμ (Hollaender and Duggar, 1936; Siegel and Norman, 1958; Rushizky, Knight and McLaren, 1960). The action spectrum differs from the absorption spectrum of the intact virus, its nucleic acid or its protein. The action spectrum of strain U2, which is more susceptible than the type strain to inactivation, slightly resembles the absorption spectrum of nucleic acid, for it has a peak near to 260 mμ. The nucleic acid behaves very differently, and its action spectrum closely resembles its absorption spectrum. Infective particles made by recombining nucleic acid with virus protein give action spectra similar to undisrupted virus (Rushizky et al, 1960).

The protein of tobacco mosaic virus protects from inactivation, not only or even mainly by shielding the nucleic acid from the radiation, but by making it more resistant to inactivation by absorbed radiation. Thus, to inactivate by the same proportion, the nucleic acid within particles of tobacco mosaic virus must absorb five times more radiation per unit weight than when it is freed from the protein (McLaren and Takahashi, 1957). The protein of different strains protects from inactivation to different extents, for whereas the type strain and U2 when intact differ greatly in their susceptibility, their free nucleic acids inactivate at the same rate (Siegel, Wildman and Ginoza, 1956). The protection is presumably afforded by the bonds between the nucleic acid and the protein, and the differences suggest that these bonds differ in different strains. In this context it may be relevant that strains that differ in their susceptibility to inactivation by ultraviolet radiation are those with distinctive amino-acid compositions and that are only distantly related serologically. To what extent the protein of other viruses protects their nucleic acids from inactivation by the radiation has not been studied, but results with a tobacco necrosis virus suggest that it is little if any more resistant than its free nucleic acid (Kassanis, 1960). Recombining the nucleic acid and protein of type tobacco mosaic virus may not restore all the bonds normally occurring, for preparations of reconstituted virus were more readily inactivated than undisrupted virus (Siegel, Wildman and Ginoza, 1956).

Some irradiated bacteriophages and animal viruses (Luria and Dulbecco, 1949; Henle and Liu, 1951) show the phenomenon of "multiplicity reactivation," which means that proportionally more infections are obtained with concentrated than with dilute inocula, suggesting that damaged particles that are inactive singly can infect when several enter the same cell. There is no evidence that damaged particles of any plant virus can supplement one another in this way. Indeed, instead of increasing more than proportionally with increasing concentration of inocula, the numbers of infections often decrease, because concentrations of inactive virus of 0.01% or more can inhibit infection by active particles. However, effects differ with difference viruses, and whereas irradiated tomato bushy stunt does not inhibit infection by active particles of this or of other viruses, irradiated tobacco mosaic and tobacco necrosis viruses do, giving a small unspecific inhibition and a large specific one (Bawden and Kleczkowski, 1953). The effect probably comes from the protein of the viruses, for the protein produced by disrupting tobacco mosaic virus with alkali similarly inhibits infection by active particles (Bawden and Pirie, 1957a). One effect of ultraviolet radiation on this disrupted protein is to aggregate it regularly into discs and short rods (Kleczkowski, 1959).

Photoreactivation. The phenomenon called photoreactivation was discovered by Kelner (1949), who found that the proportion of *Streptomyces griseus* conidia that survived ultraviolet irradiation was greater when they were exposed to visible light than when kept in darkness. Visible light has since been found to counteract effects of irradiation in many biological systems, including viruses and leaf cells of flowering plants (Bawden and Kleczkowski, 1952, 1953). The infectivity of irradiated virus preparations is not affected by exposing them to visible light *in vitro*, and the phenomenon with them operates through some light-sensitive system in the host cells; it shows by the fact that the proportion of virus remaining infective after irradiation is greater when inoculated plants are kept in the light than when they are kept in darkness. Keeping plants in light or darkness before they are inoculated has no effect on the proportion of virus in irradiated preparations that infects. Whether visible light reverses changes in the virus particles caused by the radiation, or in some other way aids damaged particles to infect, is unknown, but it seems to reverse changes in a bacteriophage and so probably also does so with plant viruses (Lennox, Luria and Benzer, 1954). Whether or not photoreactivation operates, the inactivation of viruses follows first-order kinetics; its operation has the effect of slowing the apparent rate of inactivation and is equivalent to decreasing the dose of radiation by a factor that is characteristic of different viruses. Thus, with a radiation dose v, the proportion p of remaining active virus is $p = e^{-k_{\text{dark}} v}$ without photoreactivation and $p = e^{-k_{\text{light}} v}$ with. The ratio of $k_{\text{dark}}/k_{\text{light}}$ indicates the extent of photoreactivation, which as Table 10–2 shows, differs with different viruses. Of the viruses tested, tobacco mosaic (several strains) and tobacco rattle give a ratio of 1, indicating no photoreactivation, but all others give a larger ratio, and potato virus X shows more photoreactivation than any other yet tested. It may be significant that the two with a ratio of 1 both have particles of the same kind, rigid rods, whereas the particles of the others are either flexible threads or isometric. Tables 10–2 also shows that, although intact tobacco mosaic and tobacco rattle viruses do not show the phenomenon, their nucleic acids do when irradiated free from their proteins (Bawden and Kleczkowski, 1955, 1959; Harrison and Nixon, 1959). This could

TABLE 10–2

Photoreactivation with Different Viruses and Inocula

Preparation Irradiated	$\dfrac{k\text{dark}^*}{k\text{light}}$
(1) Tobacco mosaic virus	
(a) type strain	1.0
(b) Datura strain	1.0
(c) Strain U2	1.0
(d) Bean form of cowpea strain	1.0
(e) Tomato aucuba strain	1.0
(2) Tobacco rattle virus	1.0
(3) Tomato bushy stunt virus	1.2
(4) Rothamsted tobacco necrosis virus	1.2
(5) Cucumber mosaic virus	1.5
(6) Tobacco ringspot virus	1.9
(7) Cabbage black ring virus	2.0
(8) Potato virus X	3.0
(9) Nucleic acid from type tobacco mosaic virus	2.0
(10) Nucleic acid from tobacco rattle virus	1.9

* Value of k derived from $p = e^{-kt}$ where p is the proportion of original infectivity remaining after exposure to ultraviolet radiation for t minutes: $k$dark is value from plants placed in darkness after irradiation and $k$light from plants in the light. The extent of photoreactivation is shown by the amount by which the ratio $k$dark/$k$light exceeds 1.0.

have two interpretations: (1) the protein may protect the nucleic acid against the kind of damage that is photoreactivable or (2) it may prevent light from counteracting the damage. That the first is correct is shown by the fact that photoreactivation occurs only with nucleic acid irradiated as such and not with inocula of nucleic acid prepared from virus irradiated while intact.

Photoreactivation increases the infectivity of irradiated virus preparations but does not restore it to its initial level. Hence, irradiation produces at least two kinds of change in the nucleic acid, one reversed in infected cells by visible light and the other not. The fact that inactivation, with or without photoreactivation, follows first-order kinetics suggests that the two kinds of change are independent of one another, for if the reversible change in a particle had to precede the irreversible one, the proportion of infective particles with photoreactivation would depart from first-order kinetics (Kleczkowski, 1960).

To halve the infectivity of nucleic acid preparations from type tobacco mosaic virus requires the absorption of about 0.4 joules per mg with photoreactivation and 0.2 without, about one-tenth as much as needs to be absorbed by the nucleic acid in intact virus (Bawden and Kleczkowski, 1959; McLaren and Takahashi, 1957).

Hence about half the energy absorbed by free nucleic acid is concerned with causing the kind of damage reversible by photoreactivation and half with the irreversible damage. Apparently the protein protects the nucleic acid from being damaged by 90% of the energy it absorbs and this includes the 50% that would have caused reversible damage. The protection against the reversible kinds of damage seems to be provided equally by the kind of bonding in all strains, but protection against the irreversible kind of change differs with different strains.

Experiments with irradiated potato virus X allow the process of photoreactivation to be approximately timed. At 20°, most reversibly damaged particles require about 30 minutes after being inoculated to leaves before they reach the state in which their ability to infect is affected by exposing the leaves to visible light; once in this state exposure to daylight for 15 minutes gives almost complete reactivation, but the state is temporary and within an hour most particles have become irreversibly inactivated in plants kept in darkness. Irradiated nucleic acid of tobacco mosaic virus becomes susceptible to photoreactivation almost immediately after leaves are inoculated, and inoculated leaves must be exposed to visible light within an hour of inoculation to get any effect (Bawden and Kleczkowski, 1955, 1959). Some irradiated particles are reactivated by exposing leaves to light of 80 f.c.; others need brighter light, but increases in intensity above 600 f.c. produce no additional response. The action spectrum of photoreactivation has not been determined, but tests with filters show that it is light of wavelength shorter than 450 mμ that is effective (Chessin, 1958).

The structural changes in the nucleic acid of viruses responsible for inactivation by ultraviolet radiation have still to be determined. As pyrimidines are the more susceptible, it is reasonable to suspect changes in them rather than in the purines. A reversible hydrolysis in the double bond between positions 5 and 6 in cytosine and uracil is a possible explanation for the reversible change (Shugar and Wierzchowski, 1958), but although this is reversed by some treatments, whether light does so has yet to be determined.

REFERENCES

BABOS, P. 1962. Rep. Rothamst. exp. Sta. for 1961, p. 104.
———, and B. KASSANIS. 1962. Virology 18: 206.
BAWDEN, F. C., and A. KLECZKOWSKI. 1952. Nature, Lond. 169: 90.
———, and ———. 1953. J. gen. Microbiol. 8: 145.
———, and ———. 1955. Ibid. 13: 370.
———, and ———. 1959. Nature, Lond. 183: 503.
———, and N. W. PIRIE. 1937. Proc. roy. Soc. B. 123: 274.

240 PLANT VIRUSES AND VIRUS DISEASE

BAWDEN, F. C., and N. W. PIRIE. 1938. Brit. J. exp. Path. 19: 66.
————, and ————. 1940. Biochem. J. 34: 1258.
————, and ————. 1940a. Ibid. 34: 1278.
————, and ————. 1943. Ibid. 37: 70.
————, and ————. 1957. J. gen. Microbiol. 17: 80.
————, and ————. 1957a. Ibid. 16: 696.
————, and ————. 1959. Ibid. 21: 438.
CADMAN, C. H. 1962. Nature, Lond. 193: 49.
CHESSIN, M. 1958. Ann. appl. Biol. 46: 388.
FISCHER, M. A., and M. A. LAUFFER. 1949. J. Amer. chem. Soc. 71: 3800.
FRAENKEL-CONRAT, H. 1956. J. Amer. chem. Soc. 78: 882.
————. 1957. Virology 4:1.
————. 1962. Surv. biol. Progr. 4: 59.
————, and B. SINGER. 1957. Biochim. biophys. Acta 24: 540.
GIERER, A. 1957. Nature, Lond. 179: 1297.
————, and G. SCHRAMM. 1956. Nature, Lond. 177: 702.
GINOZA, W. 1958. Nature, Lond. 181: 958.
————, and A. NORMAN. 1957. Nature, Lond. 179: 520.
HARRISON, B. D., and H. L. NIXON. 1959. J. gen. Microbiol. 21: 591.
HENLE, W., and O. C. LIU. 1951. J. exp. Med. 94: 305.
HOLLAENDER, A., and B. M. DUGGAR. 1936. Proc. nat. Acad. Sci., Wash. 22: 19.
HOLLINGS, M., and R. A. LELLIOTT. 1960. Plant Pathology 9: 63.
JOHNSON, J. 1927. Wis. Agric. exp. Sta. Res. Bull. 63.
KASSANIS, B. 1960. Virology 10: 353.
————, and A. KLECZKOWSKI. 1944. Biochem. J. 38: 20.
KELNER, A. 1949. Proc. nat. Acad. Sci., Wash. 35: 73.
KLECZKOWSKI, A. 1954. Biochem. J. 56: 345.
————. 1959. Virology 7: 385.
————. 1960. Ann. N.Y. Acad. Sci. 83: 661.
KNIGHT, C. A. 1956. Meth. Enzymology 3: 684.
LAUFFER, M. A. 1959. Biochemistry of Viruses, p. 167. Pergamon Press, New York
————, and W. C. PRICE. 1940. J. biol. Chem. 133: 1.
LEA, D. E., and K. M. SMITH. 1942. Parasitology 34: 227.
————, K. M. SMITH, B. HOLMES, and R. MARKHAM. 1944. Parasitology 36: 110.
LENNOX, E. S., S. E. LURIA, and S. BENZER. 1954. Biochim. biophys. Acta 15: 471
LURIA, S. E., and R. DULBECCO. 1949. Genetics 34: 93.
MCKINNEY, H. H. 1947. Phytopathology 37: 139.
MCLAREN, A. D., and W. N. TAKAHASHI. 1957. Radiation Res. 6: 532.
MALKIEL, S. 1947. J. Immunol. 57: 55.
MANIL, P. 1938. C. R. Soc. Biol., Paris 127: 1464.
OSTER, G. 1947. J. gen. Physiol. 31: 89.
————, and A. D. MCLAREN. 1950. J. gen. Physiol. 33: 215.
PIRIE, N. W. 1954. Biochem. J. 56: 83.
PRICE, W. C. 1940. Arch. ges. Virusforsch. 1: 373.
ROSS, A. F., and W. M. STANLEY. 1938. J. gen. Physiol. 22: 165.
RUSHIZKY, G. W., C. A. KNIGHT, and A. D. MCLAREN. 1960. Virology 12: 32.
SANGER, H. L., and E. BRANDENBURG. 1961. Naturwissenschaften 48: 391.
SCHRAMM, G., G. SCHUMACHER, and W. ZILLIG. 1955. Z. Naturf. 10b: 481.
SHUGAR, D., and K. L. WIERZCHOWSKI. 1958. Postepy Biochem., Polska Akad. Nauk
  4: 243.
SIEGEL, A., and A. NORMAN. 1958. Virology 6: 725.
————, S. G. WILDMAN, and W. GINOZA. 1956. Nature, Lond. 178: 1117.
STANLEY, W. M. 1939. J. biol. Chem. 129: 405.
————. 1940. Ibid. 135: 437.
WENT, J. C. 1937. Phytopath. Z. 10: 480.

Virus Multiplication

Viruses are invisible and multiply only inside cells, plant viruses usually in multicellular tissues bounded by a cuticle, so their multiplication cannot be observed directly. Future developments in electron microscopy, especially improvements in techniques for preparing thin sections, together with methods for selecting cells at known intervals after they have become infected, may show exactly where and how viruses multiply, but this is still a distant prospect. Meanwhile, conclusions about the sequence of events between a plant contracting infection and new virus becoming detectable within it can be only tentative. This is not because phenomena occasioned by these events are lacking but because their interpretations are uncertain and derive plausibility largely from the extent to which they fit the behavior of such bacterial viruses as T2 coliphage, about whose multiplication much more is known. A discussion of how plant viruses multiply is perhaps best introduced by summarising this knowledge about T2 and by pointing out some differences between bacteriophages and plant viruses that make extrapolation from one to the other something that calls for caution.

The three major differences are: (1) T2 differs chemically from plant viruses in containing deoxy ribose and not ribose nucleic acid; (2) tadpole-shaped, with a complicated tail consisting of a central core surrounded by a contractile sheath and ending in six threads, T2 is morphologically much more complex than even the largest known plant virus; (3), and no doubt because of (2), it organises its own transmission and spreads unaided, whereas plant viruses depend on other organisms to transmit them.

Infection by T2 has long been known to be followed by an "eclipse phase" during which the virus apparently disappears, for

extracts from newly infected bacteria are not infective, do not read
with T2 antiserum, and contain nothing recognisable as virus pa
ticles in the electron microscope. This remained unexplained unt
the discovery that infection entails little except the virus nuclei
acid entering the infected bacterium, a fact first established b
using as inocula bacteriophages labelled either with radioactiv
sulphur in their protein or with radioactive phosphorus in the
nucleic acid, and confirmed by electron microscopy. The infectio
process begins by T2 particles attaching themselves tail first to th
bacterium, at first loosely and then firmly. The tail contains a
enzyme able to soften the wall of the bacterium, and also about 10
molecules of adenosine triphosphate, the hydrolysis of which pro
vides the energy for the sheath to contract. After this has hap
pened, the nucleic acid moves from the head, down through th
core of the tail into the bacterium, leaving the empty membrane
of the head adhering to the outside of the bacterium. Similar empt
particles can be produced by subjecting T2 to osmotic shock, whic
releases the nucleic acid from their hexagonal heads and destroy
their infectivity, but leaves them with their specific antigenicit
unimpaired and still able to attach themselves specifically to ho
cells.

The failure to detect T2 particles in bacteria disrupted durin
the eclipse phase, therefore, is simply explained, for there is non
to detect. It is a phase during which the virus nucleic acid fir
apparently associates with, or becomes part of, the genetic syster
of the bacterium, whose metabolism then changes in various way
the most striking being the synthesis of 5-hydroxymethylcytosin
which T2 nucleic acid contains in place of the cytosine usual i
deoxyribose nucleic acids and which has not been detected in un
infected bacteria. Exposure to ultraviolet radiation early in th
eclipse phase readily prevents infection from developing, but resis
ance to this inactivation soon increases and, after a while, inactiva
tion curves change from the straight lines obtained initially to curve
of a "multi-hit" type, suggesting that more than one unit now ha
to be inactivated to prevent infection from developing. The pro
tein metabolism of infected bacteria also alters, but whether coir
cident with or after the synthesis of T2 nucleic acid is uncertai

The reappearance of infectivity in bacterial extracts coincide
with the first occurrence of the characteristic tadpole-shaped pa
ticles early in the second half of the period between infection an
lysis of the bacterium. From then on, both infectivity and the nun
bers of such particles increase linearly with time until the bacteriu
lyses. Shortly before the tadpole-shaped particles occur, protei

with the serological specificity of T2 becomes detectable and electron microscopy shows, first round particles of a similar size to the head of the bacteriophage and, later, such particles with tails but still lacking nucleic acid and infectivity. These protein particles of different forms and complexities almost certainly represent stages in the formation of T2 particles, but by what mechanisms they are put together and their heads come to contain the nucleic acid is unknown. The assembly may not demand exacting conditions, for tobacco mosaic virus particles can be reassembled *in vitro* by a process reminiscent of crystallisation, in which disaggregated protein comes together in a regular manner around the nucleic acid, but T2 particles are so much more complex that this analogy may well be inappropriate. However, there can be little doubt that the actual formation of T2 particles differs from what is usually regarded as a multiplication process and results from assembling already existing parts; if any part directly multiplies or replicates, this seems to be only the nucleic acid, which also causes the other parts to be made and later combines with them to produce complete virus particles.

Plant viruses show many phenomena that can plausibly be interpreted as indicating they behave much like T2. Many results obtained from work on their multiplication are compatible with the idea that the nucleic acid of infecting particles becomes freed from its protein and enters some cell component, where it is protected from inactivation and either replicates or organises its synthesis elsewhere. There are also observations compatible with the idea that virus protein is synthesised separately from the nucleic acid and the two are then assembled into complete virus particles. Indeed, there is little that conflicts with this current concept of infection and virus multiplication, and no better one can be advanced. It is, therefore, particularly important to stress that there is no unequivocal evidence to support it and that it rests on unproven interpretations of phenomena. Plausible as are current interpretations of many phenomena, plausibility is no guarantee of correctness. Ideas about virus multiplication have often changed greatly in the past and may well do so in the future. Meanwhile, let us examine some of the phenomena, and try to distinguish between what is established and what is inferred.

Detecting and measuring virus increase. The usual method of studying factors that affect virus multiplication is to inoculate leaves with virus, wash them to remove surplus inoculum from their surface, then macerate them at intervals and assay the successive extracts for their virus content. In this way, reproducible curves showing changes in virus content with time after inoculation can be obtained with a given inoculum and host, provided conditions are kept constant. After an interval ("latent period"), the length of which depends on the temperature, the virus content of the inoc-

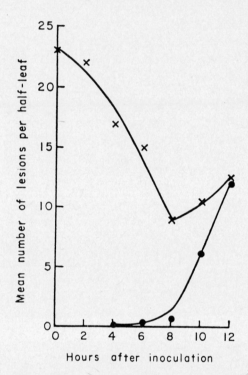

Fig. 11–1. The relative infectivities of extracts made from French bean leaves at different intervals after they were inoculated with either intact tobacco necrosis virus (X—X) or its nucleic acid (O—O) and then kept at 24°. The extracts were inoculated to other French bean plants and the results are the mean number of lesions produced per half-leaf on these plants. (B. Kassanis, 1960, Virology 10: 353).

ulum and the sensitivity of the assay method, newly produced virus becomes detectable and the content of successive extracts then increases rapidly. The latent period has obvious similarities with the "eclipse phase," except that, when the initial inoculum is concentrated enough to give the shortest interval between inoculating and detecting new virus, leaf extracts made during the interval are usually infective (Harrison, 1956b; Kassanis, 1959, 1960). Even this difference disappears when the nucleic acids of plant viruses are used as inocula, for leaf extracts made within a few hours of inoculation are then not infective(Fig. 11–1).

The time when new virus first becomes detectable is also more clearly evident with inocula of nucleic acid than with intact virus. This has led to conclusions that new virus is produced sooner by inoculating with nucleic acid, which in turn have been advanced as evidence that intact virus releases its nucleic acid before it can multiply and that the time needed for the release is indicated by the difference between the latent periods obtained with the new types of inocula. However, the difference found by different workers differs greatly: the one of 10 hours reported by Schramm and Engler (1958) at 23° is about the length of the latent period found by other workers for inoculations with intact tobacco mosaic virus (Yarwood, 1952) and four times as long as the difference reported by Kassanis (1959). Whether even the shorter difference is meaningful can be questioned, because the time when new virus first becomes detectable, and the amount that is detectable in successive extracts for some time afterwards, depends on the number of infections in the leaves being sampled and can be made to differ by far more than four hours simply by changing the concentration of the initial inoculum. Similarly, although new virus can be unequivocally demonstrated sooner in leaves inoculated with the nucleic acid of tobacco necrosis virus (Kassanis, 1960), this does not mean it was necessarily produced any sooner. As Fig. 11–1 shows, extracts from leaves inoculated with intact virus were the more infective at this time and the infectivity of successive extracts was still decreasing. Hence new virus could have been produced simultaneously in similar amounts in both lots of leaves, but in those inoculated with intact virus this amount would have been too little to compensate for the inactivation of the inoculum that was apparently still continuing.

The reason for the inactivation in inoculated leaves of such stable viruses as tobacco mosaic and tobacco necrosis has still to be determined, although leaves contain systems that inactivate tobacco necrosis *in vitro* (Bawden and Pirie, 1957). It is also unknown whether the infectivity of successive extracts made during the latent period falls because the stability of virus particles changes during an essential step in the process of initiating infection or because surplus inoculum is inactivated by processes irrelevant to infection. Interpretation of the changes in infectivity is complicated by the need to wound leaves to produce infections and by the uncertainty about the proportion of inoculum retained by a washed leaf that actually infects. Washing unrubbed leaves with water removes

more than 99% of virus that is simply sprayed over them, wherea
about 6% remains on leaves rubbed before they are washed (Yar
wood, 1952; Harrison, 1956a). Washing immediately after rubbing
slightly decreases the number of infections obtained, whereas an
hour or so later it has no effect. These results again can be fitted
into the story of bacteriophage infection. Thus, the virus retained
by rubbed leaves may be retained because it has become specifically
attached to infection sites, and the fact that washing soon ceases to
affect infection may mean that attachment is at first more loose than
it is later. However, equally, virus retained by rubbed leaves may
be mechanically entrained in wounds and washing may have no
effect after an hour simply because wounds through which viru
particles might earlier have escaped are now healed.

Although washing removes most of the virus rubbed over leaves
about 1,000,000 particles remain for every lesion that develops
How many of these actually engage in infection and how many are
incidental is unknown, but the need to apply such numbers to get
an infection makes it impossible to decide the significance of the
fall of infectivity during the latent period or to know exactly what
the first rise in infectivity reflects. The rise obviously shows newly
produced virus that is stable in leaf extracts, but whether this is the
first infective material that is formed or whether it is even the first
crop, or generation, of stable virus particles is less certain. Experi
ments with viruses and hosts that give necrotic local lesions, such
as tobacco mosaic in *Nicotiana glutinosa* or tobacco necrosis in
French bean, suggest that the fall in infectivity may largely reflect
the inactivation of surplus inoculum and that the rise may not begin
until some time after new virus has been formed, because infectivity
continues to fall until shortly before lesions become visible, when
some hundreds of mesophyll cells are already infected and dying at
each lesion. If, as there is reason to think, inoculation introduces
virus only into epidermal cells, this implies that a cycle of infection
and virus multiplication in the epidermis occurs undetected and
that there is a second cycle in the mesophyll before the infectivity
of leaf extracts starts to increase.

Further evidence for this conclusion comes from exposing inoculated leaves to ultraviolet radiation at different times after inoculation. Moderate exposures inactivate virus in the epidermis but not
in deeper tissues, and there comes a time when exposures many
times greater than those that earlier prevented lesions from developing no longer do so. This time, which is presumably when virus
has become established in the mesophyll, is approximately half the
interval between inoculation and when new virus becomes detect-

ble in leaf extracts (Harrison, 1956a). As it is also about the same ime when removing the epidermis no longer prevents lesions form- ng in leaves inoculated with cucumber mosaic (Welkie and Pound, 958) or tobacco mosaic virus (Dijkstra, 1962), there is good reason o correlate it with virus moving into deeper tissues. What is less vell established is the identity of the virus that moves, whether it s from the inoculum or is virus newly produced in the epidermis. f it is from the inoculum it takes half the latent period to move hrough the epidermis. This is a possibility that cannot be excluded, ut it seems much more probable that the virus that moves was roduced in the epidermis; not only is it an unlikely coincidence hat the inoculum would take as long to move through the epidermis s does a cycle of infection and virus production in the mesophyll, ut evidence will be given later suggesting that virus from the inocu- um undergoes changes much sooner than the mesophyll becomes nvaded.

Thus, the evidence favours the conclusion that, although infec- ivity tests detect smaller amounts of virus than any other method, hey fail to detect virus produced by the first cycle of infection. Various explanations can be offered. The infective material first roduced may be unstable in leaf extracts although able to move nto and infect nearby cells; nucleic acid might fit this requirement. Or the first-formed virus may all become specifically and firmly at- ached to infection sites in nearby sites and never become free in eaf extracts. Analogies for these two suggested types of behaviour are provided by the behaviour of some strains of tobacco rattle (Sanger and Brandenburg, 1961; Cadman, 1962) and tobacco ne- rosis (Babos and Kassanis, 1962) viruses, which cause lesions in- volving hundreds of cells but sap from such lesions is not infective or only slightly so; extracting the lesions with phenol gives highly nfective inocula, but whether this means that the infective material was already present in the host cells as nucleic acid or as virus par- ticles contained in some cell component not disrupted when making customary leaf extracts, is uncertain. Such possibilities for failing to detect multiplication sooner cannot be excluded, but a simpler explanation is that the first-formed virus, although enough to infect many nearby cells in the infected leaf, is not enough to make leaf extracts infective. To be infective, extracts need to contain more than a million virus particles per ml, and there is no reason to con- sider that such a concentration would be achieved immediately virus is first produced in the epidermal cells infected at inoculation.

Understandably enough, virus increase has been most studied with viruses and hosts with which infection is readily obtained and virus multiplication is readily demonstrable. With such virus-host combinations, once new virus becomes detectable, the infectivity of successive leaf extracts increases rapidly, giving a normal kind of growth curve, rising steeply for some days and then flattening. This increase will reflect increasing virus content of already infected cells and increasing numbers of cells becoming infected as the virus moves through the inoculated leaf. Most workers have not distinguished between these two factors influencing the content of successive leaf extracts, but Harrison (1956a) concluded that whereas the amount of a tobacco necrosis virus in extracts from French bean leaves continued to increase at 22° for a week or more after inoculation, the virus content of cells reaches its maximum in about 36 hours after they become infected. When fully infected such cells contain about a million particles; this also seems to be the order of magnitude that tobacco mosaic virus particles average in tobacco leaf cells, with large hair cells containing about 10^8 (Nixon, 1956). As we shall largely be concerned with viruses in hosts where they reach these large populations in infected cells and also readily move from cell to cell within inoculated leaves, it is perhaps well to stress that this behaviour may be exceptional rather than general, for the expectation that virus multiplication is readily detectable in all host plants can lead to invalid conclusions. It is, indeed, highly probable that many plants reported as immune to a given virus may be hosts, but with the virus multiplying only in cells directly infected at inoculation, or spreading only to few cells and not reaching a concentration large enough in leaf extracts to provide an inoculum.

Virus multiplication is not always readily demonstrable in plants that undoubtedly are hosts because they produce necrotic local lesions, so failure to demonstrate it in symptomless ones is obviously not conclusive evidence that they are insusceptible. Further, different hosts differ greatly in their susceptibility to infection and an inoculum of tobacco mosaic virus that readily infects and leads to a large virus content in tobacco leaves may fail to multiply detectably in another host, such as *Rhoeo discolor*, which is both more resistant to infection and also supports virus multiplication much less well. This plant has been described as immune to infection when inoculated with intact virus but susceptible when inoculated with nucleic acid (Gordon and Smith, 1960), which if true would be strong circumstantial evidence for the idea that infection necessitates the nucleic acid separating from the protein and that some plants are immune because they lack the mechanisms able to disrupt virus particles. However, *R. discolor* can be infected by intact virus, but inoculum needs to be very concentrated, which inevitably means that much virus remains attached to the rubbed leaves even after they are thoroughly washed. This complicates the interpretation of subsequent assays, for the virus multiplies so little in some infected leaves that, even after many days, extracts from them may be no more infective than immediately after inoculation. Inocula of concentrated nucleic acid leave no residual infectivity, so extracts made immediately after inoculation are not infective and any infectivity demonstrable later clearly indicates multiplication, even though it may be less than that of leaves immediately after they are inoculated with concentrated virus solutions.

The extent to which tobacco mosaic virus increases in R. discolor depends greatly on the conditions in which inoculated leaves are kept; at high light intensities multiplication is usually enough to give extracts 6 days after inoculation that are more infective than extracts made immediately after, but in dim light the later extracts often never reach the infectivity of the first. However, the infectivity of successive extracts usually falls at first and then rises, indicating that new virus has been produced. In plants that seem not to be hosts the infectivity of successive extracts falls steadily and those made three or more days after inoculation are usually not infective (Bawden, 1961).

Light intensity can also greatly affect the extent to which tobacco mosaic virus increases in plants that are more susceptible and better hosts than R. discolor. For example, when inoculated pieces of tobacco leaf are floated in water or nutrient solution, a technique much used to study factors that affect virus increase, extracts from pieces kept in the light contain much more virus than those from pieces kept in darkness, and those floated in solutions of sucrose and $Ca(H_2PO_4)_2$ contain more than those floated in water (Bawden and Kassanis, 1954).

Assays, whether of infectivity, antigen content or some other specific character, made on successive extracts are often reported as though they directly indicate the extent of virus multiplication, but whether they always do is another matter. What they measure are changes in the relative amounts of infective particles or related materials that are released in the extracts and are stable there. Increases shown in successive assays are doubtless primarily determined by the extent of virus multiplication, but they may well be affected by other factors. Not all the virus in a leaf passes into the sap when leaves are ground and pressed, and it is assumed rather than established that a constant proportion of that present is always released. If it is not, but different proportions are released from leaves containing different amounts, the assays will measure what is released

rather than what has been produced in the leaf. Similarly, if infec
tive particles differ in their stability in sap at different stages of the
multiplication cycle, the assays will indicate only the stable ones and
not necessarily the true amount of multiplication. Further, assay
may underestimate virus multiplication, because, in addition to mul
tiplying, virus may also be inactivating in the leaf. There is evi
dence that this happens in some conditions, and it must be accepted
as a possibility even in conditions where there is no evidence for it

Evidence that virus is inactivated *in vivo* comes mainly from
work with infected plants kept at high temperatures, but there is no
reason to assume that inactivation does not also occur more slowly
at lower temperatures. Indeed, that it does is strongly suggested by
the fact that the temperature at which the virus content of succes
sive leaf extracts increases fastest is often much above the tempera
ture at which the leaves ultimately give extracts containing the
most virus. The rates of all biological processes depend on tem
perature and are increased by increasing temperatures up to an
optimum. Different processes have different optima and when con
flicting processes, such as virus synthesis and degradation, are pro
ceeding simultaneously, assays will not show either process unequiv
ocally but only the balance between the two. Table 11–1 shows the

TABLE 11–1

The Relative Amounts of a Tobacco Necrosis Virus in Extracts from Inoculated
French Bean Leaves Kept at Different Temperatures

Temperature	Intervals Between Inoculation and Sampling		
	23 Hours	47 Hours	71 Hours
	Relative Virus Content [*]		
10	1	3	37
14	2	422	3,935
18	31	3,875	33,750
22	208	19,100	158,000
26	79	3,015	7,550
30	6	97	163

[*] The relative virus amounts were calculated by multiplying the number of lesions
produced by the highest dilution of each extract assayed by its dilution.

relative contents of a tobacco necrosis virus in successive extracts
from leaves kept at six different temperatures after inoculation. The
virus obviously multiplies over the whole range tested, and there is
little doubt that increases in temperature up to 22° increased the
rate of multiplication, but what happens at higher temperatures is

less certain. Multiplication may proceed fastest at 22°, but this is made doubtful by the fact that lesions appear sooner at higher temperatures. Probably the optimum is above 22°, but the fact is obscured by effects on the rate of inactivation, which become increasingly important as either the temperature or virus content increases. Evidence that this happens comes from results of putting bean plants that have already been at 22° for two days after inoculation and so contain a considerable amount of virus, at 30°; although, as Table 11–1 shows, the virus multiplies at 30°, leaf extracts made after a day at 30° will contain less virus than those made when the plants were transferred from 22° (Harrison, 1956b).

Although tobacco necrosis viruses may inactivate in leaves more readily than some others, there is no reason to think they are exceptional. The very different tobacco mosaic virus also inactivates at 36° (Kassanis, 1957), and most viruses whose multiplication has been studied ultimately reach higher concentrations in plants below rather than above 20°, although they initially increase faster at higher temperatures. Some viruses may create conditions in their hosts that inactivate them, for having increased rapidly for several days to reach a maximum, they then decrease very rapidly. Alfalfa (lucerne) mosaic virus is a striking example of this phenomenon (Ross, 1941); the virus content of successive extracts from infected plants is greatest at about two weeks after inoculation and then decreases so much that within another two weeks it will be less than one-tenth the maximum. Most other viruses behave differently, and having reached their maximum content remain at or around this for considerable periods, provided the host plants are well supplied with nutrients and their other growing conditions are unchanged. The content achieved differs greatly with different viruses, and it may be significant that only viruses that are unusually stable *in vitro* give extracts containing large amounts of virus.

Initiation of infection. Presumably the sequence of events that culminates in virus multiplying in cells that become infected by inoculation is repeated in each cell that becomes infected subsequently by virus spreading from cell to cell, but there is no evidence that this is so and knowledge about the infection process is limited to cells that become infected by inoculation. This evidence comes from three main types of work; studies of treatments that interfere with the establishment of infection, of which the most used have been pancreatic ribonuclease and exposure to ultraviolet radiation; studies of photoreactivation of virus damaged by ultraviolet radiation; comparisons of the differences between leaves inoculated with intact virus particles and with virus nucleic acid. Selected results from these various lines of work can be pieced together to form a story consistent with the idea that a first step in the normal infection process is for the virus nucleic acid to separate from its protein and become associated with some cell component in a way that protects it from inactivation, but there is nothing that establishes this definitely and there are results that make it open to question.

The fact that the infectivity of successive extracts made from inoculated leaves falls before it begins to rise has already been commented on and is *prima facie* evidence that viruses stable *in vitro* become unstable in leaves. Whether this fall depends on changes in virus particles that are initiating infection is uncertain, but the fact that it does not become appreciable until some hours after other changes can be detected in the inoculated leaves, and is still continuing after new virus has been formed in them, does perhaps indicate that what is being inactivated is mostly surplus inoculum.

The first change in the state of virus particles in inoculated leaves shows by the failure of washing with water, or of dipping in solutions of pancreatic ribonuclease, to prevent infections. This need mean no more than that the wounds produced in cells by inoculation have healed and that virus particles can no longer escape or the enzyme enter. Pancreatic ribonuclease is a powerful inhibitor of infection when inoculated along with any virus yet tested, although its inhibiting action differs greatly in different host species; it does not destroy virus particles *in vitro*, but rapidly hydrolyses their nucleic acids (Loring, 1942; Kleczkowski, 1946). Applied to leaves after they have been inoculated with viruses, it inhibits infection less than when applied before or when contained in the inoculum, and has little effect one hour after inoculation (Bawden and Harrison, 1955; Bawden and Kleczkowski, 1955), although Casterman and Jeener (1955) reported effects with tobacco mosaic up to 6 hours when inoculated leaves were infiltrated instead of being dipped or rubbed with solutions. Casterman and Jeener suggest that the enzyme inhibits infection because it hydrolyses the virus nucleic acid when it becomes free from the protein as an initial step in the infection process. This is a possibility that cannot be denied, but is a plausible explanation for the behaviour of the enzyme rather than establishing that the nucleic acid does become free, and there is much to be brought against the idea. First, there are other substances that are powerful inhibitors of infection but have no ribonuclease activity. Secondly, leaf ribonucleases, which readily hydrolyse virus nucleic acids *in vitro*, are not powerful inhibitors of infection. Thirdly, pancreatic ribonuclease inhibits infection of *Rhizobium* sp. by bacteriophages, which there is no reason to think contain ribonucleic acid (Kleczkowski and Kleczkowski, 1954). Fourthly, it has considerable effects on cell metabolism, and these effects, like those caused by exposing leaves to ultraviolet radiation, could be what prevent infection rather than any direct action of the enzyme on the virus nucleic acids.

Further evidence for the idea that viruses soon change their state and become susceptible to inactivation in inoculated leaves comes from photoreactivation studies on potato virus X (Bawden and Kleczkowski, 1955). Two changes are indicated by putting plants in light or darkness at different intervals after inoculation with appropriately irradiated preparations. At first, as *in vitro*, the ability of damaged particles to infect is not affected by visible light; a few particles move from this to the second state within 15 minutes at 20°, but most take 30 minutes and some as long as 2 hours. In this state, a few minutes' exposure to daylight is all that is needed to change the particles so that they then can infect and cause lesions, but it is an unstable state and particles not photoreactivated within an hour or so are irreversibly inactivated. Comparable tests have yet to be made with irradiated nucleic acid from potato virus X, so it is unknown whether this would be photoreactivable sooner than inocula of intact virus particles, but it may be significant that irradiated nucleic acid from tobacco mosaic virus seems to become photoreactivable almost immediately it is inoculated to leaves (Bawden and Kleczkowski, 1960). Indeed, unless such leaves are exposed to visible light within 30 minutes of inoculation, most of the damaged nucleic acid seems to be irreversibly inactivated, for later exposure has little effect on the numbers of infections. Comparable tests with intact tobacco mosaic virus cannot be made, because the nucleic acid in intact particles is protected against the kind of radiation damage that is reversed by visible light (Bawden and Kleczkowski, 1959). To draw conclusions from inoculations with intact particles of one virus and nucleic acid of another is a highly questionable procedure, but obviously the results do fit a pattern suggesting that intact particles of potato virus X may have to release their nucleic acid before they can be photoreactivated and that, while in this state *in vivo*, they are at risk of irreversible inactivation.

Exposing leaves to ultraviolet radiation at different intervals after they are inoculated with either intact virus particles or nucleic acid preparations provides further circumstantial evidence for the idea that infection normally entails the nucleic acid becoming free, and indicates a series of changes occurring in infected cells. Irradiation can prevent infections from developing, but the amount required to do so differs at different intervals after inoculation. After inoculating with intact virus, there is a period during which a constant amount of radiation produces a constant effect, but afterwards the resistance of infection centres to inactivation increases steadily. The duration of this period depends on the temperature and on the identity of the virus or virus strain; at 20° it is about 2 hours with tobacco

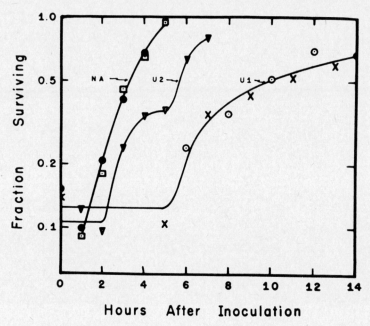

Fig. 11–2. The survival of infective centres when leaves were exposed to ultraviolet radiation at different times after inoculation with intact type tobacco mosaic virus (open circle and X), intact strain U2 (triangle), nucleic acid of type strain (solid circle) and U2 nucleic acid (square). Exposure to radiation, nucleic acids and intact U2, 90 seconds: intact type strain, 5 minutes. (A. Siegel, W. Ginoza and S. G. Wildman, 1957, Virology 3: 554).

necrosis virus and the U2 strain of tobacco mosaic virus and about 5 hours with the type strain of tobacco mosaic virus (Bawden and Harrison, 1955; Siegel and Wildman, 1956). An explanation for this lag period as being the time required for the virus nucleic acid to separate from the protein was suggested by Siegel, Ginoza and Wildman (1957), who showed that it was abolished by using nucleic acid as inoculum and that the infection centres initiated by nucleic acids of the two strains of tobacco mosaic virus increased their resistance to inactivation simultaneously (Fig. 11–2). Infection centres initiated by the nucleic acids from tobacco necrosis virus and red clover mottle virus also start to increase their resistance to inactivation almost immediately after inoculation (Kassanis, 1960; Bawden and Sinha, 1961), so the abolition of the customary lag period by the use of this form of inoculum is probably a general phenomenon.

If it were established that infection entails the nucleic acid separating from the protein, there would be little need to question the interpretation of the lag period as the time taken for this to happen, but rather more caution is needed before accepting that the differences between behaviour of nucleic acid and intact virus prove such separation to be necessary. What the radiation experiments show is that infection centres initiated by nucleic acid increase their resistance to inactivation by ultraviolet radiation sooner than those initiated by intact virus. As both kinds of inocula lead to the same end result, new virus and local lesions, their effects must coincide somewhere, but where is open to question. Because infection centres initiated by both increase their resistance to inactivation by irradiation, it is plausible to assume they coincide at this early stage, but this is only an assumption. The increased resistance quickly gained by nucleic acid may come from a process quite different from the one whereby infective centres initiated by intact virus slowly increase their resistance. The nucleic acid of tobacco mosaic virus is much more readily inactivated by irradiation when free than when combined in virus particles, and if the nucleic acid were to combine with some cell component to form a complex in which it was as well protected as in intact virus particles, this would immediately enhance its resistance to inactivation. Hence, it may be that the free nucleic acid acquires resistance sooner because it dresses, rather than that the intact virus is slower because its nucleic acid has to undress.

Observations on other differences between the behaviour of inocula of intact virus and free nucleic acid have also been advanced as evidence for the idea that normal infections involve removing the protein from the virus nucleic acids. The claims that inocula of nucleic acid lead to new virus being formed sooner were discussed earlier in this chapter and shown to be of doubtful validity. Similarly open to question is the conclusion that inocula of nucleic acid lead to lesions being produced sooner (Fraenkel-Conrat, Singer and Veldee, 1958) and that the difference between the time when half the final number of lesions produced by each kind of inoculum can "be defined as the average time required for the protein to be stripped off the intact virus" (Fraenkel-Conrat, 1959). When the two kinds of inocula are applied to opposite halves of the same leaves, the first lesions will appear simultaneously on the two halves, provided there is not a great disparity between the total numbers of lesions produced. When there is, lesions will appear first on those halves that ultimately produce the most. The difference between the two kinds of inocula, whether of tobacco mosaic or tobacco necrosis viruses (Kassanis, 1960), is that inocula of intact virus continue to produce lesions over a much longer period. In other words, infections with nucleic acid are better synchronised. This difference does not require the explanation that intact virus particles must undress to infect, for it is plausibly explained by the greater instability of the nucleic acid. Nucleic acid that does not quickly take some step in the infection process that stabilises it seems to become inactivated, and the almost synchronous behaviour of infections by nucleic acid may be a character necessitated by its fragility *in vivo*.

Evidence for this fragility of nucleic acid *in vivo* also comes from irradiation experiments. Exposing leaves to ultraviolet radiation can render them insusceptible to infection by viruses to which they are normally susceptible (Bawden and Kleczkowski, 1952), permanently when the leaves are kept in darkness for some hours after irradiation but only temporarily when kept in the light. In other words, the capacity of the leaves to support infection can be destroyed by radiation and photoreactivated. When leaves are inoculated with intact tobacco mosaic virus immediately after appropriate irradiation, exposing the leaves to light increases the number of lesions to the same extent as when irradiated leaves are kept in light for some hours before they are inoculated. By contrast, leaves inoculated with nucleic acid immediately after this irradiation produce no more lesions when kept in the light than when kept in darkness; irradiated leaves kept in the light for some hours before inoculation with nucleic acid, however, produce more lesions than comparable leaves kept in the dark after irradiation. Hence, the capacity of leaves to support infection by either kind of inoculum can be photoreactivated, but this takes a few hours and whereas intact tobacco mosaic virus apparently survives unharmed through this period of leaf restoration, the nucleic acid does not (Bawden and Kleczkowski, 1960).

The effect of photoreactivation on the capacity of leaves to support infection depends on the radiation dose and the sensitivity of the leaves; it sometimes enhances the original capacity, sometimes restores it partially and sometimes completely. Not all intact viruses seem as stable as tobacco mosaic *in vivo*, and when inoculated to leaves whose capacity to support infection has been temporarily destroyed, few particles of tobacco necrosis (Bawden and Kleczkowski, 1952) or of red clover mottle (Bawden and Sinha, 1961) viruses survive through the period while light restores the capacity, although many do in leaves given smaller doses of radiation. Indeed, inoculum of intact virus often produces more lesions in leaves that are in the light after brief exposure to ultraviolet radiation than in unirradiated leaves, whereas inoculum of nucleic acid produces fewer. The extent to which a given dose of radiation affects the capacity of the leaves differs greatly with leaves in different physiological states, and various treatments that increase susceptibility to infection by viruses also increase susceptibility to damage by the radiation. These effects of radiation on the host greatly complicate interpretations of radiation experiments in terms of changes in the infecting virus particles, and the assumption that such complications are avoided by keeping irradiated plants in daylight is unwarranted.

The fact that infections initiated by intact virus particles can lead to lesions appearing simultaneously with those initiated by nucleic acid suggests that, if infection by intact particles requires that the nucleic acid becomes free, some particles must disrobe almost immediately they enter inoculated cells. This is possible, but again is not the only necessary interpretation. Although they rarely state it implicitly, most workers who compare the behaviour of the two kinds of inocula assume that all infection sites are similar and equally open to infection by intact virus particles and free nucleic acid. However, this is not necessarily so and this assumption probably derives from another, most likely unjustified, that infection sites for intact virus particles are uniform, with differences between leaves of different susceptibilities reflecting differences in quantity rather than quality of infection sites. It is odd that this assumption should continue to be made, because, as stated in Chapter 7, the analysis of dilution curves is incompatible with the idea that infection happens from chance encounter between single virus particles and uniform infection sites, and compatible only with the idea that different sites differ in the size of dose needed to infect them. Sites, too, could differ in other ways, such as their relative susceptibilities to infection by nucleic acid and intact particles, or the speed with which they accept infection and allow new virus to be formed. If nucleic acid can infect only one of several kinds of site open to intact particles, and this one the type where infection is established most speedily, the fact that some intact particles produce changes more slowly is not evidence that they have to undress to establish infection. It may mean no more than that the undressed nucleic acid is restricted by its nakedness to doing things where they can be done speedily. That sites do differ in the speed with which major changes become apparent is obvious enough simply from observing the times when lesions appear in leaves of *Nicotiana glutinosa* plants inoculated with tobacco mosaic virus; even in the same leaf some lesions may take twice as long as others to develop and, on leaves of different ages, differences can be even greater. The fact that the relative infectivities of inocula of nucleic acid and intact virus can differ by several orders of magnitude when tested on N. *glutinosa* plants of different ages also shows that infection sites where intact particles readily establish themselves are often not open to infection by nucleic acid. Again, though, how to interpret the differences is uncertain; the important factor may not be differences in the character of infection sites, but the instability of the nucleic acid, which may be harmed in some cells before it reaches the infection sites.

What these sites are can only be guessed at, but current ideas about normal ribonucleic acids in cells suggest two possibilities, the nucleus and microsomes, with the instability of inocula of virus nucleic acids equating it to the "messenger" nucleic acid that is thought to pass from the nucleus to the microsomes. If virus particles or nucleic acid do enter or associate with such cell components rich in nucleic acids, this obviously would explain the initial gain in resistance of infection centres to inactivation by ultraviolet radiation. Also, if this association led to increased accumulation of purines and pyrimidines locally as a preliminary to synthesis of virus nucleic acid, this could explain the increased resistance with increasing time. Inactivation curves obtained by irradiating inoculated leaves are at first straight and steep, but become increasingly less steep with increase in time and Siegel and Wildman (1956) show later curves as being of the "multi-target" type. This change from straight lines to curves they consider shows when the virus begins to multiply and the number of virus particles at the infection centres increases. However, this interpretation is questionable, for the doses of radiation needed to inactivate infection centres some hours after inoculation are much larger than early on, and these doses probably considerably affect leaf capacity, the destruction of which does not follow first-order kinetics (Bawden and Harrison, 1955).

Although irradiation of virus-infected leaves shows phenomena that reflect changes produced by infection, it does not show the nature of the changes. Soon after inoculation with virus nucleic acids, or with intact particles of viruses that are more easily inactivated than tobacco mosaic by ultraviolet radiation, infection centres can be destroyed by so little radiation that this probably happens mostly from the direct inactivation of the inoculum, but effects later cannot be clearly identified as on either the virus or the host. Indeed, it may be mistaken to try to make such a distinction, for the establishment of infection may well imply that the virus has become integrated into the mechanism that controls the synthesis of the cell, which has consequently become a different metabolic system from what it was before. Two features of tobacco mosaic virus seemed to provide the possibility of getting unequivocal evidence on the behaviour of the infecting particles; one is the greater sensitivity of the nucleic acid than intact virus to inactivation by ultraviolet radiation and the other that nucleic acid irradiated free from the protein can be photoreactivated. Hence, if the nucleic acid becomes free from the virus protein *in vivo,* this might have been shown by two effects; an increase in susceptibility of infection centres to inactivation and a simultaneous enhanced effect of photoreactivation. However, irradiating leaves at different intervals after inoculation with intact virus showed neither effect (Bawden and Kleczkowski, 1960). The resistance of infection centres to inactivation remained constant during the lag period after which it increased steadily, and the amount of photoreactivation, which was all attributable to effects on leaf capacity, also remained constant until some hours after the lag period. Although photoreactivation of leaf capacity may have obscured any of the nucleic acid that became free in infected cells, the results of these experiments do not suggest any change in the virus particles making them resemble inocula of nucleic acid; in particular, whereas free nucleic acid inoculated to leaves while they are being photoreactivated fails to infect, there was no suggestion that infective material failed to survive through this period at sites inoculated with intact virus, regardless of whether leaves were irradiated immediately after inoculation or near the end of the lag period. Hence, if infection requires particles separating into their two major components, this seems to happen in surroundings where the nucleic acid is protected from risks run by inocula of nucleic acid and where it is equally protected against damage caused by ultraviolet radiation as it is in virus particles. In other words, if the nucleic acid undresses, it seems immediately to take on a new garment that behaves much like its old one.

Synthesis and assembly. Analyses of virus particles have as yet shown only one component that differs from any found in uninfected plants. This is the polyamine, bis(3-aminopropyl)amine (Johnson and Markham, 1962), and its synthesis is presumably initiated by infection. As the nucleic acid and protein of the viruses contain no novel nucleotides or aminoacids, their formation requires the assembling in new ways of materials already being made rather than the making of new compounds. There is no need to assume that the formation of virus nucleic acids and proteins differs fundamentally from that of other nucleic acids and proteins in uninfected cells. Indeed, current ideas about the role of individual nucleic acids in initiating the synthesis of normal proteins derive much of their support from the fact that infections with virus nucleic acids lead to the production of specific proteins. Obviously, whatever effects the virus protein may have later, the changes in nucleoprotein metabolism that culminate in new virus particles can all be initiated by the nucleic acid. Hence, the nucleic acid must do at least two things, which can be summarised simply, by saying that it acts as a pattern for more of itself to be formed and also determines the sequence in which aminoacids join to form polypeptide chains. This could be elaborated into current theories of nucleic acid replication and of sequences of nucleotides providing codes translatable into sequences of aminoacids, with perhaps three successive nucleotides responsible for coding each aminoacid, but there seems little point in doing so while it is still unknown whether the nucleic acid and protein of virus particles are produced at the same site and simultaneously or separately and consecutively.

The structure of virus particles, composed as they are of many protein units of similar sizes enclosing nucleic acid, suggests they are likely to be made by an assembly process of separately synthesised parts, and the ready way that tobacco mosaic virus can be taken apart and reassembled *in vitro* reinforces the suggestion. Also, studies on the fractionation of the specific products occurring in extracts from infected leaves provide evidence compatible with the idea that protein and nucleic acid can be produced separately, although this is not proven. That virus protein commonly occurs on its own has long been known from work with extracts from plants infected with turnip yellow mosaic (Markham and Smith, 1949) and tobacco mosaic viruses (Takahashi and Ishii, 1952, 1953); in the former such protein usually amounts to about one-third of the total virus protein and occurs as empty shells of the same size as particles containing nucleic acid; in the latter, it accounts for only a small proportion of the total virus protein and occurs as small particles resembling those produced when the virus is disrupted by alkali. It has been suggested that both these types of proteins represent intermediate stages in the assembly of virus particles, for they acquired a much greater specific radioactivity than either virus particles or normal plant proteins when infected plants were kept for a few days in air containing $C^{14}O_2$ (Jeener, 1954; van Rysselberge and Jeener, 1955). However, although this makes it unlikely they are formed by the degradation of virus particles, it does not prove they are materials that were destined to be incorporated into virus particles; it simply shows that they are unstable *in vivo* and need to be continually renewed. As the small pieces of tobacco mosaic virus protein readily aggregate *in vitro* to form virus-like rods, they have obvious potentialities for being intermediaries in the assembling of particles *in vivo*, but this does not prove that this is what they are. They may well be end products of a process that was never going to end in complete virus particles. They and the infective rods are far from being the only kind of particles that occur, for there are also nucleoprotein particles ranging in length from about 30 to 300 mμ long, and it seems that virus multiplication does not proceed smoothly from the initiation of specific syntheses of required parts in amounts that are then fully used to assemble one kind of finished product. Rather it seems that synthesis of parts and assembly are sometimes out of balance, although to attribute the range of products to faulty workings of the system may be wholly unwarranted, for although many may be unable to initiate infection, all the products may have some activity in the cells where they are formed.

That differences in end products cannot be simply attributed to random errors in assembly is suggested by the behaviour of tobacco rattle virus, which, like tobacco mosaic virus, occurs in a range of particle sizes, but two predominate and these are such that could not be derived from one another by breaking or aggregation (Harrison and Nixon, 1959). The more common one is not infective, but as the major part of the specific material present at any time, it can hardly be regarded as anything other than an end product. Perhaps the lengths of these anisometric particles are determined by the length of the nucleic acid thread along which protein units aggregate. Incomplete threads or broken pieces of completed threads could then give rise to the particles of random lengths, but to get particles of two main lengths seems to indicate the synthesis of nucleic acid threads of two specific lengths.

If the small particles of tobacco mosaic virus protein represent intermediaries in virus assembly and are not separate products or faulty pieces of synthesis, they might perhaps be expected to form a larger proportion of the total protein in the early than in later stages of infection. However, they do not, but become detectable only when infected leaves already contain much virus, and although they may thereafter fluctuate unpredictably they usually increase more or less in proportion to the total virus content (Commoner and Rodenberg, 1955; Bawden and Pirie, 1956). Again, though, this may mean no more than that virus nucleic acid and protein are not always produced in the same proportions. If nucleic acid multiplication is a necessary preliminary to protein synthesis, then soon after infection there will be nucleic acid immediately ready to combine with protein units as soon as they are formed, whereas later the two may not always be in step and protein may be produced in excess of nucleic acid.

The effect of thiouracil on the multiplication of turnip yellow mosaic virus perhaps provides evidence in support of the idea that, once the synthesis of virus protein has started, it can proceed without equivalent quantities of virus nucleic acid being produced (Francki and Matthews, 1962). When thiouracil is applied to leaves some days after they are inoculated, virus protein continues to increase rapidly but not the nucleoprotein particles, which usually amount to about two-thirds of the total specific particles, and the ratio of protein shells to total particles increases by four or more times. This seems to happen because of failure to synthesise nucleic acid rather than because of failure to incorporate it in the particles, for there is no increase in total leaf nucleic acid to parallel the increase in protein shells. The usual proportion of protein shells may also reflect excess protein synthesis, for when nucleoprotein particles become readily detectable, at about a week after inoculation, they are not accompanied by protein shells, which appear a few days later and then for a while their proportion of the total increases steadily. Again, this sequence conflicts with expectation if the protein shells are precursors of the nucleoprotein particles, and fits better with the idea that they are end products.

Non-infective particles seem to be a constant feature of infections with many different viruses, but their biological significance is unknown, and there is no need to postulate they all have a similar origin or function. Some may represent stages in virus assembly. Others may be breakdown products from virus particles, for virus formation is likely to resemble other forms of nucleoprotein metabolism and be a dynamic process, with conditions at any one time representing the balance between synthesis and degradation. Still others may be side products, made separately from the main line of virus synthesis and degradation and using material that was not destined to form part of an infective particle.

Particles consisting of only virus protein, or nucleoprotein particles that differ in size or other character, are relatively easy to detect because they are stable in leaf extracts. The position is different with virus nucleic acids, which are readily inactivated in sap and hydrolysed by the ribonuclease there. Nevertheless, there have been claims that free virus nucleic acid occurs in leaves where tobacco mosaic virus is rapidly increasing. That infection soon stimulates the synthesis of nucleic acid is compatible with the increasing resistance to inactivation by ultraviolet radiation gained by infective centres, and Commoner (1954) reported analyses showing that the amount of insoluble nucleic acid in infected leaves increases before tobacco mosaic virus can be extracted in comparable amounts, and then decreases as the virus content of sap increases. Also, the free purines and pyrimidines that are usually detectable in tobacco leaf sap disappear when tobacco mosaic virus is multiplying, indicating that the virus nucleic acid is assembled from the common pool, which is further suggested by the fact that the virus produced in leaves treated with 8-azaguanine (Matthews, 1953b) or 2-thiouracil (Jeener and Rosseels, 1953; Matthews, 1956) contain these materials in place of guanine or uracil.

To demonstrate the occurrence of free virus nucleic acid in leaves requires extracting in conditions where the nucleic acid will be stable and by methods that do not disrupt the virus. Cochran and Chidester (1957) first claimed to have done this, but Whitfield and others (1960) state that the method does not isolate infective nucleic acid. As evidence that infective nucleic acid is formed as a precursor of tobacco mosaic virus, Engler and Schramm (1959) reported experiments showing that, in the first three days after infection but not later, extracts made by macerating leaves in the presence of phenol were more infective than those made by first macerating leaves normally and treating with phenol later. This difference they attributed to infective nucleic acid being inactivated when leaves were macerated ordinarily but being preserved by direct maceration in phenol. However, Bawden and Pirie (1960) could not confirm that the water extracts of leaves macerated in phenol were more infective than those of leaves pulped normally and later treated with phenol, and it is doubtful whether the technique is adequate to give meaningful differences. Maceration with phenol does not extract a constant proportion of the total infective material contained in leaves, and some samples of sap after treatment with phenol give aqueous extracts containing materials that strongly inhibit infection by nucleic acid. These materials are removed by dialysis, which often increases the infectivity of such extracts many times. The best evidence that recently infected leaves may contain free nucleic acid of tobacco mosaic virus has been provided by Diener (1962), who ground leaves in solutions of sodium chloride buffered at pH 9 to 10, where leaf ribonucleases are inactive, and then fractionated the extracts by density-gradient centrifugation. Diener reports considerable infectivity, which is destroyed by ribonuclease and sediments more slowly than virus particles, in extracts from leaves infected for only a few days, but not from those infected for 3 weeks, or from uninfected leaves to which purified virus was added. The simplest interpretation of these results is that the unstable infective material detected in extracts from recently infected plants is virus nucleic acid that existed as such *in vivo* and would later have combined with protein to form stable virus particles, but work with tobacco rattle and tobacco necrosis viruses shows that infective material extractable by such means is not necessarily a precursor of stable virus particles.

When local lesions caused by inoculating tobacco plants with some strains of the rattle virus are macerated singly and their extracts used as inocula, most produce few infections whereas about 5% produce very many. Plants inoculated with readily transmissible isolates become systemically infected in about a week, show evanescent symptoms, their sap contains many of the characteristic rod-shaped particles, both 75 and 175 mμ long, is highly infective and the infectivity is stable. Plants inoculated with the other isolates take some weeks to become systemically infected, symptoms persist, their sap contains few rods and these all 75 mμ long, is poorly infective and the infectivity is ephemeral (Cadman and Harrison, 1959). Phenol extracts of plants infected with readily transmissible isolates are less infective than sap, whereas such extracts of plants infected with isolates normally difficult to transmit are much more infective than sap (Sanger and Brandenburg, 1961; Cadman, 1962). The infective material in phenol extracts is free nucleic acid, but it seems unlikely that it is in this form in leaves infected with the poorly transmissible isolates, because sap extracted normally, although itself with little infectivity, gives highly infective aqueous extracts when treated with phenol. Indeed, it continues to do so for a few hours, though nucleic acid is rapidly inactivated in sap, so the infectivity is at first protected against ribonuclease and other inactivating agents in sap, though it is much less stable than the rod-shaped virus particles.

Cadman (1962) suggests that the infective material is virus nucleic acid contained in nuclei, for much of the infective material that can be extracted by phenol sediments when sap is centrifuged at 10,000 rpm. He further suggests that, whereas the nucleic acid of isolates readily transmissible by sap moves easily into the cytoplasm where it initiates the synthesis of virus protein, with which it combines to form the rod-shaped particles, the nucleic acid of isolates difficult to transmit remains in the nucleus. However, if this is so, it is difficult to see how both kinds of isolate cause similar local lesions and become systemic, for this implies spread, not only from cell to cell but over distances. There is no *a priori* reason why nucleic acid should not do this, but at least it would have to emerge from the nucleus. If the isolates not readily transmissible by sap do occur as nucleic acid only, this also carries the implication that symptoms are caused by aberrations in the nucleic acid synthesis and that the virus protein has no effect on the host cells, but serves simply as an inert protector of the virus nucleic acid. Much more information will be needed before these fascinating results can be interpreted with certainty. There seems little doubt that the isolates difficult to transmit by ordinary methods of extraction rarely produce the rod-shaped particles characteristic of those easy to transmit, but this does not prove that they fail to produce other kinds of specific particles, less distinctive, less able to protect the nucleic acid from inactivation and less well adapted for transmission by inoculation. The range of rod-shaped particles produced by the multiplication of the readily transmissible variants is already large, but there may be still other kinds of particle awaiting discovery.

Tobacco rattle virus is not unique in occurring in variants that differ in their transmissibility by sap inoculation. Most single lesions produced by tobacco necrosis virus when macerated and used as inocula produce many infections, but about one in twenty produces very few (Babos and Kassanis, 1962). However, this minority of lesions will give highly infective inocula when extracted with phenol or macerated in alkaline buffers with bentonite, although they behave differently from tobacco rattle in that treating even freshly extracted sap with phenol does not give infective inocula. The two obvious explanations for this are that the infective material either is not extracted when leaves are simply macerated, or is extracted in such a state that it is immediately inactivated in sap. Infective nucleic acid would be such a state and this may be how the variant exists in leaves, but if so it seems remarkably robust. Leaves infected with these isolates develop typical necrotic lesions and within a few days will collapse, but many days later still give highly infective extracts when extracted with phenol or alkaline buffers. It seems probable that the nucleic acid would need some protection to survive in such an environment, but how this is conferred can only be surmised. Sap from such plants has a little infectivity, which is also stable; this no doubt resides in the few particles in sap that resemble the many present in sap from plants infected with the readily transmissible isolates. Using stored sap as inoculum does not increase the transmissibility of the isolates by sap inoculation, so it seems their multiplication leads to two very different end products, of which the minority is in the form of customary virus particles readily extractable and stable in sap and the majority of

unknown nature demonstrable only by special extraction methods
Whether the readily transmissible isolates also give two such end
products differing so much is unknown, but it is clear that they
readily change into the forms that do. As with tobacco rattle virus,
there is no evidence that the change is reversible and that isolates
difficult to transmit by sap inoculation ever become readily transmissible.

Tobacco mosaic virus (Siegel, Zaitlin and Sehgal, 1962) has
also been found to produce variants that are defective in their ability
to produce stable nucleoprotein particles, and although these discoveries are too recent to know whether they will apply at all generally, it can confidently be expected that at least some other viruses
will behave in comparable ways. Until the phenomena have been
much further studied, their interpretation can be little except speculation, but meanwhile they serve as a salutary warning to those studying virus multiplication. Although the accuracy of assays for infective particles stable in sap has always been open to question, they
have long provided the bases for estimating virus multiplication, but
only now has it become obvious how misleading they can be, with
the demonstration that most of even the infective products of multiplication may differ in kind from the inoculum and be undetected
by tests on sap. Clearly, work up to the present with many viruses
may have given little indication of the range or amounts of products
that are specific to infected cells.

It is unknown wherein infected cells virus particles are formed,
but most accumulate in the cytoplasm, either individually or aggregated into inclusion bodies; viruses that form intranuclear inclusions presumably also accumulate in nuclei. The extent to which
different viruses occur as extractable nucleoprotein or protein differs greatly; the amount of some is too little to affect the electrophoretic pattern of sap, whereas others become the major part of
the soluble protein (Bawden and Kleczkowski, 1957). The idea
used often to be advanced that virus multiplication simply entails
the change of a normal host component, in a manner analogous to
that in which trypsin converts an inactive precursor, trypsinogen,
into active enzyme. Indeed, there has been one claim that normal
tobacco plants contain a protein serologically related to tobacco
mosaic virus, but this is contrary to the experience of all other
workers. Similarly unsubstantiated is the claim that tobacco mosaic
virus multiplies directly at the expense of the dominant protein
component present in tobacco leaf sap (Wildman, Cheo and Bonner, 1949). This component is unstable and its concentration fluc-
tuates but also decreases as leaves age (Commoner, Newmark and

Rodenberg, 1952). Its concentration is not correlated with the amount of virus present in extracts from infected leaves and is no more affected by simultaneous infection with potato virus X and tobacco mosaic virus, each of which exceeds the amount of this normal component, than by infection with either alone (Bawden and Kleczkowski, 1957). The only sense in which normal plant proteins might be precursors for virus protein is that aminoacids or other nitrogen compounds produced by their breakdown are used as sources of nitrogen for virus formation. There seems no reason why viruses should not be made from the pool of aminoacids used for general protein synthesis, but Commoner (1954) states that the aminoacids contained in tobacco mosaic virus are synthesised anew from ammonia in the host.

Inhibitors of multiplication. Of the substances that when incorporated in inocula decrease the number of infections, some also inhibit virus increase when applied to leaves in which infection is already established. These are all substances with small molecules that readily diffuse into leaf cells and most are analogues of purines and pyrimidines, of which the most used have been 2-thiouracil (Commoner and Mercer, 1951, 1952; Mercer, Lindhorst and Commoner, 1953; Nichols, 1953; Bawden and Kassanis, 1954; Badami, 1959; Sinha, 1960; Francki, 1962a, 1962b; Francki and Matthews, 1962) and 8-azaguanine (Matthews, 1953a, 1953b). Like substances with large molecular weights that inhibit infection by viruses, or other substances with small molecular weights, such as trichothecin (Bawden and Freeman, 1952), that affect virus increase, the effect of thiouracil depends on the identity of the host species; for example, whereas the increase of tobacco necrosis virus is greatly affected in tobacco, it is much less so in French bean. Its action also depends on the condition in which infected leaves are kept. Table 11–2 shows the relative amounts of tobacco mosaic virus in extracts from leaf pieces macerated a week after inoculation and kept for the previous 6 days in the specified conditions. Keeping in daylight and floating in the nutrient solution both increased virus content, which was everywhere decreased by thiouracil but by such different amounts in the different conditions that, although with daylight and nutrient the virus content was four times as much as with darkness and water, in the presence of thiouracil it was thirty-two times as much with darkness and water as with daylight and nutrient. The reason for thiouracil inhibiting tobacco mosaic virus increase so much more in conditions where otherwise the virus would increase most remains undetermined, but its inhibiting action

TABLE 11–2

The Effect of Thiouracil on the Amount of Tobacco Mosaic Virus in Extracts from
Infected Leaves Kept in Different Conditions *

| Illumination | Leaves Floated in | | | |
	Water		Nutrient Solution	
Daylight	Water only	64	Nutrient only	192
	Thiouracil	8	Thiouracil	1
Darkness	Water only	48	Nutrient only	128
	Thiouracil	32	Thiouracil	2

* Thiouracil was used at 100 mg/l and the nutrient solution contained 10 g/l
sucrose and 0.2 g/l $Ca(H_2PO_4)_2H_2O$. The different treatments were started a day
after the leaves were inoculated and the leaves were macerated 6 days later. The
numbers are the reciprocals of the highest dilutions at which clarified sap from the
leaves precipitated specifically with virus antiserum (Bawden and Kassanis, 1954).

is counteracted by uracil and a possible explanation is that leaves
kept in darkness without nutrient may have more free uracil because
less nucleic acid is synthesised than in daylight with nutrient.

The effect of thiouracil and azaguanine also differs with different
viruses. In tobacco, for example, whereas thiouracil can greatly
inhibit increase of tobacco mosaic virus, it has little effect on cucumber mosaic virus; by contrast azaguanine, which has little effect on
tobacco mosaic virus, greatly inhibits the production of alfalfa
(lucerne) mosaic and cucumber mosaic viruses (Matthews, 1953a;
Badami, 1959). Again, this specificity remains unexplained, but it
seems not to lie in the amounts of uracil and guanine contained in
the viruses, because tobacco mosaic virus contains less uracil and
more guanine than does lucerne mosaic virus; all that can be suggested is that the production of tobacco mosaic virus depends more
on some host-cell system demanding uracil and less on one demanding guanine than does lucerne mosaic virus.

When leaves infected with tobacco mosaic virus are treated with
azaguanine (Matthews, 1953b) or thiouracil (Jeener and Rosseels,
1953; Matthews, 1956), these substances become incorporated in the
virus nucleic acid and replace some of the guanine and uracil.
Here is an obvious possible explanation for these substances affecting virus multiplication, but even those who argue most forcibly for
the idea that particles containing these analogues are "sterile" produce little convincing evidence that this sterility is adequate to
explain the inhibition. For example, alhough Francki (1962b) reports that virus formed in the presence of thiouracil is less infective
than usual, the largest decrease he shows is to one-fifth, and the

virus produced in treated leaves always has considerable infectivity. That virus formed in the presence of thiouracil is intrinsically able to multiply *in vivo* is clearly shown by the fact that when leaves in which virus increase is being inhibited by thiouracil are treated with uracil, or the thiouracil is removed, the virus immediately starts to increase. Further, in normal leaves where virus has been multiplying for some days and so already contains much infective virus, thiouracil will slow the rate of further increase. There has been no work to decide whether these inhibitors act by decreasing the amount of virus produced in individual cells or by decreasing the number of cells that become infected, but it may well be that they prevent new cells from becoming infected rather than preventing virus being produced in already infected cells. This could happen because they affect the nucleic acid metabolism of the host cells so as to make the cells resistant: an analogy is perhaps provided by the temporary insusceptibility of cells to infection while being photoreactivated after exposure to ultraviolet radiation.

There are several additional reasons for seeking other explanations of the inhibitory action than that the analogues become incorporated in virus particles. Thiothymine inhibits the increase of tobacco mosaic virus, which does not contain thymine; this action, like that of thiouracil and thiocytosine, is counteracted by giving uracil to the leaves, but not by giving thymine or cytosine (Mercer, Lindhorst and Commoner, 1953), which again perhaps suggests the main factor may be a uracil-dependent system of the host. Also, thiouracil is as effective in inhibiting the increase of turnip yellow mosaic as of tobacco mosaic virus, but is not incorporated in its nucleic acid (Francki and Matthews, 1962). Further, trichothecin (Bawden and Freeman, 1952) and coumarin (Knypl and Gubanski, 1960) act much like these analogues of purines and pyrimidines in inhibiting virus increase, but they are far removed from them chemically and would not be incorporated in the virus particles.

When well developed detached leaves are treated with thiouracil they show few signs of being affected, but that metabolism is greatly changed is readily shown by the effects on young tissues when whole plants are treated, for the young leaves rapidly become pale and apical growth is arrested. This may be relevant to effects on virus multiplication, for young tissues are more likely than already mature leaves to depend on the continuing synthesis of nucleic acid and proteins. That thiouracil does primarily affect such syntheses is indicated by chemical studies on treated leaves (Porter and Weinstein, 1957; 1960), which show accumulation of free amino- and amide-nitrogen because of arrested protein synthesis. Virus multiplication is itself essentially an aberration in the nucleic acid and protein metabolism of host cells and almost certainly the mechanisms, enzymes and energy sources used in the synthesis of normal cell components are used to synthesise virus nucleic acid and protein. When these syntheses are already being disturbed by such substances as thiouracil, it is perhaps little surprising that the cells should not also readily accommodate the second aberration of virus production.

Thiouracil has no therapeutic action on plants infected with tobacco mosaic virus; it slows virus increase, but virus already formed remains unaffected. However, it can decrease the virus content of plants infected with some less stable viruses, probably not because it inactivates them but because they are intrinsically unstable *in vivo* and thiouracil prevents new particles being synthesised to replace those that become degraded. There is no record yet of a systemically infected plant being made virus-free by its use, but potato plants had their content of potato virus Y much decreased and cultures of tobacco callus tissues were freed from this virus by prolonged exposure to thiouracil (Kassanis and Tinsley, 1958).

Effects of other viruses. It has long been known that infections by some pairs of viruses, such as potato X and Y, cause more severe symptoms than either causes alone. The increased severity of symptoms is correlated with an increase in amount of potato virus X extractable from leaves (Rochow and Ross, 1955), and it seems that infection with virus Y removes some factor that otherwise limits the concentration of virus X. This concentration depends on the temperature at which plants are growing, it decreases greatly with increases in temperature above 20° and is very little above 30°. Virus Y increases the amount of virus X over this whole temperature range; it produces the greatest effect on total amount of virus at the lower ones, but proportional increases are greatest at the higher ones. Thus, at 32° virus Y increased the concentration of virus X more than ten times over that in plants infected with X alone, but this extra production of virus X was less than that obtained by virus Y doubling the concentration at 19° (Stouffer and Ross, 1961). Infection with virus Y, then, has consequences on virus X concentration similar to those of lowering the temperature, which suggests two possibilities for its action; the multiplication of virus Y may remove some metabolic product that inhibits virus X and accumulates increasingly as the temperature increases, and for this it would be reasonable to expect some breakdown product of protein; or it may increase the amount of some material needed by virus X and that is increasingly demanded by host metabolism as the temperature rises. More work is needed to decide whether the limiting factor is something positive, i.e. an inhibitor of virus increase, or negative, i.e. some missing metabolite; also, to decide whether the effect of temperature and virus Y on the concentration is primarily one of determining the extent virus X increases in individual cells or the readiness with which it spreads between cells.

Work on tobacco necrosis has provided what seems an example

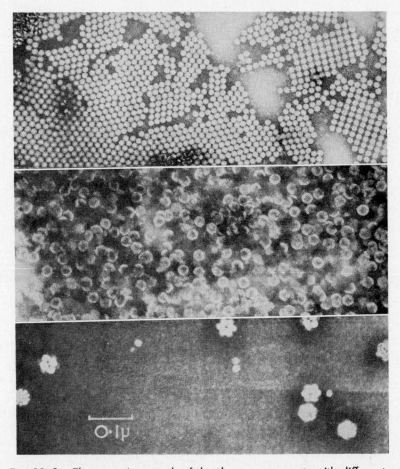

Fig. 11–3. Electron micrograph of the three components with different sedimentation constants from the Rothamsted culture of tobacco necrosis virus: all stained with phosphotungstate. *Top:* the satellite virus, sedimentation constant 50S. *Centre:* the infective tobacco necrosis virus, 116S. *Bottom:* aggregates of 12 particles of the satellite virus, 240S. (B. Kassanis and H. L. Nixon, 1961, J. gen. Microbiol. 25: 459).

of a virus that is wholly dependent on another for its ability to multiply. Extracts from plants infected with the Rothamsted culture of tobacco necrosis virus have long been known to contain specific particles of three sizes, of which the smallest seemed non-infective, were the most stable and were thought to be derived as products of the multiplication of the larger ones (Bawden and Pirie 1945; 1957). However, Kassanis and Nixon (1961) showed that this culture consists of two serologically unrelated viruses, one with polyhedral particles about 17 mμ in diameter (sedimentation constant 50S) and the other with polyhedral particles about 30 mμ in diameter (sedimentation constant 116S). A more rapidly sedimenting component than either of these sometimes occurs, which consists of aggregates of 12 of the 50S particles (Fig. 11–3). Only the 116S particles cause lesions when inoculated to leaves and the lesions they cause are uniformly large; such infections give leaf extracts containing only 116S particles. Leaves inoculated with the 50S particles not only produce no lesions, but extracts from them contain nothing that reacts with virus antiserum. When leaves are inoculated with mixtures of the 116S and 50S particles, leaves produce lesions of two sizes, and the proportion of large to small decreases as the proportion of 50S particles in the inoculum increases (Table 11–3). Extracts from leaves inoculated with such mixtures contain both sizes of particles, again roughly in the proportions in which they were contained in the inoculum. The 50S particles do not share antigens with the 116S particles. In brief, one virus, which Kassanis (1962) has termed the satellite virus, seems to depend for

TABLE 11–3

The Effect of Satellite Virus on the Lesions Produced by a Tobacco Necrosis Virus (TNV) *

Concentration of Virus (Mg/l)		Number of Lesions on 8 Half-Leaves of French Bean	
Satellite	TNV	Large Lesions	Small Lesions
80	0.0	0	0
20	0.8	4	295
5	0.8	20	274
1.2	0.8	44	199
0.3	0.8	157	95
0.08	0.8	217	0

* Satellite virus does not produce lesions, but changes the size of lesions caused by TNV and the proportion of small to large lesions increases as its concentration increases. (Results from Kassanis and Nixon, 1960; 1961).

its ability to multiply on the simultaneous infection by a second, larger one to which it is unrelated, but whose multiplication it slightly inhibits.

More than one of the tobacco necrosis viruses can activate the satellite virus, but tobacco mosaic and several other viruses tested do not. What the tobacco necrosis viruses do to allow the satellite virus to multiply detectably is not known. The satellite virus has the smallest particles of any known virus and Kassanis and Nixon (1961) suggest that the nucleic acid is inadequate to function independently and needs to borrow activities from the nucleic acid of the other virus, but if this is so, the borrowing does not show in the antigenic constitution of the satellite virus. Also, in plants at 34° potato virus X often fails to multiply detectably unless virus Y is also present, but its nucleic acid is clearly adequate in other conditions.

The satellite virus can remain apparently latent in leaves for several days and still be activated by inoculation with a tobacco necrosis virus. In the context of the idea that infection requires virus particles to separate into protein and nucleic acid, this fact carries the suggestion that the satellite virus on its own cannot make this separation. However, this is unlikely to explain its inability to multiply on its own because inoculum of satellite virus disrupted with phenol is no better as an inoculum than intact particles. The nucleic acid is effective when inoculated together with the tobacco necrosis virus, but is much less so than intact virus when it is inoculated to leaves some days before the activating virus, though it does have some effect, which perhaps suggests that it must do something in the host cells to preserve its activity.

In considering what happens to the satellite virus when inoculated alone, it is again necessary to stress the limitations of current techniques for recognising virus increase. The tests so far made give no indication that the satellite virus can unaided multiply at all but, as said earlier in this chapter, testing techniques might fail to detect multiplication that was restricted to cells actually infected at the time of inoculation. What the aiding virus may do is increase the multiplication of the satellite virus and enable it to invade many cells, so that it reaches detectable amounts in leaf extracts. However, an equally possible explanation of its behaviour is that the satellite virus on its own enters into a condition in the inoculated leaf cells comparable to that of bacteriophages in lysogenic bacteria, from which latent state it is roused by the activating tobacco necrosis viruses as are pro-phages by ultraviolet radiation and some other stimuli.

From being a neglected subject, the study of virus multiplication in plants is now very active and its complexity is only just becoming apparent by the many new and unexpected phenomena recently disclosed. In simple outline it is possible to see virus production as a special form of nucleoprotein synthesis, using host-cell mechanisms but able to divert these mechanisms in the necessary directions only when many unknown conditions are fulfilled. The subject is still largely in the stage of uncovering phenomena rather than explaining them, but if questions cannot be answered but only speculated on, it is at least becoming more clear what questions most need asking.

REFERENCES

Babos, P., and B. Kassanis. 1962. Virology 18: 206.
Badami, R. S. 1959. Ann. appl. Biol. 47: 78.
Bawden, F. C. 1961. J. biol. Chem. 236: 2760.
——, and G. G. Freeman. 1952. J. gen. Microbiol. 7: 154.
——, and B. D. Harrison. 1955. J. gen. Microbiol. 13: 494.
——, and B. Kassanis. 1954. J. gen. Microbiol. 10: 160.
——, and A. Kleczkowski. 1952. Nature, Lond. 169: 90.
——, and ——. 1955. J. gen. Microbiol. 13: 370.
——, and ——. 1957. Virology 4: 26.
——, and ——. 1959. Nature, Lond. 183: 503.
——, and ——. 1960. Virology 10: 163.
——, and N. W. Pirie. 1945. Brit. J. exp. Path. 26: 277.
——, and ——. 1956. J. gen. Microbiol. 14: 460.
——, and ——. 1957. Ibid. 16: 696.
——, and ——. 1960. Rep. Rothamst. exp. Sta. for 1960, p. 112.
——, and R. C. Sinha. 1961. Virology 14: 198.
Cadman, C. H. 1962. Nature, Lond. 193: 49.
——, and B. D. Harrison. 1959. Ann. appl. Biol. 47: 542.
Casterman, C., and R. Jeener. 1955. Biochim. biophys. Acta 16: 433.
Cochran, G. W., and J. L. Chidester. 1957. Virology 4: 390.
Commoner, B. 1954. In The Dynamics of Virus and Rickettsial Infections. The Blakiston Co., New York.
——, and F. L. Mercer. 1951. Nature, Lond. 168: 113.
——, and ——. 1952. Arch. Biochem. Biophys. 35: 278.
——, P. Newmark, and S. D. Rodenberg. 1952. Ibid. 37: 15.
——, and S. D. Rodenberg. 1955. J. gen. Physiol. 38: 475.
Diener, T. O. 1962. Virology 16: 140.
Dijkstra, J. 1962. Virology 18: 142.
Engler, R., and G. Schramm. 1959. Nature, Lond. 183: 1277.
Fraenkel-Conrat, H. 1959. In Perspectives in Virology, p. 7. (M. Pollard, ed.). Wiley, New York.
——, B. Singer, and S. Veldee. 1958. Biochim. biophys. Acta 29: 639.
Francki, R. I. B. 1962a. Virology 17: 1.
——. 1962b. Ibid. 17: 9.
——, and R. E. F. Matthews. 1962. Virology 17:367.
Gordon, M. P., and C. Smith. 1960. J. biol. Chem. 235: PC 28.
Harrison, B. D. 1956a. J. gen. Microbiol. 15: 210.
——. 1956b. Ann. appl. Biol. 44: 215.
——, and H. L. Nixon. 1959. J. gen. Microbiol. 21: 569.
Jeener, R. 1954. Biochim. biophys. Acta 13: 307.

———, and J. ROSSEELS. 1953. *Ibid.* 11: 438.

JOHNSON, M. W., and R. MARKHAM. 1962. Virology 17: 276.

KASSANIS, B. 1957. *Ibid.* 4: 187.

———. 1959. J. gen. Microbiol. 20: 704.

———. 1960. Virology 10: 353.

———. 1962. J. gen. Microbiol. 27: 477.

———, and H. L. NIXON. 1960. Nature, Lond. 187: 713.

———, and ———. 1961. J. gen. Microbiol. 25: 459.

———, and T. W. TINSLEY. 1958. Proc. 3rd Conf. Potato Virus Diseases, Lisse-Wageningen.

KLECZKOWSKI, A. 1946. Biochem. J. 40: 677.

KLECZKOWSKI, J., and A. KLECZKOWSKI. 1954. J. gen. Microbiol. 11: 451.

KNYPL, J. S., and M. GUBANSKI. 1960. Naturwissenschaften 13: 308.

LORING, H. S. 1942. J. gen. Physiol. 25: 497.

MARKHAM, R., and K. M. SMITH. 1949. Parasitology 39: 330.

MATTHEWS, R. E. F. 1953a. J. gen. Microbiol. 8: 277.

———. 1953b. Nature, Lond. 171: 1065.

———. 1956. Biochim. biophys. Acta 19: 559.

MERCER, F. L., T. E. LINDHORST, and B. COMMONER. 1953. Science 117: 558.

NICHOLS, C. W. 1953. Phytopathology 43: 555.

NIXON, H. L. 1956. Virology 2: 126.

PORTER, C. A., and L. H. WEINSTEIN. 1957. Contr. Boyce Thompson Inst. 19: 87.

———, and ———. 1960. *Ibid.* 20: 307.

ROCHOW, W. F., and A. F. ROSS. 1955. Virology 1: 10.

ROSS, A. F. 1941. Phytopathology 31: 410.

RYSSELBERGE, C. VAN, and R. JEENER. 1955. Biochim. biophys. Acta 17: 158.

SANGER, H. L., and E. BRANDENBURG. 1961. Naturwissenschaften 48: 391.

SCHRAMM, G., and R. ENGLER. 1958. Nature, Lond. 181: 916.

SIEGEL, A., W. GINOZA, and S. G. WILDMAN. 1957. Virology 3: 554.

———, and S. G. WILDMAN. 1956. *Ibid.* 2: 69.

———, M. ZAITLIN, and OM. P. SEHGAL. 1962. Proc. nat. Acad. Sci. Wash. 48: 1845.

SINHA, R. C. 1960. Ann. appl. Biol. 48: 749.

STOUFFER, R. F., and A. F. ROSS. 1961. Phytopathology 51: 5.

TAKAHASHI, W. N., and M. ISHII. 1952. *Ibid.* 42: 690.

———, and ———. 1953. Amer. J. Bot. 40: 85.

WELKIE, G. W., and G. S. POUND. 1958. Virology 5: 362.

WHITFIELD, P. R., M. F. DAY, K. HELMS, and D. G. VENABLES. 1960. *Ibid.* 11: 624.

WILDMAN, S. G., C. C. CHEO, and J. BONNER. 1949. J. biol. Chem. 180: 985.

YARWOOD, C. E. 1952. Amer. J. Bot 39: 613.

Movement Within Host Plants

Viruses are economically important only in plants in which they cause systemic infections, that is, plants in which they can move from primary infection sites to other cells, not only those immediately adjacent to the primary sites but to distant tissues. As viruses are usually first encountered and mostly studied in such hosts, their apparent ability to move freely through vegetative cells and tissues is often accepted without question, although such behaviour is most unexpected with particles of their size. Ready movement between plant cells and tissues is usually regarded as an attribute peculiar to molecules small enough to diffuse through semi-permeable membranes, something virus particles or their nucleic acids are far too large to do. The fact that viruses seem to move with a freedom denied to normal plant proteins, or to other indiffusible cell components such as starch, suggests that their movement may be more than passive transport and depend on some specific activity of virus particles. However, despite appearances, it would be premature to conclude that viruses move between cells or through tissues any more freely than do other indiffusible cell contents. The difference between viruses and other large particles may lie not in their relative abilities to move but in the ability of viruses to multiply in the cells they reach after they have moved. The movement of some particles of, say, normal protein from leaves to roots or fruits passes unnoticed, whereas the movement of virus particles will become obvious, not necessarily because more of them moved, but because the ones that moved multiplied at the new site and reached detectıble amounts. The apparent ease with which a virus such as tobacco mosaic invades tobacco or tomato plants gives an impression of ready and purposeful movement but this impression may be misleading. Instead of virus moving in quantity over distances, systemic infection may be the end result of the chance escape from leaf parenchyma of only a few of the virus particles produced at initial infection sites. Some evidence in support of the idea that there is no bulk movement comes from an analysis of the strains of tobacco mosaic virus that become systemic in plants inoculated with distinctive strains mixed in different proportions (Cohen *et al*, 1957).

Localised infections. Not all viruses become systemic in all their hosts. The local infections that attract most attention are those in which the host reacts with necrotic lesions, and the restricted spread has received a ready explanation on the assumption that, as viruses are obligate parasites, they are prevented from moving by the death of the host cells. Although plausible, for several reasons this explanation has never been adequate. First, necrosis does not always stop the further spread of a virus. The necrotic lesions produced by tobacco mosaic virus in *Nicotiana glutinosa,* for example, appear in 2–3 days at 20°, but the lesions slowly increase in area for a further week. Also, when plants with fully developed necrotic lesions are placed at over 30°, the virus resumes its spread and moves into new cells. Secondly, localised infections are not peculiar to virus-host combinations that react necrotically. Holmes (1938, 1946) found that tobacco mosaic and tobacco etch viruses infect and multiply locally in many plants in which they cause neither necrosis nor systemic infections. More than half the 199 species he found to be hosts for tobacco mosaic virus failed to become systemically infected and of the 108 species in which the virus multiplied only locally, more than 80 remained symptomless and most of the others developed only chlorotic lesions. Similarly, tobacco necrosis viruses seem to move no more freely in *Primula obconica* in which they cause no local lesions than in species where they cause necroses. Indeed, they are more narrowly confined to initial infection sites in leaves of *P. obconica* than of French bean, in which the necrotic lesions may increase until the whole of the inoculated leaf is invaded. In each host the viruses occasionally pass from an inoculated leaf to infect an uninoculated one, but this movement leads only to another localised infection and not to a full systemic infection (Bawden and Kassanis, 1947). Thirdly, systemic infections are obtained with some virus-host combinations that give necrotic local lesions similar to those in others where infection is localised. For example, potato viruses C and Y produce similar black local lesions in several potato varieties, but virus Y usually becomes systemic whereas virus C does not. Similarly, bean stipple streak virus becomes systemic in French beans, though it produces similar local lesions to other tobacco necrosis viruses that are restricted to the inoculated leaves.

All these facts suggest that movement from infection foci is not necessarily an intrinsic property of viruses that is interfered with only by the death of infected cells, but is rather a reflection of some other specific virus-host interaction. Perhaps this can be put more positively by saying that ability to multiply in cells to which viruses move may be the limiting factor, rather than inability to move. This is strongly suggested by work with tobacco mosaic virus in bean (Yarwood, 1953, 1960) and tobacco (Ross, 1961a, 1961b) varieties in which it causes necrotic local lesions. The regions around the necrotic lesions become highly resistant to infection by tobacco mosaic virus introduced by new inoculations, and concentrated inocula either fail to infect or produce only very few, minute lesions. The acquired resistance in tobacco is greatest near to the necrotic lesions, but there is also an effect at a distance, for infection of one half only of a leaf makes the other half resistant, and infection of some leaves only on a plant increases the resistance of the other leaves. This acquired resistance presumably reflects changes in the physiology of the uninfected cells caused either by something diffusing into them from the necrotic lesions or by something diffusing from them towards the lesions. As described in Chapter 4, the oxidising enzymes are increased in leaves that react necrotically, and Farkas, Kiraly and Solymosy (1960) report that tobacco mosaic virus multiplies without causing necrotic local lesions in leaves of Nicotiana glutinosa supplied with high concentrations of ascorbic acid. In such leaves necrosis and localisation of infection are correlated and are probably cause and effect, but the fact that the still living cells resist infection implies that localisation may have other explanations than that the virus cannot move from cells that react necrotically to infection.

The acquired resistance is not specific against the virus causing the necrotic local lesions, for the green parts of hypersentitive leaves infected with tobacco mosaic virus resist infection by tobacco necrosis and some other viruses; similarly, the green parts of leaves carrying tobacco necrosis lesions resist infection by tobacco mosaic virus. The resistance is not acquired when the hypersensitive hosts infected with tobacco mosaic virus are kept at above 30° or are simultaneously infected with potato virus X, conditions in which the spread of the virus is not restricted (Ross, 1961a). There are host plants in which some but not all strains of this virus are localised in necrotic lesions. For example, tomato aucuba mosaic virus is normally localised in inoculated leaves of *Nicotiana sylvestris*, whereas the type strain is not and causes a systemic mottling, but in plants inoculated with a mixture of both strains, both become systemic (Benda, 1957). Obviously, in some way infection with the type strain makes it possible for the other to move through and from the inoculated leaves, perhaps because infection with the type strain prevents cells around the necrotic lesions normally caused in this host by the aucuba strain from acquiring resistance to infection.

A consideration of all the evidence suggests that viruses remain localised less because they fail to move from cells they have infected than because the cells to which they move do not accept infection. Movement through leaf parenchyma is probably along a concentration gradient created by virus multiplication. As long as each lot of cells that is newly invaded supports virus multiplication, the gradient will be created again by a new cycle of multiplication, but should the cells be resistant the necessary gradient will not be established. Also, if tissues that are intrinsically resistant, or cells that have become so from effects of infection in other cells, can inactivate virus particles that enter them, they would completely bar further spread. The localisation of tobacco mosaic virus in hypersensitive hosts seems likely to depend on the production of such a barrier in the leaf parenchyma rather than that the virus cannot move into or out of the vascular tissues, for when *N. glutinosa* stems are grafted with infected tobacco or tomato scions the virus invades the young shoots and produces a lethal systemic infection.

Spread between adjacent cells. When systemic hosts are inoculated by rubbing their leaves with a virus preparation, there is clear evidence for movement of two different kinds. For some days virus spreads slowly from the initial infection points moving equally in all directions through the leaf parenchyma. Then, when the virus reaches the vascular tissue, it moves rapidly down the vein into the petiole and stem and soon reaches tissues remote from the site of infection. Fig. 12–1 illustrates the two patterns of movement, one producing the circular local lesion and the other the lesion spreading along the vein. The rate of spread from cell to cell in the leaf parenchyma, like every other process, depends on the temperature, and can be roughly gauged from the rate at which local lesions, either necrotic or chlorotic, increase in size; at 20° this may average about 1 mm a day, but the rate of increase and the ultimate size of lesions depends greatly on the physiological conditions of the inoculated leaves. In young plants that are growing rapidly and are highly susceptible to infection, lesions both increase in size faster and become larger than in older plants that are more resistant to infection, suggesting that the speed and distance of movement both depend on the extent to which the virus multiplies.

Fig. 12–1. Leaf of tobacco plant inoculated with diluted sap from plants infected with tobacco yellow mosaic virus. Treated with iodine eight days after inoculation. The uninfected leaf tissue has stained darkly, and the local lesion and the path taken by the virus down the vein to the petioles show clearly. (G. Samuel, 1931, Ann. appl. Biol. 18: 494).

Uppal (1934) measured the interval of time between rubbing the upper epidermis of *Nicotiana sylvestris* leaves with tobacco mosaic virus and detecting virus in the lower epidermis and calculated the average rate of movement to be about 8 mμ an hour, but it is unlikely that movement proceeded steadily and continuously at this rate. As discussed in Chapter 11, there are various reasons for thinking that virus in the inoculum rarely directly infects cells other than epidermal ones and that infections in deeper cells are caused by virus produced in the epidermis. Hence, such tests as Uppal's, or those in which the upper epidermis is removed at intervals after inoculation to see when this no longer prevents lesions from developing (Dijkstra, 1962), probably greatly underestimate the rate at which virus moves within and between cells, for most of the time measured is probably occupied not by moving but by successive cycles of virus multiplication. There is no evidence to show over what distance, or through how many cells, virus produced in one leaf cell can move to infect other cells, but at 20° the leaf mesophyll is infected within 10 hours of inoculation and lesions appear within 48 hours, when there are already several hundreds of cells not only infected but dying. This suggests that spread may be further than to cells contiguous to infected ones, but definite conclusions about distance of spread are impossible because it is unknown how many cells become directly infected from the inoculum at sites where lesions later develop.

How virus moves between leaf cells is also unknown, but the plasmodesmata, cytoplasmic strands that connect the cells, provide an obvious route, and it is generally accepted that movement is along these (Livingston, 1935; Sheffield, 1936; Martin and McKinney, 1938). Virus particles in infected cells seem to occur predominantly in the cytoplasm rather than the vacuolar sap, and the active streaming of the cytoplasm will certainly soon distribute virus particles throughout the cell and ensure they reach all the plasmodesmata. However, knowledge is so slight that, even if it is safe to assume plasmodesmata provide the paths, the identity of what moves along them has still to be established; as virus nucleic acids can initiate infection, and strains of some viruses seem not to produce readily extractable nucleoprotein particles that are stable in sap, spread of infection between parenchymatous cells may reflect movement of virus nucleic acid rather than of fully formed virus particles. The smaller size and the greater flexibility of nucleic acid seem obvious advantages in moving along the narrow plasmodesmata. In uninfected cells, "messenger" nucleic acid synthesised in the nucleus is thought to move through the cytoplasm and determine protein synthesis in the microsomes; similarly, virus nucleic acid synthesised in one cell may move along the plasmodesmata and affect the metabolism of other cells, but this still remains to be demonstrated.

There seems only one reason for questioning whether the plasmodesmata are the paths along which viruses, or their nucleic acids, move from cell to cell. Kassanis, Tinsley and Quak (1958) found that tobacco mosaic virus moves from infection sites in tobacco callus tissue growing in culture, but they failed to find any plasmodesmata connecting the individual callus cells or any holes in the walls of the callus cells comparable to those penetrated in normal cell walls by plasmodesmata. They state that the rate of movement, 1 mm per week, is approximately the rate at which the virus invades leaf parenchyma, but it is considerably slower, for lesions up to 4 mm in diameter are formed in leaves within less than a week. If movement depends on diffusion along a concentration gradient, it could be expected to be slower in callus tissue, because the virus reaches greater concentrations in leaf parenchyma. The apparent lack of plasmodesmata in the tissue cultures does not deny their role in normal tissues, but it does suggest that there is perhaps another way in which viruses may spread between cells.

Movement over distances. Movement through veins, petioles and stems can happen at speeds and over distances much greater than movement through leaf parenchyma (Holmes, 1930; 1931;

Fig. 12–2. Two leaves from the centres of plants becoming systemically invaded with tobacco yellow mosaic virus. Before staining with iodine these showed clearing of the veins. The darkly staining parts at the tips are not infected, the virus being restricted to the areas around the veins which are differentiated by the iodine staining. (G. Samuel, 1931, Ann. appl. Biol. 18: 494).

1932; Samuel, 1931; 1934). Whereas it may take a virus some days to produce a local lesion 3–4 mm in diameter, after reaching a vein it may move many centimetres in the next hour and occur in both the young leaves and roots. This movement, down the veins of inoculated leaves (Fig. 12–1), and up the veins of systemically infected leaves (Fig. 12–2), is far too fast to occur by diffusion along concentration gradients set up by virus infecting and multiplying in successive lots of parenchymatous cells in the phloem or xylem. That this rapid movement depends on the carriage of virus over long distances was first shown by Samuel (1934). He inoculated one terminal leaflet of tomato plants with tobacco mosaic virus and then at intervals after inoculation cut the plants into many portions, which were incubated to allow any virus in them to multiply, and then tested for the presence of virus. Virus was restricted to the inoculated leaflet for 3–days, but then rapidly spread to roots and young leaves. At the time virus was first moving into the stem, its distribution was not correlated with the position of the inoculated leaf, and stem portions near to this leaflet were often virus-free while ones further away contained virus. Hence virus particles (or something able to initiate infection) passed through considerable lengths of stem without infecting them. Samuel suggested that this movement over long distances occurs in the phloem and that its direction is determined by the flow of food coming from the leaves. Developing fruit trusses often became infected at the same time as roots and young leaves, whereas mature leaves adjacent to the trusses remained free from virus for weeks. All the leaves of small plants became infected soon after the youngest ones, but three weeks were needed for this to happen in medium-sized plants, and two months for plants in the fruiting stage. Fig. 12–3 is a diagram showing the invasion of a medium-sized plant. In large plants, infection of mature leaves is usually restricted to limited areas around the main veins even three months after the initial inoculation.

Other workers (Kunkel, 1939; Capoor, 1939; Matsumoto, 1941a, 1941b) confirmed Samuel's results, except that they did not find that tobacco mosaic virus always first moved to the roots. Kunkel found that roots and young leaves usually become infected simultaneously and that, when they did not, movement to the leaves first was as likely as to the roots. On first entering the stem, virus moved as much as 17 cm in an hour and, during this period of rapid transport, there were often virus-free pieces of stem positioned between pieces containing virus. Capoor (1939) got similar results with other viruses, which differed from one another and from tobacco mosaic virus only in the length of the interval between inoculating a leaf and the time when virus first entered the stem. All then soon travelled long distances and each often moved through stem pieces without infecting them, so these phenomena seem general.

Such tests show without doubt that infective material can pass through intrinsically susceptible tissues without multiplying in them, and they suggest that, at least when infective material starts to move from inoculated leaves, it does so only intermittently and not steadily. They also measure rates of movement, by showing where infective material has reached at a given time, but they do not show what would have been its destination had the plants not been cut into pieces. There is no reason to doubt that some infective material that reaches the stem from an initially inoculated leaf will travel the whole length of the vascular system to the youngest leaves or roots, but the extent to which such carriage over long distance is responsible for the ultimate systemic invasion shown in Fig. 12–3 is uncertain. During the many days taken to infect the mature leaves, there will be opportunities for virus to multiply wherever cells chance to become infected and there is no way to assess the relative contributions of local spread from these sites and of movement over long distances. It is to be expected that virus produced at every new site of infection will contribute its quota to the amount of infective material that is carried over long distances in the conducting tissues, but travel over long distances is something that can be measured only when virus is either moving into uninfected tissues or through tissues in which it does not multiply.

Whether ability to travel through the conducting tissues is an essential prerequisite to causing systemic infection is uncertain, but it seems likely. However, it is also likely to be something that all viruses can do equally, provided they get into the conducting tissues. The more important difference between virus-host combinations that result in systemic infections and those that do not may lie in the differing abilities of viruses to enter and leave the conducting tissues. The critical factor determining this difference may be whether or not cells near to the conducting tissues are susceptible to infection and support a high concentration of virus. The speed of travel when virus first enters the stem shows that they must be moving in the sieve tubes or the wood vessels; a virus that initially infects leaf epidermis and then the mesophyll will obviously have more chances of entering sieve tubes or wood vessels if it also multiplies in the companion cells and wood parenchyma than if it does not. A virus can pass through a piece of stem of a plant that is insusceptible, for instance when an infected scion of one variety is grafted to a stem piece of an immune one and this stem is then grafted onto a susceptible stock, but its passage is much more assured when the stem is susceptible. All that is needed to transmit viruses that infect dodder (*Cuscuta* sp.) is to have an infected and an uninfected plant simultaneously parasitised, whereas to transmit viruses that do not multiply in the dodder requires such extra treatments as keeping the uninfected plant in darkness while the infected one is in the light, plus drastically pruning the dodder (Cochran, 1946). These extra treatments are likely to increase the flow of metabolites through the dodder stems from the infected to the uninfected plant and so presumably increase the chances that any virus particles entering the dodder will be carried through the stems to the uninfected plant.

The fact that there are two possible ways of virus moving through a stem in which it multiplies may explain the conflicting conclusions

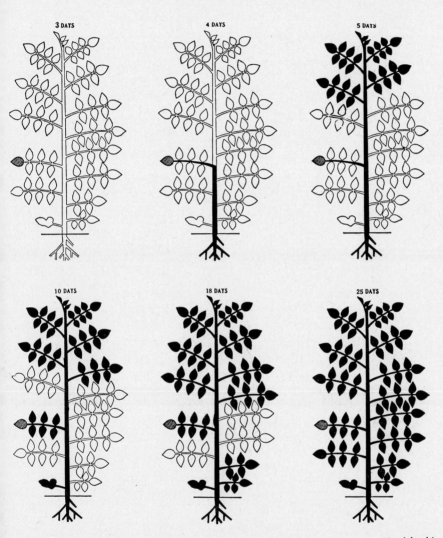

Fig. 12–3. Diagram showing the progress of tobacco mosaic virus (in black) through a medium-sized, young tomato plant. Based on tests made with Dwarf Champion plants about 15 in. high, growing in 6 in. pots in an unheated green-house. The inoculated leaflet is shown shaded. (G. Samuel, 1934, Ann. appl. Biol. 21: 90).

about the movement of tobacco mosaic virus, with which most workers have detected a rapid movement over considerable distances early in systemic invasions but some (Caldwell, 1930; 1931; 1934; Grainger, 1933) have reported only a steady, slow rate, suggesting diffusion along a concentration gradient. Caldwell showed that tobacco mosaic virus did not pass through pieces of stem killed by steaming, and he also concluded that, when the virus is experimentally introduced into the wood vessels, it remains there without causing a systemic infection unless the vessels are mechanically damaged. This points to the sieve tubes being the usual place where rapid movement occurs, and to other movement following multiplication in the stem cells that are susceptible.

The rates at which mechanically transmissible viruses move when they first enter stems resemble those at which viruses initially move when introduced by vectors that feed on the phloem or wood. Thus, sugar beet curly top virus has been found to move away from infection sites at 2.5 cm a minute (Bennett, 1934) and to travel 18 cm in 30 minutes (Severin, 1924); similarly, maize streak virus was detected 40 cm from infection sites in 2 hours (Storey, 1928). Both these viruses are transmitted by phloem feeders and there is much evidence that curly top occurs predominantly in the phloem, so these rapid movements probably occurred in the sieve tubes. However, similar rates have also been reported with the virus causing Pierce's disease of the grape, movement that presumably occurred in xylem vessels, for this virus is transmitted by xylem feeders (Houston, Esau and Hewitt, 1947). Similarly, there is evidence connecting the virus that causes phony disease of peach with the xylem (Hutchins, Cochran and Turner, 1951) and southern bean mosaic virus seems able to move in the xylem, at least in Pinto beans, for it regularly passed through pieces of stem killed by steaming (Schneider and Worley, 1959a, 1959b). Pinto bean is a local-lesion host for this virus and in these tests was either grafted to systemically infected Black Valentine beans or the virus was injected into their stems. The demonstration that the virus moved through the wood vessels in these unusual circumstances may not be relevant to what happens in normal systemic infections, but does suggest that movement through the wood should be considered more than it has been, and particularly interesting was the demonstration that the virus moved both upwards and downwards through the wood.

Most workers have concluded, usually from the direction of movement, that movement over distances occurs through the sieve tubes, but there have been few critical experiments to exclude movement through other tissues. Bennett (1934; 1937; 1956) found that

ugar beet curly top virus does not move across pieces of tobacco
tem in which the continuity of the phloem is broken by ringing
nd has produced much other evidence that this virus may be
argely confined to the phloem. He (1939; 1940) also found that
obacco mosaic virus did not cross ringed stems of *Nicotiana glauca*,
ι host in which it multiplies poorly, but cucumber mosaic virus, for
vhich *N. glauca* is a good host, did. Similarly, breaking the phloem
·ontinuity in tobacco stems only delayed and did not prevent the
)assage of tobacco mosaic virus, presumably because it could multi-
)ly in the tissues around the broken phloem and pass the gap in
his way. There is no call to question that most viruses can move
n the phloem or, indeed, that they usually do, and for viruses like
;ugar beet curly top this may be the only tissue in which movement
s possible, but viruses less limited in the type of cells in which they
nultiply readily may also have alternative ways of moving.

Movement through phloem has usually been postulated because
when moving to cause systemic infections viruses usually go in
lirections that metabolites could also be expected to take. Thus,
rom mature leaves, movement is to growing points, of both stem
ιnd roots, or to other points actively using food, such as fruit trusses.
Also, the direction of movement and the tissues that soon become
nfected can be changed by changing conditions that might be
·xpected to change the direction of food streams. For instance,
viruses in raspberry plants usually invade only inoculated canes and
their roots in the year of infection, but other canes of the plant will
ιlso become infected if they are pruned to force lateral shoots (Bennett, 1927). Keeping inoculated leaves in darkness will delay the
movement of virus from them, whereas keeping uninoculated mature leaves in darkness will make them become infected sooner than
they would if in the light. The many changes in direction of movement, with such different viruses as tobacco mosaic and sugar beet
curly top, described by Bennett (1934; 1937; 1939; 1940) as a result
of differential defoliation or etiolation, are all compatible with the
idea that the treatments acted by altering the translocation of metabolites, but this is not the only effect of defoliation and etiolation on
host-plant physiology that might determine whether virus reached
and multiplied in a given tissue. Roberts (1952) showed that several mechanically transmissible viruses could move from leaves
starch-free when inoculated and subsequently kept in darkness, conditions in which sugars were moving into the leaves. He also found
that when two different viruses were inoculated separately, one to
an upper and one to a lower starch-free leaf, both viruses later
occurred in both leaves, showing that there had been movement

downwards and upwards. Hence, although there is much evidenc
that movement, especially over long distances, may largely be deter
mined by the direction in which the main food stream is moving
viruses can also move against this stream. It is doubtful whethe
any large quantity of virus is moved over long distances in suc]
food streams. When potato plants are setting tubers, sugars wi]
flow from the leaves to the tubers in large quantities over a lon,
period, but immature tubers formed by plants infected with potat
virus X give extracts containing less than one-thousandth as mucl
virus as do leaf extracts. The amount of virus that reaches the tuber
is all important in assuring their infection and the perpetuation o
the virus, but the amount is trivial compared with what was in th
leaves of the parent plant or occurs later in the mature tuber whe
the virus multiplies in the sprouts (Bawden, Kassanis and Roberts
1948).

Several viruses that move rapidly into the roots from infected
shoots when inoculated to roots have been found either to remai
there or move into the shoots only after a long period (Bennett, 1940
Fulton, 1941; Roberts, 1950). The chances that infection will spread
from roots to shoots are increased by keeping plants in the dark, b
removing most of their leaves, or by cutting off their tops. This als
is compatible with the idea that these treatments reverse the usua
flow of food and, by encouraging the upward flow in the root siev
tubes, increase the chances of virus particles in them being carried
to the shoots, but the treatments may also be having other effect
on the behaviour of the viruses in the roots. Shoots of unpruned
plants growing in ordinary conditions often do become infected
from their roots, so movement against the usual food stream is pos
sible. Indeed, it seems to happen regularly from stem bases; when
these are inoculated below the lowest leaf, where presumably flow
through the sieve tubes is in the same direction as in the tap root
virus soon moves to infect the young leaves. Hence, there may b
another factor than the usual downward flow through the sieve
tubes responsible for the greater difficulty viruses have in moving
from roots to shoots than from shoots to roots. What this facto
is still remains to be determined, but it need be no more subtle thar
that the viruses usually multiply more readily and reach higher con
centrations in stem and leaf tissues than they do in root tissues.

Movement and multiplication of viruses are, of course, differen
things, but to treat them as though they are unconnected, as has
often been done, is very misleading. That virus has moved is usually
evident only because it multiplies in the cells to which it has moved
and whether it moves from an infected cell or tissue probably de-

pends more often than not on the extent to which it multiplies in that cell or tissue. When studying movement, it is important also to study virus multiplication, to try and see which of the two is primarily affected by changing conditions. For example, when tobacco plants inoculated with potato virus X are kept at over 30°, the virus rarely becomes systemic but will do so in such plants whose leaves are simultaneously infected with potato virus Y (Close, 1962). Virus Y obviously makes it possible for virus X to move, but how it does this is less certain. The movement may be only a secondary effect, simply an inevitable consequence of the fact that virus Y greatly increases the multiplication of virus X in leaves at 30° and so allows it to reach amounts that ensure it reaches and enters the veins. Similarly, the fact that systemically infected plants growing at high temperatures often produce virus-free shoots is not conclusive evidence that high temperatures prohibit movement through stems, for an equally likely explanation of the phenomenon is that high temperatures act by their effect on virus multiplication. The chances that virus will move will be decreased by decreasing the virus content of already infected cells and any that does move is less likely to multiply because infection by some viruses is prevented by high temperatures.

Many viruses that can ultimately invade all the mature vegetative tissues of their hosts are not seed-transmitted in these hosts. Something bars their entry to pollen and egg mother cells. This something is unlikely to be lack of continuity between such cells and vegetative cells, because some viruses do infect these cells. Hence, the critical factor determining seed-transmission may be whether the cells surrounding the reproductive ones are susceptible to infection and allow virus to move through them by maintaining a concentration gradient resulting from continued multiplication. That immature cells are less favourable hosts than mature cells for tobacco mosaic virus is suggested by the great increase in virus content of sap extracted at increasing distances from the apical meristems in both roots and stems (White, 1943; Limasset, Cornuet and Gendron, 1949; Kassanis, 1957). Hence the reason that apical meristems of plants otherwise systemically infected are often virus-free (Morel and Martin, 1952, 1955) may be because the virus is barred from them by the insusceptibility to infection of the cells immediately behind them. The multiplication of tobacco mosaic virus near to the apical meristems of tomato roots is reported to be much enhanced by treating the roots with the chelating agent ethylenediamine tetraacetate (Crowley and Hanson, 1960), which may act by disturbing the synthesis of normal nucleic acids and proteins.

Whether or not viruses occur in apical meristems, therefore, possibly depends on their ability to become established and multiply in dividing or recently divided cells, in which the synthesis of nucleic acid and protein is likely to be proceeding much more actively than in mature cells. If this is so, the less able a virus is to compete with normal syntheses, the more mature a cell will need to be before it becomes susceptible, and the further the virus is likely to be kept from any kind of apical meristem.

REFERENCES

BAWDEN, F. C., and B. KASSANIS. 1947. Ann. appl. Biol. 34: 127.
———, B. KASSANIS, and F. M. ROBERTS. 1948. *Ibid.* 35: 250.
BENDA, G. T. A. 1957. Virology 3: 601.
BENNETT, C. W. 1927. Mich. Agr. Exp. Sta. Tech. Bull. 80.
———. 1934. J. agric. Res. 48: 665.
———. 1937. *Ibid.* 54: 479.
———. 1939. Phytopathology 29: 1.
———. 1940. J. agric. Res. 60: 361.
———. 1956. Ann. Rev. Pl. Physiol. 7: 143.
CALDWELL, J. 1930. Ann. appl. Biol. 17: 429.
———. 1931. *Ibid.* 18: 279.
———. 1934. *Ibid.* 21: 191.
CAPOOR, S. P. 1939. Thesis, London University.
CLOSE, R. 1962. Ph. D. thesis, London University.
COCHRAN, G. W. 1946. Phytopathology 36: 396.
COHEN, M., A. SIEGEL, M. ZAITLIN, W. R. HUDSON, and S. G. WILDMAN. 1957. Phytopathology 47: 694.
CROWLEY, N. C., and J. B. HANSON. 1960. Virology 12: 604.
DIJKSTRA, J. 1962. Virology 18: 142.
FARKAS, G. L., Z. KIRALY, and F. SOLYMOSY. 1960. Virology 12: 408.
FULTON, R. W. 1941. Phytopathology 31: 575.
GRAINGER, J. 1933. Ann. appl. Biol. 20: 236.
HOLMES, F. O. 1930. Amer. J. Bot. 17: 789.
———. 1931. Contr. Boyce Thompson Inst. 3: 163.
———. 1932. *Ibid.* 4: 297.
———. 1938. Phytopathology 28: 58.
———. 1946. *Ibid.* 36: 643.
HOUSTON, B. R., K. ESAU, and W. B. HEWITT. 1947. Phytopathology 37: 247.
HUTCHINS, L. M., L. C. COCHRAN, and W. F. TURNER. 1951. U.S. Dept. Agr. Handbook 10: 17.
KASSANIS, B. 1957. Ann. appl. Biol. 45: 422.
———, T. W. TINSLEY, and F. QUAK. 1958. *Ibid.* 46: 11.
KUNKEL, L. O. 1939. Phytopathology 29: 684.
LIMASSET, P., P. CORNUET, and Y. GENDRON. 1949. C. R. Acad. Sci., Paris 228: 1888.
LIVINGSTON, L. G. 1935. Amer. J. Bot. 22: 75.
MARTIN, L. F., and H. H. McKINNEY. 1938. Science 88: 458.
MATSUMOTO, T. 1941a. Trans. nat. Hist. Soc. Formosa 31: 201.
———. 1941b. *Ibid.* 31: 275.
MOREL, G., and C. MARTIN. C. R. Acad. Sci., Paris 235: 1324.
———, and ———. 1955. C. R. Acad. Agric., Fr. 41: 472.
ROBERTS, D. A. 1952. Phytopathology 42: 381.

ROBERTS, F. M. 1950. Ann. appl. Biol. 37: 385.
Ross, A. F. 1961a. Virology 14: 329.
———. 1961a. Ibid. 14: 340.
SAMUEL, G. 1931. Ann. appl. Biol. 18: 494.
———. 1934. Ibid. 21: 90.
SCHNEIDER, I. R., and J. F. WORLEY. 1959a. Virology 8: 230.
———, and ———. 1959b. Ibid. 8: 243.
SEVERIN, H. H. P. 1924. Phytopathology 14: 80.
SHEFFIELD, F. M. L. 1936. Ann. appl. Biol. 23: 506.
STOREY, H. H. 1928. Ann. appl. Biol. 15: 1.
UPPAL, B. N. 1934. Indian J. agric. Sci. 4: 865.
WHITE, P. R. 1943. A Handbook of Plant Tissue Culture. Ronald Press Co., New
York.
YARWOOD, C. E. 1953. Phytopathology 43: 490.
———. 1960. Ibid. 50: 741.

chapter

13

Genetic Variability

The idea that plant viruses might vary seems not to have been readily acceptable to plant pathologists. It was not even mooted until more than 30 years after viruses were first discovered and even then was for long unappreciated by the many workers who continued the practice of giving a new name to any virus found causing a previously undescribed syndrome. Why this should have been so is puzzling, for that viruses could vary in virulence was evident enough from the work of Pasteur and his colleagues in the 1880s, before viruses were recognised as a distinct type of pathogen, in producing an attenuated form of rabies virus to use as a vaccine. It is true that workers with plant viruses had no such practical incentive to seek avirulent forms, but it is odd that they should have been so uninfluenced by work with animal viruses and have continued so long to treat viruses as immutable.

The first indications of virulence changes in plant viruses came from work by Carsner (1925), Johnson (1925) and McKinney (1926, 1929). Carsner found that passage through *Chenopodium murale* changed sugar beet curly top virus so that it produced less severe symptoms in beet. Continued propagation in beet left the attenuated form apparently unchanged, but Lackey (1932) showed later that its virulence towards beet was enhanced by passage through *Stellaria media*. Johnson found that when plants recently inoculated with tobacco mosaic virus were kept at 35–37° they not only produced less severe symptoms than at lower temperatures, but that the virus from such plants also produced only mild symptoms when inoculated to plants grown at lower temperatures. McKinney obtained forms that caused a more severe disease than ordinary tobacco mosaic by the simple procedure of taking inoculum from

292

selected areas of infected leaves. In addition to the customary mild mosaic, infected leaves sometimes show bright yellow spots (Fig. 13–1) and inoculum taken from these spots caused a general yellow mottle, very different from the usual mosaic. McKinney suggested that the virus in the yellow spots was not a contaminant in the customary use of the word but a variant derived from the ordinary type. He also noticed that plants inoculated simultaneously with mixtures

Fig. 13–1. Tobacco leaf showing symptoms of tobacco mosaic. In addition to the general mild type of mottling, the leaf shows a bright yellow spot. Inoculum taken from this spot causes a general yellow chlorosis. (L. O. Kunkel, 1934, Ann. Rep. Quebec Soc. Prot. Plants 25–26: 23).

of the two viruses showed symptoms intermediate between those caused by either alone, and that the smaller was the proportion of one virus in the inoculum, the fewer were the symptoms characteristic of it and the more slowly they developed.

McKinney's observations were the first to suggest that individual variants (forms or strains) of a given virus interfere with each other's multiplication, a phenomenon established independently by Thung (1931) and Salaman (1933), who both stressed its importance in identifying symptomatologically distinct viruses as related strains. From a tobacco plant with mosaic Thung obtained a variant that produced a white mosaic when inoculated to uninfected plants, but failed to produce any additional symptoms when inoculated to plants already systemically infected with ordinary tobacco mosaic virus. Similarly, Salaman showed that tobacco plants already infected with strains of potato virus X that cause only mild mottlings developed no further symptoms when inoculated with virulent strains that on their own cause necrotic rings or yellow mottles. The discoveries that strains of one virus seem mutually antagonistic and that plants can be protected against the effects of virulent strains by infection with an avirulent one greatly stimulated work on variability and also began to indicate its extent, for they provided a method whereby variants could be recognised as such. At about the same time another method for doing this stemmed from the discovery that plant viruses are antigenic (Beale, 1928, 1929, 1931), for the antisera produced by injecting viruses into animals proved to be group specific rather than type specific (Gratia, 1933a, 1933b; Birkeland, 1934); that is to say, strains of one virus are serologically related and react specifically with each other's antisera, but do not react with antisera made against other viruses. Serological and plant-protection tests indicated relationships between many viruses previously assumed to be unrelated, and the identification as related strains of viruses with widely different properties showed that virulence is far from being the only variable feature of plant viruses.

Range of variability. The kind of change most often reported is in pathogenicity or host range, which are indeed the only variable features yet recognised in some viruses. Whether such changes are also the commonest that happen is less certain, because they are the most sought and the easiest to recognise. Certainly there are many reports of other properties changing, as will be evident from comments in earlier chapters of this book on the behaviour of different virus strains. Indeed, it is difficult to think of a single property that has not, with some virus or other, been found to vary. Transmissibility by a given vector; stability in leaf extracts; crystal form (Fig. 13–2); resistance to inactivation by specific treatments; isoelectric point; electrophoretic mobility; antigenic structure; aminoacid composition; these are only some of the properties that have been found to differ between strains. Until recently, particle shape and size seemed a constant feature, but since the discovery that some strains of tobacco rattle virus fail to produce the customary rod-shaped particles stable *in vitro* (Cadman, 1962), even particle morphology must be placed in the category of variable characters.

The variability of most viruses has yet to be explored, so comparisons between them are suspect, but it does seem probable that different viruses, and even different strains of one virus, differ in the readiness with which they undergo change. It is true that type tobacco mosaic virus has been studied more intensively than any

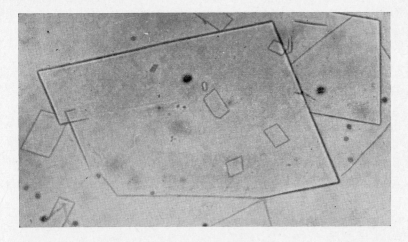

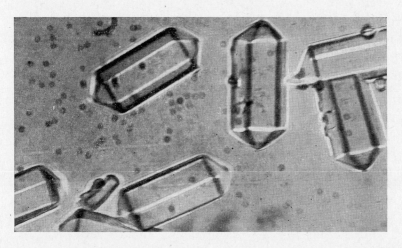

Fig. 13–2. Serologically related strains of a tobacco necrosis virus that consistently crystallise in different ways. *Above:* thin lozenge-shaped plates formed by one strain. *Below:* hexagonal prisms formed by the other. × 200.

other, and this could in part explain the fact that more variants have been described from it than from any other, but it does also seem intrinsically more variable than most, both in the frequency with which it varies and in the extent to which the variants differ from one another. Up to 2% of the lesions produced in *Nicotiana glutinosa* by inoculation with sap from systemically infected tobacco have been found to contain variants that differ in their pathogenicity from the main type (Kunkel, 1940). From such local lesions, Jensen (1933, 1936, 1937) distinguished over 50 variants by the readiness with which they infected, the kind of lesion they caused and the extent to which they multiplied in, the differential hosts tobacco, tomato, *Nicotiana sylvestris* and *N. glutinosa*, and many others have since been identified by their ability to infect cucumber (Bawden and Pirie, 1937) or French bean (Lister and Thresh, 1955) systemically, or by their different physical and chemical properties (Siegel and Wildman, 1954; Ginoza and Atkinson, 1955). By contrast, tomato aucuba mosaic virus, which is closely related serologically to tobacco mosaic virus, has been described as varying only in the intensity of mottling it causes. Also, whereas variants that in some ways resemble the aucuba strain are readily isolated from plants infected with tobacco mosaic virus, the aucuba strain seems never to have produced a variant able to cause a systemic mild mosaic in tobacco. Similarly, individual variants from tobacco mosaic virus seem to differ in stability; whereas some continue apparently unchanged through long periods and many sub-cultures, others produce further variants, some of which may be more and some less like tobacco mosaic virus than their immediate forebears.

The behaviour of mutant strains from different sources shows that some characters can change while others do not. Holmes (1936) found that the other properties of variants that cause yellow mottlings in tobacco depended on the origin of the variants; for example, those derived from an invasive line of tobacco mosaic virus themselves also rapidly became systemic in tobacco, whereas those derived from a slow invader did not. Similarly, twelve variants from a strain causing necrosis in tomato all possessed this property, whereas variants from other sources rarely did (Norval, 1938). More often than not, changes in virulence are independent of changes in aminoacid composition, and many clinically different strains, including one that causes no symptoms in tobacco, have the same composition; however, variants that cause only necrotic local lesions in *Nicotiana sylvestris* seem usually to have two or more aminoacids different from those in strains that become systemic (Tsugita, 1962a, 1962b). Not all the properties of viruses that are measured will be independent of one another, for all those that depend on the aminoacid composition will, of course, change when this changes. There is evidence with other viruses than tobacco mosaic of individual characters able to change independently of one another. From the behaviour of potato virus X in tobacco, Salaman (1938) reported five such and there may well be others, because the kind of symptoms caused in tobacco are not correlated with the ability to cause top-necrosis in specified potato varieties. Thus, although viruses have often been likened to genes, the analogy is probably inapt; they much more resemble collections of genes, each of which can change individually so that variants contain different combinations of genetic units.

Differences between parent strains and variants obtained from them experimentally have mostly been in pathogenicity, but a few variants of tobacco mosaic virus, such as the one called U2 by Siegel and Wildman (1954) and a minority of those isolated from chemically treated virus preparations (Tsugita, 1962a, 1962b), also show considerable differences in aminoacid composition and physical properties. Most strains with widely different properties from the type strain have been found in naturally infected plants, usually species taxonomically remote from tobacco, and it was reasonable to assume they had reached their current states as a result of many changes accumulated during considerable periods of evolution along separate and diverging paths. However, the changes in a strain found causing a systemic mosaic in leguminous plants when propagated in different hosts show that no protracted period of evolution is needed to produce variants that differ greatly in their composition and properties (Bawden, 1958). As obtained from systemically infected legumes, this strain differs from type mosaic virus at least as much as does any other known strain; it has a very different aminoacid composition; it is only slightly related to the type strain serologically; it has different electrophoretic behaviour, showing at least two components, the major with mobility -4.2 and the minor -9.4×10^{-5} cm.^{2} sec. $^{-1}$V.$^{-1}$, the same as the type strain; it goes insoluble in pH 7 phosphate buffer; it is much more susceptible to inactivation by ultraviolet radiation; weight for weight it causes many fewer necrotic local lesions in *Nicotiana glutinosa*, and the lesions are smaller and take twice as long to develop; in *N. glutinosa* kept at over 30° it multiplies without causing symptoms, whereas the type strain causes large chlorotic spots and rings (Fig. 2–5).

White Burley tobacco plants inoculated from leguminous plants systemically infected with this strain usually develop many small necrotic local lesions; most such plants show no other symptoms, but a few become systemically infected and the uninoculated leaves show symptoms resembling ordinary mosaic. The virus in these uninoculated leaves also closely resembles the type strain serologically, in its aminoacid composition, and in its pathogenic behaviour, including giving only black necrotic local lesions in Pinto beans. Other bean varieties in which the type strain does not produce necrotic local lesions, also give no such local lesions with this strain; most such inoculated plants remain seemingly unaffected but occasional ones become systemically infected and show mosaic symptoms, and these plants contain virus resembling the original form from legumes.

There is nothing unexpected in a stock of virus changing its behaviour as a result of passage through a new host. What was novel in the behaviour of the strain from legumes was the magnitude of the changes and that such changes should be reversible. Previous changes were explicable by inocula containing more than one variant, not all of which invade the new host systemically. Thus, Johnson (1947), who found that bulk cultures of tobacco mosaic virus were less virulent towards tobacco after passage through *Eryngium aquaticum*, readily explained this effect by tests with single-lesion isolates, which showed that bulk cultures contained virulent and avirulent variants and that the virulent ones multiplied only locally in *E. aquaticum*. Single-lesion isolates of the strain from legumes, however, behaved exactly like bulk cultures, and the reversibility of the change seems inexplicable by postulating that the different hosts act solely by differentially favouring one variant of many that infect them from the inoculum. The "purity" of single-lesion isolates is always suspect, but the tobacco form of this variant seems unlikely to be carried as such through single lesions caused in *Nicotiana glutinosa* by the legume form. Not only does the tobacco form produce its typical lesions when added in small amounts to much of the bean form, but it produces them in similar numbers as when inoculated alone. Also, if its presence were not immediately obvious from the appearance of the lesions, it should become so during a second passage in *N. glutinosa*, for the tobacco form multiplies much more extensively than the bean form in this host, but as many as 10 successive inoculations from single lesions failed to give any lesions typical of the tobacco form.

A small amount of the bean form in the presence of much of the tobacco form would pass undetected by inoculations to *N. glutinosa*, but as the bean form is much more susceptible to inactivation by ultraviolet radiation, its existence in inocula can be excluded by irradiation. It has an inactivation constant four times as large as the tobacco form, so preparations of the tobacco form irradiated to leave 10^{-5} of their initial infectivity would retain only 10^{-20} of any infectivity conferred by particles of the bean form that might have been present initially. That is, any present would all be inactivated, as indeed are preparations containing $2mg/ml$ of the bean form when exposed to this amount of radiation. Yet, when isolates obtained from single lesions produced in *N. glutinosa* by such irradiated preparations of the tobacco form were bulked in tobacco and then inoculated to French beans, some plants became systemically infected with the bean form. Hence there seemed little doubt that this bean form was derived from the tobacco form by changes happening in plants infected after the irradiation, and was not selected from a contaminant in the initial inoculum.

As described in Chapter 11, the multiplication of most viruses leads to a range of different end products and that the range may be even greater than usual with this strain from legumes is indicated by the electrophoretic pattern. Infectivity tests have given no evidence that the variability extends to the occurrence in sap from systemically infected beans of particles with the infective behaviour of the tobacco form, for even inoculum consisting of the component with the same electrophoretic mobility as the tobacco form gave no lesions in *N. glutinosa* characteristic of this form. However, this does not prove that such particles do not occur. To get lesions demands inocula containing at least 10^7 particles per ml., so that many could lie hidden in sap from beans. When multiplying in any host, therefore, each form of the strain may produce occasional particles of the other form, but only when they are produced in hosts where they, but not particles of the other form, can become systemic will they multiply enough to reach concentrations where they become detectable.

The type strain of tobacco mosaic virus and some others can also undergo changes of the same magnitude as the strain from legumes, but do so even less rarely, for very many French bean plants usually need to be inoculated to get one that becomes systemically infected; the virus in such bean plants differs greatly from the type strain and closely resembles the strain found in naturally infected legumes. Inoculations with the tomato aucuba strain, however, have failed to infect beans systemically, again suggesting it may be intrinsically less variable than the type strain. Exposing infected plants to high temperatures further suggests this. Many workers (Johnson, 1925, 1947; Holmes, 1934; Sukhov, 1956; Kassanis, 1957; Mundry, 1957a) have reported that when plants infected with the type strain are kept at about 36° they soon come to contain variants less virulent towards tobacco than the type strain and that multiply more abundantly at the high temperature, but the tomato aucuba strain produced no such variants (Kassanis, 1957). There seems little reason to doubt that such variants of the type strain are usually produced in the plants at high temperature rather than being selected from a mixed inoculum. Indeed, Johnson (1947) and Sukhov (1956) suggested that the high temperatures were actually causing the changes by increasing the normal mutation rate, but for this there is no definite evidence. Similar variants do occur in plants kept at lower temperatures, but are then less readily isolated because they compete less well with the parent strain and are fewer in proportion to the total virus content. However, as they multiply more readily than the type strain at 36°, they there soon reach proportions able to be isolated readily from single lesions. Mundry (1957a) states that a day at high temperature is all that is needed to be able to isolate such variants and that most occur when the day of treatment is immediately after inoculation. The changes in behaviour of virus strains when propagated in plants at high temperatures, as when propagated in a new host, therefore probably depend on the new conditions selecting randomly produced mutants, which in the old conditions had no property that favoured their survival in competition with the parent type.

Another virus that seems unusually variable is tobacco rattle, which in gross morphology resembles tobacco mosaic virus. Without changing host plant species or the conditions in which plants are growing, cultures of the virus can change so that within a few months they are only remotely related serologically to the stock from which they derived. Also, single-lesion isolates from plants themselves infected by inoculation from a single lesion often differ, not only in the type of lesion they cause, but also in the readiness with which they are transmitted with sap as the inoculum (Cadman and Harrison, 1959). More than half the lesions produced by a culture derived from one readily transmissible may contain virus not readily transmissible by sap inoculations; this change, apparently correlated with the loss of ability to produce the stable rod-shaped virus particles, seems to be irreversible, for although the variants are readily transmitted by using phenol-extracts of infected leaves as inocula, such transmissions have not increased transmissibility by sap inoculations (Cadman, 1962). What may be comparable changes producing variants less able than their parents to form virus particles that are stable in vitro have also been reported with tobacco necrosis (Babos and Kassanis, 1962) and tobacco mosaic (Siegel, Zaitlin and Sehgal, 1962) viruses. Presumably these defective variants must behave in vivo in some way that selects them in preference to their parents, but in what way is unknown, though more rapid multiplication of the nucleic acid, or more ready movement between cells, are obvious possibilities. This kind of variant may be much commoner than suspected, for the difficulty with which they are transmitted by customary methods of inoculation means that their occurrence would rarely be recognised unless specifically sought.

Causes of variation. The same end result is obtained whether plants are infected with inocula containing whole virus particles or preparations of disrupted virus that contain little if anything other than nucleic acid. This is evidence enough that the individual characteristics of virus strains must be determined by the identity of the nucleic acid, and that changes in behaviour reflect changes in the nucleic acid. The chemistry of nucleic acids is discussed in Chapter 8 and need not be further considered here, except to repeat that they consist of four nucleotides, which in different viruses occur in characteristically different proportions, whereas strains of one virus usually have nucleic acids with the same gross compositions. Differences between strains of viruses, therefore, are thought to depend on differences between the order in which the nucleotides are arranged in the nucleic acid, and this sequence is also thought to represent a code that determines the order in which aminoacids become incorporated in the virus proteins.

What evidence there is about the sequence of nucleotides does suggest that it differs in strains of tobacco mosaic virus with widely different aminoacid compositions (Knight *et al*, 1962), but much more evidence will be needed before sequential differences are fully established. That the character of the nucleic acid determines the kind of protein synthesised is obvious enough from the different proteins produced in the same host when infected with nucleic acids from different viruses or different virus strains. However, in these conditions nucleic acid is also multiplying, and possibly doing many other things that might affect protein synthesis, other than simply acting as a template guiding the sequential arrangement of aminoacids. Evidence in support of the idea that there is such direct guidance comes from the report that nucleic acid from tobacco mosaic virus influences the incorporation of aminoacids by a cell-free system from *Escherichia coli;* the added nucleic acid not only stimulated protein synthesis *in vitro,* but the material produced precipitated specifically with antiserum to tobacco mosaic virus and had some polypeptides resembling those in the virus protein (Tsugita *et al,* 1962). The material synthesised was not virus protein, for it had a different N-terminal aminoacid and also contained methionine and histidine, but that the virus nucleic acid had any effect on the synthesis and that there were similarities to the virus protein is perhaps more significant than that there were also differences. The interpretation of these results is far from certain, but they carry the suggestion that, if the sequence of nucleotides does represent a code translatable into aminoacid sequences, the resulting translation depends on the environment in which it is made.

The effects of treating tobacco mosaic virus with nitrous acid have also been advanced as evidence that the specificity of the nucleic acid is determined by the sequence of the nucleotides. Nitrous acid is a deaminating agent and acts on nucleic acids to convert adenine, guanine and cytosine respectively to hypoxanthine, xanthine and uracil. It does this to the nucleic acid of tobacco mosaic virus (Schuster and Schramm, 1958), so there is no reason to doubt that, by replacing cytosine with uracil, it can alter the sequence of nucleotides normally occurring in the nucleic acid. It is an inactivating agent and is generally accepted as also being mutagenic, that is able to produce changes in nucleic acid that are perpetuated in the progeny (Mundry and Gierer, 1958; Mundry 1959; Siegel, 1960; Tsugita and Fraenkel-Conrat, 1960; Rappaport and Wildman, 1962). Again, there is no doubt that nitrous acid greatly affects the qualitative behaviour of tobacco mosaic virus preparations and that variants are much more readily isolated from plants inoculated with preparations after partial inactivation with nitrous acid than before. Only Bawden (1959) has questioned whether this could be because the treatment allows already existing variants to be more readily selected rather than that it produces them. Even though everyone else has answered "no" and concluded that nitrous acid causes the reported hereditable changes, the question still seems worth the asking, for at least two reasons; first, not all the phenomena fit readily into the context of the mutants being chemically produced; secondly, as shown later, similar variants are isolated after treatment with other chemicals than deaminating agents, so if these too are producing the variants, it becomes necessary to question the idea that nucleotide sequence determines genetic specificity and protein synthesis.

There would be little need to question the action of nitrous acid if it produced variants from a homogeneous starting culture, or novel kinds of variants, but it does not. We have already seen that preparations of tobacco mosaic virus may contain about 2% of their total particles as variants distinguishable from the main type, and treatment with nitrous acid has not produced variants differing from those occurring naturally. Indeed, treatment with nitrous acid seems simply to increase the ease of getting variants from strains already known to produce them. Bawden (1961) got no evidence of mutation during the inactivation of the tomato aucuba strain and Siegel (1960) detected many fewer variants of strains U2 and U4 than of the type strain. These other strains inactivate as readily as the type strain but are intrinsically less variable, so the starting preparations contained few or no variants.

The failure to get novel variants by treatment with nitrous acid is not evidence against the idea that the acid is mutagenic, because it is reasonable to expect such a treatment to produce the kinds of changes that also occur most often spontaneously. Nevertheless, when the treatment seems only to be producing variants of the kind that existed before the treatment was applied, it is necessary to consider whether the treatment is favouring the selection of those already in existence. Mundry (1959) unhesitatingly rejects the idea that selection can possibly explain the fact that the number of necrotic local lesions formed in Java tobacco increases while the number formed in Xanthi and *Nicotiana glutinosa* falls after tobacco mosaic virus is treated with nitrous acid. In doing so he may well be correct, but it would be premature to conclude that the only possible explanation for the increased number of necrotic lesions in Java is that the particles causing them represent mutants produced by the nitrous acid. Knowledge about the infection process, the effects of nitrous acid on type tobacco mosaic, how chemically changed particles might affect infection, or how to interpret the meaning of infectivity assays made on different hosts or by comparing necrotic with chlorotic local lesions on one host, is not yet so advanced as to be sure that changes in the ability of strains to interfere with one another could not play some part in the phenomenon. If, for example, nitrous acid affects the type strain so that it multiplies and moves less readily in Java tobacco than previously but still causes lesions in Xanthi tobacco or *Nicotiana glutinosa*, the number of necrotic lesions in Java would increase proportionally to those in the other hosts simply because the existing variants that cause necrotic lesions in Java would have less competition there from the type strain. There is nothing fanciful in this suggestion, for Mundry and Gierer (1958) and Siegel (1960) both report that extracts from more than a third of the lesions produced in Xanthi or *N. glutinosa* by virus treated with nitrous acid failed to infect tobacco. Such a loss of infectivity towards tobacco is, of course, reasonably regarded to be a mutagenic action of nitrous acid, but the mutations would be in other particles than the ones causing the local lesions in Java and would not have produced the variants causing these lesions. When such things are happening as virus losing its infectivity for one host but not for another, it is more than usually necessary to be cautious about drawing conclusions from assays used to measure inactivation on one host and mutation rate on another.

The most striking effect of nitrous acid is the way it increases the ratio between the number of necrotic lesions produced in Java tobacco and the number produced in Xanthi or *N. glutinosa*, but there seems little agreement between the number of necrotic lesions produced in Java and the number produced in the other hosts that contain virus able to produce necrotic lesions in Java. Bawden (1961) tested 200 lesions produced in Xanthi leaves by a treated preparation of tobacco mosaic virus that at the dilution used was giving more than 10% as many necrotic lesions in Java as in Xanthi, but none contained virus that produced necrotic lesions in Java. The lesions tested were taken at random, so included many of the small ones which Siegel (1960) found were increased in proportion to the total number after treatment with nitrous acid. The individual lesions produced very different numbers of infections when macerated and inoculated to further Xanthi, the large ones producing many more than the small ones, some of which produced none, but lesion type was not consistently reproduced; inoculum from the large lesions always produced some small lesions and inoculum from small lesions produced an occasional large one.

While nitrous acid was the only substance known to produce these effects, for earlier claims to have produced mutations by radiations were shown by Mundry (1957b) to be explicable by selection of already existing variants, there was good reason to assume that any mutagenic action came from changes in nucleotide sequence occasioned by the deamination of cytosine to uracil. However, similar effects have now been obtained with N-bromosuccinimide and the alkylating agents methyl iodide, dimethylsulphate and propylene oxide (Fraenkel-Conrat, 1961). These, like nitrous acid, yield variants that resemble the naturally occurring ones, in that more than half differ from the type strain in pathogenicity but not in aminoacid composition, and others fall into two groups, one of which has three or fewer aminoacid differences from the type strain and the other about 16 differences (i.e. positions in the protein chain where one aminoacid in the type strain is substituted by another in the variants) (Tsugita and Fraenkel-Conrat, 1962; Tsugita, 1962a, 1962b). Those with 16 substitutions also have them scattered throughout the peptide chain, something that seems incompatible on current coding theories with the conclusion (Mundry and Gierer, 1958; Siegel, 1960) that nitrous acid causes mutations by single deaminations. There is, of course, the obvious explanation for the similarity between variants, however obtained, that they are all natural variants, but Tsugita and Fraenkel-Conrat (1962) dismiss this possibility and are fully satisfied that the variants were produced and not selected by the treatment, although there is no critical evidence that any of the variants isolated after chemical treatment has been changed chemically in a way that is perpetuated. If

t is correct to reject selection, then it must be accepted that mutation can occur for other reasons than changing the sequence of
nucleotides and that something other than the sequence of nucleotides can determine the arrangement of aminoacids in the virus
proteins. If different chemical treatments are producing the same
end results, they are unlikely to be doing so by producing chemical
changes in virus nucleic acid that are duplicated when the virus
multiplies. It seems more probable that, if the treatments have any
mutagenic action, it lies in their common ability to render inopera-
tive specific unit structures in the nucleic acid, rather than in producing any new replicating units. If the individual properties of
virus strains are determined by localised specific configurations in
the nucleic acid, then changes that prevent the normal replication
of these configurations would eliminate them individually. We have
already seen that type tobacco mosaic virus seems more variable
than most other strains and perhaps this is because it has more
dispensable characters than most others. Certainly the behaviour
of most of its variants suggests the loss of such dominating characters as ability to invade hosts systemically, to multiply extensively
and to move rapidly. Some of these characters, too, seem to be
determined by parts of the nucleic acid not responsible for coding
the sequence of aminoacids, because many pathogenically different
strains have seemingly identical proteins.

The causes of variation still remain to be identified but the possibility of identifying them is increasing so rapidly that unequivocal
evidence is likely before long. Meanwhile it is safest to assume
there will be more than one cause. Although sequence of nucleotides now seems likely to be the major thing determining genetic
specificity, it would be decidedly premature to assume that nothing
else does. Changes in genetic behaviour need not be sought only
in individual changes in nucleotides, such as the simple replacement
of cytosine by uracil. As the meaning of many words often depends
entirely on their context, so a given sequence of nucleotides may
have different effects depending on its position in the nucleic acid
particle, and rearranging the order in which the same individual
oligonucleotides are brought together could also be an important
source of genetic variability. Producing a chain of 6,000 or so
nucleotides in a required order is a process that requires remarkably
close control if there are not to be frequent errors. Single cells infected with tobacco mosaic virus may contain more than 10^6 virus
particles and a local lesion more than 10^9. An error rate in assembly
of only one in a million could give a thousand aberrant (mutant)
particles in one local lesion. With such possibilities for new variants

in these immense populations, it is the stability of bulk cultures rather than their variability that seems more cause for surprise. This stability can be attributed to natural selection, for few variants will be better fitted than their parents to survive in the conditions for which their parents have already long been selected, and the more they depart from their parents the less likely are they to be able to supersede their parents in these conditions. In constant conditions natural selection will operate mainly as a stabilising factor, but when conditions change it will operate to select any variants with extreme properties that are better fitted to survive in the new conditions. The evolutionary value of great variability is mainly in increasing the survival chances when the environment (host plant or growing conditions) is changed; its small value otherwise is shown by the fact that none of the variants yet obtained as single-lesion isolates from tobacco mosaic virus competes successfully with the type strain in tobacco plants grown under usual conditions.

Genetic recombination. To explain the variability in plant viruses there is no need to postulate any mechanism other than random mutation, for as shown in the previous paragraph, populations are such that mutation rates much smaller than those reported for many other systems would soon produce very many variants. Even with tobacco mosaic virus, of which 2% of the particles in extracts from long-infected plants may differ from the main type, there is no need to postulate an extremely high mutation rate, for variants multiplying to different extents over a considerable time could lead to this end result. Many of the variants are those that cause necrotic lesions in Java tobacco and these may well reach larger amounts per cell than the type strain but are dominated by the type strain because of its ability to become systemic. However, because there is no need to postulate another mechanism does not mean there is no other, and certainly the many variants that occur in plants infected with tobacco mosaic virus would fit more easily into a concept not demanding repeated new mutations. For instance, it seems likely that there are many genetic differences between type tobacco mosaic virus and the variants that infect leguminous plants systemically. These may, of course, happen simultaneously in one particle or *seriatim* in successive progenies of one particle, but it is equally likely that they occur in different particles and that the changed genetic units all then get assembled into one particle. Indeed, there need have been no mutation, but simply a reshuffling of already existing genetic units from many different particles to give a rare combination.

There is no critical evidence that variants of tobacco mosaic virus can exchange genetic characters, but it is well established that, when related bacteriophages infect the same bacterium, they in effect cross with one another and, of the progeny produced, some resemble the parents whereas others are new types combining characters previously specific to one or other parent. The great variability of tobacco mosaic virus itself seriously complicates work on genetic recombination, and there are other uncertainties in working with plant viruses that prevent critical experiments. First, there is the uncertainty about the genetic homogeneity of any virus stock, because it is by no means sure even when single-lesion isolates are used that the lesions from which these came were caused by single virus particles. Secondly, it is impossible to test the virus content of single cells, and by the time extracts from local lesions are infective, virus has multiplied in many cells. Thirdly, customary inoculation methods always leave in doubt whether two variants ever simultaneously infect the same leaf cell. The fact that inocula containing artificial mixtures of strains give very different results from inocula containing each strain separately suggests they do, but is inconclusive because infection of nearby cells may also affect the outcome of using mixed inocoula.

There seems no reason why inoculation with a mixture of two strains should not introduce both into the same cell, but those who have assumed this to happen have drawn different conclusions about the outcome. Thus, Siegel (1959), who inoculated strains U1 and U2 to *Nicotiana sylvestris,* concluded that the two were mutually exclusive and that when one infected the other was precluded from doing so, whereas Wu and Rappaport (1961), who inoculated the same two strains to Pinto beans, concluded that when both entered the same cell neither multiplied. In each of these hosts one only of these strains causes local lesions and these different conclusions were drawn from the fact that this strain caused fewer lesions when mixed with the other than when alone. Only Benda (1956) has inoculated single cells with mixtures of virus strains, hair cells of N. *glutinosa* with type tobacco mosaic and the tomato aucuba strain; he tested 20 lesions produced by such inoculations and recovered the type strain alone from 14, aucuba alone from 1 and both from 5. Virus was identified as the type strain when it became systemic in N. *sylvestris* without causing necrotic local lesions and caused the usual mottling in Turkish tobacco, and as the aucuba strain when it produced necrotic local lesions in N. *sylvestris* and a yellow mosaic in Turkish tobacco. These results leave little doubt that, when two strains are introduced simultaneously into the same cell, both can infect and that specific effects are detectable in progeny from the double infection, but whether the progeny were all alike one or other of the parents and whether only one or other strain infected at 15 of the inoculation sites is less certain. These two strains do interact, for the type strain can not only prevent the aucuba strain from producing its characteristic local lesions in N. sylvestris (Kunkel, 1934; Sadasivan, 1940), but can also allow it to spread to the uninoculated leaves (Benda, 1957). Both these things can be explained by postulating that the type strain decreases the multiplication of the aucuba strain so that it does not reach amounts enough to cause necrotic lesions and because of this the aucuba strain can move. However, another possibility is that, instead of the aucuba strain as such moving, what moves may be particles that combine characters from the two strains, and when these multiply in the uninoculated leaves they produce fresh recombinants some of which resemble the aucuba strain.

The results reported by Siegel (1959) and Wu and Rappaport (1961) seem not to differ in essence from earlier ones described as illustrating the seeming mutual antagonism between strains, which shows most vividly when plants fully infected with one strain show no or few further symptoms when inoculated with a second strain that on its own would produce characteristic symptoms. Various explanations for this phenomenon have been advanced, such as that variants of one virus occupy the same infection sites or use the same materials for their synthesis, but Best (1954) pointed out that it might also be explained by genetic recombination. If strains of different virulence exchange genetic determinants, this would help to account for the intermediate symptoms usually resulting from inoculations by mixtures of strains and it would adequately explain the protection against further effects of other strains by previous infection with one. A specific determinant for some activity, such as virulence towards a given host, when introduced into a leaf already infected with one strain would amount to only a quantitatively minor component of the total genetic pool; although it might be preserved by genetic recombination and add to the potential variability of the virus stock, it would have little effect on the total behaviour of the stock, unless it was associated with unusual survival value in the host. On this idea, the different extents to which strains interfere with one another or protect plants against one another would depend on the extent to which they can exchange genetic determinants.

Of the evidence in favour of genetic recombination in plant viruses, most has come from work with tomato spotted wilt (Best and Gallus, 1955; Best, 1961). From plants infected simultaneously with two distinctive strains, single-lesion isolates were obtained differing in behaviour from either of the starting strains and combining characters from each. From an analysis of the behaviour of the original strains and of the new isolates, Best (1961) suggests that the genetic constitution of the starting strains can be represented as Abcdefg and abCDEfg respectively, and the constitution of three recombinants as aBCdefg, abCdEfg and abCdeFg. Both the original strains and the new isolates reproduced their characteristic behaviour when propagated through single lesions obtained at limiting dilutions for infection. If the new isolates are not recombinants, then it seems probable that mixtures of the two original strains were always being carried through single lesions or that simultaneous infection with two strains increased the usual mutation rate of one or other, or both, of the two strains.

Results also suggestive of genetic recombination have been reported by Watson (1960) from work with potato viruses C and Y, which are closely related serologically but cause distinctive symptoms in many potato varieties and whereas potato virus Y is readily transmitted by the aphid *Myzus persicae,* virus C is not. From *Nicotiana glutinosa* plants simultaneously infected with both, however, aphids transmit viruses that have the pathogenicity of virus C for potato varieties but that continue to be aphid-transmissible when apparently free from the original virus Y. It could be that virus Y is always present and that virus C is being transmitted as such by aphids because it has in some way been made transmissible by the presence of virus Y; also, the range of reactions produced in potato by aphid-transmitted virus may depend on the degree of interference between viruses C and Y, but the simplest explanation is that aphid-transmissibility and virulence towards potato are determined by individual genetic units that can be exchanged between the two viruses when they are multiplying.

In summary, then, although conclusive evidence for genetic recombination in plant viruses has yet to be gained, there are many facets of their behaviour that at present are more readily explained than in any other way by assuming that genetic units can segregate and come together in new arrangements. Recombination may be very rare, for it is to be expected that individual strains will usually be behaving as clones and reproducing asexually, but its occurrence is suggested by the fact that even the most divergent strains still fall into well-defined groups, whereas if multiplication were always asexual, mutation in independent strains could be expected to produce so many differences as to eliminate the distinctive group characters. Their retention indicates that strains undergoing changes that otherwise would take them along divergent courses of evolution are kept together by at least occasional genetic exchange.

REFERENCES

BABOS, P., and B. KASSANIS. 1962. Virology 18: 206.
BAWDEN, F. C. 1958. J. gen. Microbiol 18: 751.
———. 1959. Nature, Lond. 184: 27.
———. 1961. *In* Microbial reaction to environment. Cambridge University Press.
———, and N. W. PIRIE. 1937. Brit. J. exp. Path. 18: 275.
BEALE, H. PURDY. 1928. Proc. Soc. exp. Biol., N.Y. 25: 702.
———. 1929. J. exp. Med. 49: 919.
——— 1931. Contr. Boyce Thompson Inst. 3: 529.
BENDA, G. T. A. 1956. Virology 2: 438.
———. 1957. *Ibid.* 3: 601.
BEST, R. J. 1954. Aust. J. biol. Sci. 7: 415.
———. 1961. Virology 15: 327.
———, and H. P. C. GALLUS. 1955. Enzymologia 17: 297.
BIRKELAND, J. M. 1934. Bot. Gaz. 95: 419.
CADMAN, C. H. 1962. Nature, Lond. 193: 49.
———, and B. D. HARRISON. 1959. Ann. appl. Biol. 47: 542.
CARSNER, E. 1925. Phytopathology 15: 745.
FRAENKEL-CONRAT, H. 1961. Biochim. biophys. Acta 49: 169.
GINOZA, W., and D. E. ATKINSON. 1955. Virology 1: 253.
GRATIA, A. 1933a. C. R. Soc. Biol., Paris 114: 923.
———. 1933b. *Ibid.* 114: 1382.
HOLMES, F. O. 1934. Phytopathology 24: 845.
———. 1936. *Ibid.* 26: 896.
JENSEN, J. H. 1933. *Ibid.* 23: 964.
———. 1936. *Ibid.* 26: 266.
———. 1937. *Ibid.* 27: 69.
JOHNSON, J. 1925. Science 64: 210.
———. 1947. Phytopathology 37: 822.
KASSANIS, B. 1957. Virology 4: 187.
KNIGHT, C. A., D. M. SILVA, D. DAHL, and A. TSUGITA. 1962. Virology 16: 236.
KUNKEL, L. O. 1934. Phytopathology 24: 437.
———. 1940. Pub. Amer. Ass. Advanc. Sci., No. 12, 22.
LACKEY, C. F. 1932. J. agric. Res. 44: 755.
LISTER, R. M., and J. M. THRESH. 1955. Nature, Lond. 175: 1047.
McKINNEY, H. H. 1926. Phytopathology 16: 893.
———. 1929. J. agric. Res. 39: 557.
MUNDRY, K. W. 1957a. Z. Indukt. abstamm. u. VererbLehre. 88: 407.
———. 1957b. *Ibid.* 88: 115.
———. 1959. Virology 9: 722.
———, and A. GIERER. 1958. Z. Indukt. abstamm. u. VererbLehre. 89: 614.
NORVAL, I. P. 1938. Phytopathology 28: 675.
RAPPAPORT, I., and S. G. WILDMAN. 1962. Nature, Lond. 195: 1029.
SADASIVAN, T. 1940. Ann. appl. Biol. 27: 359.
SALAMAN, R. N. 1933. Nature, Lond. 131: 468.
———. 1938. Phil. Trans. 229: 137.
SCHUSTER, H., and G. SCHRAMM. 1958. Z. Naturf. 13b: 697.
SIEGEL, A. 1959. Virology 8: 470.
———. 1960. *Ibid.* 11: 156.
———, and S. G. WILDMAN. 1954. Phytopathology 44: 277.

——, M. ZAITLIN, and OM. P. SEHGAL. 1962. Proc. nat. Acad. Sci., Wash. 48: 1845.

UKHOV, K. S. 1956. Reprint by Akad. Nauk S.S.S.R., Moscow, p. 29.

HUNG, T. H. 1931. Z. Ned.-Indisch Natuurwetensch. Congr. Bandoeng, Java, 450.

TSUGITA, A. 1962a. J. mol. Biol. 5: 284.

——. 1962b. *Ibid.* 5: 293.

——, and H. FRAENKEL-CONRAT. 1960. Proc. nat. Acad. Sci., Wash. 46: 636.

——, and ——. 1962. J. mol. Biol. 4: 73.

——, ——, M. W. NIRENBERG, and J. H. MATTHAEI. 1962. Proc. nat. Acad. Sci., Wash. 48: 846.

WATSON, M. A. 1960. Virology 10: 211.

VU, J. H., and I. RAPPAPORT. 1961. Virology 14: 259.

Classification

Before considering what criteria to use in classifying viruses, it is necessary to consider for what purpose the classification is being made. This is true whatever is being classified and would hardly be worth the saying except that many taxonomists give the impression that the only possible type of classification for biological systems is one based on natural relationships, by which is usually meant that groupings should reflect current ideas about evolution. To speak of the classification of plants, for example, automatically conveys the idea of Latin binomial names putting the basic units of species into genera, these into families and these into orders, groupings now acceptable for phylogenetic reasons whatever may have been the first reasons for making them. Plants can be grouped, though, for other things than natural relationships and regularly are by those engaged in agriculture. The farmer uses such criteria as weeds or crops; cereals, roots or pastures; spring-sown or autumn-sown; annual, biennial or perennial; early or late maturing; and so on. His needs are easily met and categories set up have the virtue of being factual and permanent.

Similarly, viruses can be classified objectively and simply for various utilitarian reasons; for the farmer, again, by such criteria as susceptibility of a given crop, method of spread, kind of symptoms caused, and method of control. However, to expect such criteria to give groupings that reflect natural relationships between viruses would be as unrealistic as to expect the farmer's classification of plants to coincide with that of the academic taxonomist. The classifications of plant viruses so far proposed are of the utilitarian type, derived mainly to provide systems of nomenclature, and whether in Smith's (1937) scheme, in which viruses are grouped under the host plant in which they were first encountered, or in Holmes' (1939, 1948), in which they are grouped according to the main kind of symptom caused, it is only too obvious that very different viruses occur in the same group.

Holmes' scheme carries the air of reflecting natural relationships, for he uses the Linnaean binomial nomenclature which implies not only that viruses can be distinguished at the species level but that species can then be assigned to that most important Linnaean category, the genus. The higher categories of families and orders set up by Holmes matter less, though their erection does suggest a common origin for all viruses, and for this there is no evidence. However, the most important consideration in deciding whether a classification of viruses analogous to that of plants can be attempted is to decide whether viruses can first be analysed into species, which can then be allocated to genera. The fact that Holmes' genera were highly heterogeneous and unacceptable to most virus workers is unimportant, for genera can be changed. What is important is to decide whether there are criteria acceptable as indicating near relationships and recent common origins. If there are, then a classification analogous to those used for organisms becomes possible, but if there are not then little more can be done than cataloguing under specified headings. As phylogeny plays such a prominent part in the classification of organisms, it will be well to devote some space to considering ideas about the origins and evolution of viruses.

Virus evolution. In Chapter 1 viruses were defined as sub-microscopic, infective entities that multiply only intracellularly and are potentially pathogenic. There is nothing in this definition demanding that all viruses should have originated in the same way. The viruses whose constitution is known consist largely of two substances, nucleic acid and protein, which also occur in every kind of organism. Every living cell has components containing these two substances, components such as chromosomes and microsomes that seem to share with viruses the ability to be reproduced only intracellularly. They differ primarily from viruses in not being infective or pathogenic, but as the nearest biological analogues to viruses they seem to be the most likely source for producing viruses. Beyond this, however, it is difficult to go, for although it may be tempting to assume that viruses originated in the kinds of host they currently infect, the fact that some individual ones multiply readily both in flowering plants and insects shows they can use as hosts organisms that phylogenetically are separated by vast gulfs. Thus, although knowledge about the chemical constitution of viruses suggests a general source, it is no guide to the origin of specific viruses.

Because they are among the simplest known reproducing systems, viruses often feature prominently in discussions on the origin of life. However, as they demand such a complex environment before they can multiply, it seems highly unlikely that entities closely resembling the viruses currently studied existed in the pre-biotic world. Rather than stages in the development of cellular organisms, they are more probably late evolutionary forms, products of an already elaborate biological system. They may, nevertheless, have played a considerable part in the evolution of some organisms, not only indirectly in causing diseases that may have influenced the survival of some species, but also by becoming incorporated into the metabolic mechanisms and increasing the complexity of organisms. In the context of seeking origins for viruses, the similarity between them and normal cell components has already been mentioned, but at this level of organisation it is more than usually difficult even to guess which way evolution has proceeded. Some nucleic acids or nucleoproteins that now behave as normal components of some organisms may have originated as infections by viruses, which have now not only lost both infectivity and pathogenicity, but may also confer some benefit on the organism. There are several known examples of viruses gaining or losing either transmissibility by a given method or pathogenicity towards a given host. In an organism where it lost both transmissibility and pathogenicity, a virus would currently be indistinguishable from a normal component. Contrarily, a normal component needs only to acquire transmissibility and pathogenicity to become a virus. Perhaps, indeed, it may need to acquire only transmissibility, for when introduced into another organism in which it can also multiply it may not be accommodated without disturbing the normal functioning.

From the great variability of viruses described in Chapter 13, it will be obvious that natural selection has had opportunities to work on many variants and that the viruses currently studied were not produced by single changes in "normal" nucleoproteins. They will have undergone many evolutionary changes and the fact that some now have a characteristic morphology and differ in other ways from normal nucleoproteins is no more a barrier to assuming a common ancestor than the differences between giraffes and other mammals preclude their evolution from a common stock. Their forbears, which first began to behave like viruses, probably differed greatly from the current particles and may well have been much less well equipped for transmission and survival outside cells. In this con-

text, it is worth stressing that the viruses about which most is known
are those that differ most from normal components, for only these
are readily isolated and characterised. The causes of conditions now
described as "non-transmissible" tumours of animals, or "non-infec-
tious" chloroses and other abnormalities of plants, are obscure, but
they are possibly aberrant nucleoproteins and they perhaps indicate
the original behaviour of some current viruses that are now highly
adapted for ready transmission.

An origin for viruses that is often mooted is by the degeneration
of pathogenic micro-organisms, which after a long parasitic existence have lost their independent metabolism and come to depend
wholly on the host's synthetic systems. In effect this postulates that
some reproducing system of the micro-organism now manages to
reproduce in the host cell rather than in the micro-organism. There
is no reason to exclude this as a possible origin for some viruses, but
equally there is no reason to expect it to apply generally. All other
kinds of organisms also contain reproducing systems based on nucleic
acids, and the only reason for selecting pathogenic micro-organisms
as sources of viruses is that they are obviously in a favoured position for introducing potential viruses into other organisms. It is,
indeed, the generality of nucleic acids and proteins that prohibits
conclusions about the phylogeny of individual viruses. Every living cell has the necessary materials to produce viruses and whether
any virus that today infects flowering plants originated in a flowering plant, a bacterium or fungus, an insect or some other animal, is
likely always to remain in doubt. The only common ancestry for
all currently studied viruses may lie very far back, in whatever was
the successful precursor of nucleic acid that allowed it to be selected
and to develop into its present dominating position whereby it is the
basis of replicating systems responsible for genetic continuity.

When there is no reason to conclude that all the entities now
called viruses are related to one another by an evolutionary sequence
such as is generally held to relate plants or animals in any given
natural order, it is doubtful whether attempts to classify viruses in
a similar way to organisms are justified. However, it is less the lack
of factual knowledge about virus evolution that prevents such a classification, than the fewness of pieces of information on which to base
a classification. Linnaeus classified plants and animals without considering evolution and many of his groupings are still accepted as
valid; also, the fossil record of many groups of organisms is so incomplete that phylogeny is inferred from the classification rather
than classification depending on proven evolutionary steps. Nevertheless, it is vain to expect to do similar things with viruses. Tax-

onomists of higher organisms have advantages denied to virus taxonomists. Classification becomes easier with increasing size and complexity of the things being classified, and phylogeny can be inferred with more assurance the more specialised structures organisms have, and the more complex these become. As Pirie (1962) pointed out, more information of taxonomic value can be gained by glancing at a flower than by a year's work on a virus.

In attempting any groupings that undoubtedly reflect intrinsic characters of viruses, criteria must come from information independent of features in which the host might play a part, i.e., they must come from such things as particle morphology, chemical constitution and stability *in vitro*. It is obvious that viruses can be grouped according to whether they contain deoxy or ribose nucleic acid, and the plant viruses can be grouped according to their shapes and sizes, or the proportion of nucleic acid to protein in their particles. Whether such groupings would reflect natural relationships cannot be decided objectively. Probably most people would be prejudiced in favour of the idea that viruses containing deoxy nucleic acid are more nearly related to one another than to those containing ribose nucleic acid, but beyond that there would be much less agreement. An obvious and convenient way of grouping is according to gross morphology, and it is plausible to think that similar morphology may indicate ancestral resemblances. However, there may well be only a few ways in which nucleic acid and protein, wherever they originated, can be assembled to give arrangements allowing particles to be transmissible. If this is so, the viruses grouped because of similar morphologies may well be examples of convergent evolution rather than that they had a recent common ancestor. Viruses with different morphologies contain different proportions of nucleic acid to protein, which might be accepted as evidence indicating that gross morphology does indicate close relationship, but equally it may be that the most efficient structure for containing 5% nucleic acid in 95% protein is in a spiral arrangement demanding a long particle, whereas 15 or more percentage of nucleic acid can be contained only in particles of other shapes.

The grouping of strains. Compared with the number of species in many of the major divisions in the classification of organisms, the known plant viruses are very few, probably only two to three hundred. Although it would be desirable to be able to place these in categories showing their degree of similarity, what is far more urgent and important is the other taxonomic exercise of analysing the viruses into basic units. The great confusion in virus nomenclature arises, not from the number of viruses, but from the plethora of virus strains and the fact that strains of a previously known virus are often described as new viruses and given separate names. The first requirements for virus classification are agreed criteria for deciding whether a newly encountered virus is something entirely new or whether it is a strain of an already known virus. Although it has long been obvious that host range and pathogenicity are valueless for this purpose, these characters have continued to be used and have led to the multiplicity of synonyms that plagues virus nomenclature and defeats the certainty of identification required by a name. These two characters are the prime ones for showing differences between strains that otherwise behave alike, but have no use in deciding the relationships between viruses.

Even what to call the basic units that would be obtained by grouping strains together is uncertain. Species are the basic units for classifying organisms and the ability to interbreed is the now generally accepted criterion for placing differing individuals within the same species. Mayr (1953) states that "the most objective property of species is perhaps the gap between species. It is the place where gene exchange is interrupted." Because of this, the species concept is clearly inapplicable to systems that reproduce asexually, as it is to be assumed that viruses normally do. Mayr therefore suggests for groups of clones that have probably derived from a common ancestor the name "collective species," and I shall follow this suggestion. The placing of virus strains into such collective species need present no great problems, though of course as with any biological classifications there will always be some dubious conclusions.

For allocating strains to a given collective species, the one criterion that seems of outstanding value is serological relationship. All viruses so far found to be closely related antigenically also resemble one another in other such intrinsic properties as particle morphology and chemical composition, not only ratio of nucleic acid to protein but also the relative proportions in which the four nucleotides occur in their nucleic acid. The use of serology to group strains of different pathogenicity has been urged in previous editions of this book and elsewhere (Bawden, 1953, 1955), and the more that is found out about viruses, the more useful it seems to become. Particle size and shape do not serve the same purpose, for although all viruses of greatly different sizes and shapes are serologically unrelated, not all those of the same size and shape share antigens and those that do not usually also differ in other characters. Perhaps the nucleotide composition of the nucleic acid would be equally valuable and

would perhaps give much the same groupings, for the protein composition of viruses, which determines their serological behaviour,
presumably reflects the structure of the nucleic acid. However, determining the nucleotide composition is tedious and requires considerable amounts of purified virus, whereas serological tests are
done quickly and need not demand highly purified virus preparations. A serious limitation to the use of serology seemed to be set
by early failures to demonstrate serological reactions with some
viruses, but with better techniques for preparing antigens, both for
injecting into animals and for testing against the resulting antisera,
it seems probable that a large majority of the known plant viruses
will prove amenable to study by serological techniques. Matthews
(1957) reported that antisera had been prepared against 32 individual viruses and since 1957 they have also been prepared against
several others.

The first step required for classifying plant viruses is to select
a specific strain to act as the type for each collective species and to
prepare an antiserum against it. Then, the allocation of individual
virus strains to a named collective species will be determined by
the antiserum with which they react specifically. What kind of
test will be used to detect the reaction will depend on the circumstances, but the precipitation test in one form or other is more likely
to be favoured for work with plant viruses than complement fixation
or neutralisation of infectivity. Only positive reactions with unknown viruses will be meaningful. The lack of a reaction may truly
mean there is no serological relationship but, unless there is an antiserum with which the unknown virus reacts specifically, failure to
react may mean no more than that the preparation contained too
little of the virus. To establish serological unrelatedness requires
producing antisera against two viruses and showing that each fails
to react with antiserum to the other in conditions in which it reacts
with its own. It is also necessary to make tests over a wide range
of antigen/antibody ratios, for when serological relationships are
distant precipitation may happen only over a narrow range and may
demand the use of antiserum much more concentrated than is required when serological relationship is close. A word of caution is
also needed about positive results. These will be meaningful only
when the preparation of the type strain used to produce the antiserum contained no other antigen, either other virus or normal plant
constituent, and when the preparation used as a test antigen contains only one virus. Animals will produce antibodies against any
antigens injected into them and the resulting antisera will react with
all these antigens later. In using serological tests to set up collec-

tive species, the specificity of the antiserum and the freedom of the
test antigen from other viruses are all important. This may be obvious, but needs stressing for mixtures of viruses have often led to
false identifications.

There are two unsatisfactory features about using serology as
the basis for allocating virus strains to collective species. One is
that the nature of the structures responsible for forming specific
antibodies is unknown. The other is that an antiserum against a
virus is not an exact and reproducible reagent, but different antisera produced by injecting the same virus preparation will differ
not only in their total antibody content, as indicated by their different precipitation titres, but also qualitatively. When the antibody
content of a serum is increased, either by repeated injections of a
virus intravenously or intraperitoneally, or more strikingly by intramuscular injections of virus with an adjuvant, the number of different kinds of antibodies also increases and the antiserum becomes
increasingly less specific. Viruses are multiple antigens and when
injected into animals produce a range of antibodies. This is evident
from serum absorption experiments, for an antiserum prepared
against, say, type tobacco mosaic virus can still react with it after
all the antibodies that react with another strain have been removed
by precipitation with that strain. The proportion of the total antibodies removed can differ greatly with different strains, and from
the residual titre of the absorbed antiserum the degree of serological
relatedness can be assessed. For example, absorption of antiserum
to type tobacco mosaic virus with tomato aucuba mosaic virus may
remove more than 90% of the antibodies, whereas absorption with
cucumber virus 3 or 4 will remove fewer than 10% (Bawden and
Pirie, 1937). To show that the type strain and the aucuba strain
are antigenically different requires such absorption tests, but that
there are large differences between the type strain and cucumber 3 is
evident from simply titrating their antisera against the two strains,
for the titres will be many times greater when tested against the
homologous than against the heterologous strain. When animals are
given a single intravenous injection of 1 mg of the type strain, the
antiserum may have a titre smaller than 1/100 and, at this stage,
although it will also precipitate some other strains such as tomato
aucuba, it will probably fail to precipitate cucumber 3. With further injections, the titre against the type strain increases and the
antiserum now also precipitates strains such as cucumber 3 that are
only remotely related to it.

With methods of preparing sera that give titres of not more than
1/1,000 or so, serological relatedness has been demonstrated only

between viruses that have particles of the same size. By intramuscular injection of virus plus adjuvant, antisera have been prepared with titres against the homologous virus of more than $1/100,000$ and some of these have reacted with viruses previously thought to be serologically distinct and that have particles of different lengths. Thus, an antiserum to bean yellow mosaic virus (particle length 750 mμ) with a titre for this virus of $1/128,000$ gave a titre of $1/128$ with potato virus Y (particle length 730 mμ) and $1/32$ with bean mosaic virus (particle length 730 mμ); similarly, an antiserum against potato virus Y with a titre for this virus of $1/16,000$ gave a titre of $1/128$ with beet mosaic virus and one of $1/8$ with bean yellow mosaic virus (Bercks, 1960). These results with potent antisera show that serological tests do not always measure what Mayr describes as the most objective property of a species, that is the gap between species, for whether there is a gap can sometimes depend on the potency of the antiserum used. However, even with the most potent sera yet tested there is still great specificity, for potato virus X (particle length 515 mμ) did not react with the sera prepared by Bercks against either potato virus Y or bean yellow mosaic virus.

What importance to attach to these remote serological relationships, which need imply no more than one similar configuration somewhere in the protein, can be only a subjective decision. However, so that the allocation of viruses to collective species can be as objective as possible, there is obviously much in favour of grouping together all viruses that react with each other's antisera, however slightly. If the lack of serological relationship is accepted as the basis for putting into different collective species, uncertainties should be restricted to tests made with antisera that give only small reaction end points when titrated against their homologous viruses. To assess what significance should be attached to negative results, the potency of the sera used should always be known. Serology will relate most viruses to the type strain of a collective species unequivocally, and the uncertainties about those that may be only remotely related to it will be few compared with the many that now so confuse virus nomenclature.

Serology can do more than simply allocate viruses to collective species. It can do something to show degrees of relatedness within the collective species. Kassanis (1961) suggested that terms should be used to indicate different degrees of serological relationship, and proposed restricting strains to those that have most of their antigenic groups in common and the use of the term "sero-type" for those that have only a few in common. However, this proposal postulates a knowledge of viruses that does not exist. Not only has the nature of any antigenic group yet to be determined, but it is unknown how many or how many kinds of antigenic groups any virus has. The fact that different strains or "sero-types" have specific antigenic groups is inferred from the behaviour of the antisera made against them when used in absorbtion experiments or when titrated against a range of strains. Of the two reactants in serological tests the only one analysable into specific components is the antiserum, for whereas antibodies are precipitated individually, virus particles precipitate in total when they have combined with enough total antibody, regardless of how many kinds of their antigenic groups may still be uncombined. If all antigenic groups are equally able to stimulate antibody production in animals, the relative proportions of different kinds of antibodies in the serum will reflect the relative proportions of specific antigenic groups in the virus, but if they are not, the most common antibodies may reflect not the most abundant antigenic groups but those most active in stimulating antibody production. If strain and sero-type are to be used as distinguishing terms they should perhaps be defined by what actually distinguishes them, which is antibody production. Strain would then indicate viruses that produce antisera in which most of the antibodies react similarly, and serotype would indicate viruses that produce antisera containing only a small proportion of their antibodies in common. The dividing line between strains and serotypes can be drawn only arbitrarily and could well become a subject for heated debate, but the antisera to the viruses Kassanis put in the category of sero-type contained from 64 to 512 times as many antibodies reacting with the homologous as with the heterologous virus.

Serological tests demand stable virus protein and they will therefore fail to identify such variants as those newly described of tobacco rattle (Sanger and Brandenburg, 1961; Cadman, 1962) and tobacco necrosis (Babos and Kassanis, 1962) viruses, which seem to be defective in their ability to form protein. Such variants may well be common and their allocation to collective species will be possible only when they have clearly derived from a stable form of a virus that can be worked with serologically.

Tests of interference. So many viruses have now proved amenable to study by serological techniques that it can confidently be expected that many others will also. However, not all may be and there is need for an alternative method for allocating viruses to collective species. Obviously this must be a method that will usually give similar groupings to those arrived at by serological tests and the only one that meets this requirement is the plant-protection test, or some other test that shows whether or not two viruses interfere with one another's multiplication. Such tests have the advantages over serological ones in not demanding considerable amounts of virus stable *in vitro* and that they can be made with viruses that are transmissible only by grafting or animal vectors. With viruses

Fig. 14–1. Two leaves of *Nicotiana sylvestris* as they appeared 5 days after both had been inoculated with tomato aucuba mosaic virus. The leaf on the left was healthy whereas that on the right was suffering from tobacco mosaic at the time of inoculation with aucuba mosaic virus. The local lesions appear only on the leaf which was healthy at the time of inoculation. (L. O. Kunkel, 1934, Phytopathology 24: 437).

that multiply in their vectors, tests of interference can be made both in the animal and plant hosts (Kunkel, 1955). They have the disadvantage that they can only be used with viruses that share a common host and produce distinctive symptoms.

There are various ways of testing for interference, but the most usual is to infect a plant with an avirulent virus and then see whether this infection protects it against the effects of a virulent one, whether these effects are distinctive local lesions (Fig. 14–1) or systemic symptoms. For making such tests, ideally two strains of a named collective species are needed, one virulent and the other avirulent. Then, when the unknown virus being tested is virulent, plants will first be infected with the avirulent named strain, to see whether they are protected against the unknown virus; when the unknown virus is avirulent, plants will first be infected with it, to see whether they are then protected against the virulent named strain. With viruses that initially cause ringspot symptoms from which plants later recover, a convenient technique is to inoculate an unknown virus to plants that have recovered from the effects of named viruses and see in which it still causes ringspot symptoms. Interference can also be assessed by inoculating healthy plants simultaneously with a named and unknown virus of different virulence and comparing the result with that of inoculating plants with each separately (Holmes, 1956). With two related strains, the mixture will usually cause symptoms intermediate between those caused by each separately, whereas with unrelated viruses, the symptoms caused by the mixture will be at least as severe as those caused by the more virulent virus alone and often will be even more severe and perhaps of a different kind.

McKinney (1941) pointed out that the extent to which different strains interfere with one another often differs and he considered this to be a limitation for determining relationships, but provided tests of interference are adequately controlled by inoculating the unknown virus alone to healthy plants, there is rarely any difficulty in deciding whether the two are antagonistic. When two strains are inoculated together, even if one ultimately dominates the other, it will usually take longer to produce its characteristic symptoms than when inoculated alone; similarly, should a virus inoculated to an already infected plant later come to dominate the symptom picture, it will take very much longer to do so when the plant contained a related strain than when it contained an unrelated virus. When the first virus is unrelated to the second, the second will usually produce its effects, local lesions and systemic symptoms, as rapidly as in a previously healthy plant of the same age.

It is probably too much to expect that tests of interference will give such unequivocal results as do serological tests, and when both can be used but give different results grouping should be by serology. The discrepancies so far encountered are few and the agreement between serological relationships and tests of interference where these have both been applied to the same viruses is remarkably good. Indeed, the two seem closely correlated, for Matthews (1948) found that the extent to which strains of potato virus X interfered with one another in plants increased with increasing serological relatedness. Also, with other viruses, interference has usually been unequivocal with strains that are closely related sero-

logically, though with strains that are only remotely related serologically there is often little or no interference (Harrison, 1955, 1958;
Kassanis, 1961). Although protection sometimes is incomplete,
there seems to be only one reported example of complete failure
with viruses that are closely related serologically (tobacco veinal
necrosis and potato Y) (Bawden and Kassanis, 1951) and one of
a virus (tobacco etch) protecting a plant against systemic invasion
by another (potato Y) to which it is unrelated serologically (Bawden and Kassanis, 1945). Protection against systemic invasion is
a better test than effects on numbers of local lesions produced by
a given inoculum of a virus, for many things can decrease lesion
numbers. The fact that plants infected with tobacco mosaic virus
may give fewer local lesions than healthy plants when inoculated
with unrelated viruses such as cabbage blackring (Thomson, 1960),
therefore, is not surprising and is no reason for abandoning plant-
protection tests for identifying viruses as related strains, but counts
of local lesions without other evidence of interference should not be
relied upon for such identification.

Grouping in higher categories. The mechanism underlying the
competition between strains is undetermined but Best's (1954) suggestion that it depends on genetic recombination was discussed in
Chapter 13. If his suggestion should prove to be correct, plant-
protection tests provide a test analogous to that of sexual reproduction for allocating organisms to a species and the term species could
be applied to viruses without qualification. If failure to interfere
with one another does measure the point where gene exchange
ceases, that is the gap between species, the collective species derived
by grouping viruses because they share some common antigens may
give groups containing more than one species. However, until there
is critical evidence of genetical recombination with plant viruses and
that it is responsible for the interference between strains, it is probably idle to discuss further the possible correlations between antigenic similarity and ability to exchange genetic determinants.
Nevertheless, the possibility clearly exists that viruses closely related
to each other serologically may be equivalent to members of one
species, whereas those only remotely related serologically may be
more equivalent to different species of one genus. This possibility
seems at the moment the only way in which viruses can be collected into anything resembling the lower categories used to group
organisms. Up to this level of difference, from close to remote serological relationships, can safely be attributed to evolution from a
common stock, for it has been observed in process both in tobacco

rattle (Cadman and Harrison, 1959) and tobacco mosaic (Bawden, 1961) viruses. Evolution may, of course, proceed still further and produce variants antigenically distinct from their forbears, but this has not yet been demonstrated with viruses that remain antigenic, although some variants that are apparently defective in synthesising protein, and that possibly occur *in vivo* as nucleic acid only, are not directly relatable to their parents either by serological or plant-protection tests (Cadman, 1962).

Whether the category for which the name collective species has been suggested in this chapter should be regarded as equivalent to species or genus is likely to be decided differently by different people, as also are decisions about criteria for grouping in higher categories. Once the objective test of serological relationship has ceased to be applicable, decisions can be made only subjectively. Groupings can, of course, be made according to any property that can be ascertained; particle shape, size, ratio of nucleic acid to protein, ratio of nucleotides, transmissibility by a given method or type of vector, stability *in vitro*, ability to infect a given plant, or any of several other distinguishing features could be used to give groupings useful for some purpose or other. Whether any would reflect natural relationships between viruses, however, is another matter, but groupings according to shapes and sizes are likely less often than others to put into different categories viruses that are closely related serologically, and these groupings are likely to find favour with many of those who now desire to arrange viruses in a hierarchy going beyond the groupings possible by serology and plant-protection tests. Brandes and Wetter (1959) concluded that the most significant thing about viruses with elongated particles is the length of their most common particles and, on the basis of similar particle lengths, have put these viruses into twelve groups, which they regard as representing distinct species, even though some groups contain serologically related and unrelated viruses. They deal only with elongated viruses but, by treating these separately from others, are automatically accepting differing shapes as more important than differing sizes as prime reasons for setting up main divisions. In this they may be right, but in using sizes and shapes as the main divisions it is well to remember that it may give groupings more analogous to those obtained by putting plants into the categories of trees, shrubs and herbaceous plants rather than into the orders, families and genera used in the customary botanical classifications.

The Adanson (1757) method of grouping together creatures that have the most features in common, without any *a priori* decisions about the taxonomic significance of different features, seems more objective than any other, but however useful it may be with sizeable organisms that have many obvious features, has little to recommend it with entities so small as viruses. Indeed, any features that are used can be decided only from existing knowledge about viruses, for unless it is known that some virus does possess a given feature there can be no taxonomic significance in the answer "no" to the question "Does a virus have this feature?" Even when the feature is known to be possessed by some viruses, the answer "no" may still be meaningless or misleading. For example, "no" to the question "Is a virus transmitted by inoculation of sap?" has no taxonomic significance unless the identities of the plants from which the sap was taken and to which it was inoculated are specified and they are those between which other viruses are so transmitted. Again, although the answer "no" to "Is a virus transmitted by *Myzus persicae?*" may be meaningful, the same answer to "Is a virus aphid-transmitted?" can not have the same weight until all aphid species have been tested for their ability to transmit.

The only reason for attempting to classify viruses other than into the collective species suggested above seems to be that people have an irresistible urge to put knowledge, however scanty, into some order. Partly the urge reflects the idea that there is a basic design of Nature waiting to be discovered, partly because such orderly arrangements facilitate reference and may suggest additional features of individual viruses that might profitably be sought. If attempts to classify viruses into a hierarchy of categories leads to new knowledge, they will be justified, but first things should be put first and it is to be hoped that such attempts will not be made at the expense of identifying and naming at the lower level of collective species. Confusion is now rife primarily because the initial grouping and naming of strains at this level is incomplete. Classification and nomenclature are different things, but a pre-requisite of successful classification is that the entities being classified should be unequivocally identified and labelled.

REFERENCES

ADANSON, M. 1757. Histoire naturelle du Sénégal. Coquillages. Bauche, Paris.
BABOS, P., and B. KASSANIS. 1962. Virology 18: 206.
BAWDEN, F. C. 1953. Ann. N.Y. Acad. Sci. 56: 538.
——. 1955. J. gen. Microbiol. 12: 362.
——. 1961. *In* Symposia of Society for General Microbiology, XI. "Microbial reaction to environment," p. 296.
——, and B. KASSANIS. 1945. Ann. appl. Biol. 32: 52.
——, and ——. 1951. *Ibid.* 38: 402.
——, and N. W. PIRIE. 1937. Brit. J. exp. Path. 18: 275.

BERCKS, R. 1960. Virology 12: 311.

BEST, R. J. 1954. Aust. J. exp. Biol. med. Sci. 7: 415.

BRANDES, J., and C. WETTER. 1959. Virology 8: 99.

CADMAN, C. H. 1962. Nature, Lond. 193: 49.

———, and B. D. HARRISON. 1959. Ann. appl. Biol. 47: 542.

HARRISON, B. D. 1955. Ann. appl. Biol. 46: 571.

———. 1958. J. gen. Microbiol. 18: 450.

HOLMES, F. O. 1939. Handbook of Phytopathogenic Diseases. Burgess, Minneapolis.

———. 1948. In Bergey's Manual of Determinative Bacteriology, 6th edition. Williams and Wilkins Co., Baltimore.

———. 1956. Virology 2: 611.

KASSANIS, B. 1961. Eur. Potato J. 4: 13.

KUNKEL, L. O. 1955. Advanc. Virus Res. 3: 251.

McKINNEY, H. H. 1941. Amer. J. Bot. 28: 770.

MATTHEWS, R. E. F. 1948. Ann. appl. Biol. 36: 460.

———. 1957. Plant Virus Serology. Cambridge: University Press.

MAYR, E. 1953. Ann. N.Y. Acad. Sci. 56: 391.

PIRIE, N. W. 1962. In Symposia of Society for General Microbiology, XII. "Microbial Classification," p. 374.

SANGER, H. L., and E. BRANDENBURG. 1961. Naturwissenschaften 48: 391.

SMITH, K. M. 1937. Textbook of Plant Virus Diseases, 1st edition. Churchill, London.

THOMSON, A. D. 1960. Nature, Lond. 187: 761.

The Control of
Virus Diseases

It is not the aim of this chapter to prescribe control measures for specific diseases, but rather to use individual diseases to illustrate the principles and practice of control. Some practices applicable to virus diseases also apply to other kinds of infectious diseases; these include such hygienic precautions as destroying sources of infection, growing resistant varieties, using only uninfected seed or other kind of propagating material, planting in uninfested land and as far away as possible from infected crops, and a crop rotation that contains crops that differ in their susceptibility to different viruses.

General practices. These general practices are easily recommended but are often less easily applied. The systemic nature of most virus diseases means that, once infected, a plant remains so for as long as it lives, and as species and varieties of plants differ in their reactions and some are little harmed by infection, identifying infected plants can be difficult. A perennial plant that shows no clear symptoms can remain indefinitely as an unsuspected source of virus that may severely damage other plants growing near to it. Also, these other plants may be taxonomically very far removed from the perennial plant, for many viruses have extensive host ranges that include species in widely differing families. Annual plants will rarely be important sources of viruses, for although an increasing number of viruses are being found to be seed-transmitted, most are not. Sources of infection for annual crops, therefore, are likely to be plants that are perennial, biennial, or are vegetatively propagated, but this will not always be so and sometimes the source will be infested soil or annual plants that survive through from one crop to another, such as over-wintering brassicae and lettuce, or self-sown cereal plants.

To decide whether the destruction of sources of infection is a practical proposition requires a detailed knowledge of all the sources and of the epidemiology of the virus in the crop being harmed. Such epidemiological knowledge is also needed before a judgment can be made on the practicability as a control of destroying infected plants (roguing) within a crop. Roguing is likely to be effective only when spread is slow and mainly from infected to healthy plants within a crop. It may work against a given disease in one set of circumstances but not in another. In the United Kingdom, for example, removing potato plants with leaf roll or rugose mosaic, caused by potato virus Y, can improve the health of stocks in the north and west, where aphids rarely arrive in the potato crops until after infected plants can be identified and removed, but is usually valueless in the south and east where aphids are active earlier in the year (Doncaster and Gregory, 1948).

Information about sources of infection can often be gained by studying the distribution of infected plants within a crop, which may in turn suggest whether roguing is likely to be worth while. Sometimes diseased plants occur in such clearly defined patches that spread between neighbouring plants is obviously more important than infections coming into the crop, but this is not always so. On the assumption that plants infected directly by incoming vectors will be randomly distributed, whereas spread within the crop will produce groups of infected plants, van der Plank (1946) devised a test for distinguishing between the two kinds of spread, from the frequence with which infected plants occur in pairs; pairs are any two adjacent plants so that a run of three infected plants is two pairs. Of a sequence of n plants examined, in which x are infected, the number of random pairs expected is given by the expression $p = \dfrac{x(x-1)}{n}$, and for large values of n, p will have a standard error of $\sqrt{p}$. When the observed value for p differs significantly from the calculated value, spread between plants in the crop can be assumed. Measuring the incidence of infected plants in different parts of a crop can sometimes help to identify external sources of infection, provided these are not too remote, for it may show disease gradients and the main direction in which the virus is entering the crop.

Sowing date can affect losses in annual crops, for the effect of infection on yield depends greatly on the stage of growth of plants when they become infected with viruses. Thus, early-sown sugar beet suffer less loss than late-sown crops from curly top (Wallace and Murphy, 1938) and yellows (Watson, 1942). Also, some plants become increasingly resistant to infection with increasing age, and in potato "seed-growing" areas of the United Kingdom the incidence of aphid-transmitted virus may be doubled by delaying planting by a month (Cadman and Chambers, 1960). The effect of changing sowing date, however, will depend on the time when vectors are active. When vectors are active early, a virus disease may be largely avoided by delaying sowing until the spring migration has ended. Similarly, with crops like sugar beet, which are usually sown thickly and later thinned, delaying the thinning until after the main migration of vectors has ended can diminish losses. Except when aphids or leafhoppers are unusually abundant, too few infective vectors usually arrive in a crop from outside to infect the whole crop, and the number that enters will be independent of the number of crop plants per unit area. Hence, doubling the density of the stand can be expected approximately to halve the proportion of the crop that becomes infected. van der Plank and Anderssen (1945) showed this expectation was realised with tomato spotted wilt virus in South Africa, where the virus enters tobacco crops early in the growing season and spreads little in the crop afterwards. Planting at half the usual spacing, or setting two plants per hole, and thinning to the usual density after the thrips have finished coming into the crops, allows the infected plants to be removed leaving a full stand of healthy ones.

Spread within a crop can also be expected to be less damaging in dense than in thin stands, for if the number of plants infected in it is constant, the proportion infected will be less in a dense than in a thin crop. van der Plank (1947, 1948) pointed out that dense planting, by affecting the size of individual plants, can be expected a priori to slow the rate viruses spread, for a connection between spread and size of plant is implicit in the concept of systemic infections. Only one infection is needed for a whole plant to become invaded, regardless of its size. Other things being equal, a large plant is more likely than a small one to become infected, simply because it has a larger surface area exposed to chances of contracting infection; once infected, it also offers a larger volume of tissue for the virus to multiply in and vectors to feed on, so chances of spread from it are also greater than from a small plant. Hence, unless plants become increasingly resistant as they grow, there will be two factors likely to make virus diseases more important in thin stands of large plants than in dense stands of small plants. It is unlikely that this simple relation holds between size and extent of spread in field crops, but there are reports with potato, sugar-beet and cruciferous crops of large plants being more liable than small ones to contract infection (Whitehead, 1927; Edmundson, 1940; Watson, Watson and Hull, 1946; Doncaster and Gregory, 1948; Broadbent, 1957). Close spacing of groundnut plants has long been known to control rosette disease. Storey (1935) attributed this to the dense stands controlling the aphid vector, but it is likely that at least some of the effect on rosette reflects the fact that the same number of infections per unit area that could ruin a sparse stand might do no more than some useful "thinning" in a dense stand. However, close spacing will not always be beneficial; with a disease like swollen shoot of cocoa, it may well increase spread, for the mealybug vector seems rarely to move except between trees in contact with one another, and the denser the planting the sooner will trees touch and the more other trees each will be able to touch (Thresh, 1958).

The cheapest and simplest method of combating virus diseases is to grow resistant varieties, and such varieties have often permitted crops to be grown economically where otherwise they would have had to be abandoned. A striking example is sugar cane, whose survival was threatened until the resistance of P.O.J. varieties was first noticed in Java and a successful breeding programme based on them (Summers, Brandes and Rands, 1948). Similarly, new lines of sugar beet give good crops where curly top devastates old lines; Murphy (1946) reported that resistant lines yielded up to 16 tons per acre where European lines gave no measurable yield.

There are three main problems in producing useful resistant lines; (1) to find a source of genes conferring resistance, (2) to combine these genes with other desirable qualities in the crop, (3) to know whether the resistance will hold against all strains of the virus against which the variety was bred. Fortunately, there are more features offering practical resistance to virus diseases than to most other kinds of infectious diseases, but not all are equally desirable. The ideal is, of course, immunity, and although this is rare, it has been achieved in some seemingly unlikely conditions. For example, when most potato varieties grown in America were infected with potato virus X, a seedling (U.S.D.A. 41956) was bred that is immune. Similarly, although the soil-borne viruses have an enormously wide host range and devastate some raspberry varieties, other varieties are immune from them (Cadman, 1961).

Failing immunity, there are many other inherited features that can greatly diminish the losses caused by viruses. These include resistance to infection, either its initiation or the readiness with which the virus multiplies after plants have contracted infection; hypersensitive reactions, which either restrict the virus to necrotic local lesions or rapidly kill the whole plant so that, in effect, the stock does its own roguing; ability to tolerate full systemic infection without suffering large loss of yield; resistance or unattractiveness to virus vectors, which may partly explain the different incidence of rosette in different varieties of groundnuts grown in similar conditions (Evans, 1954).

Some of these features exist in varieties of crops that were not specifically bred to combat virus diseases but the fact that the varieties were resistant has sometimes contributed to their success where other varieties failed. Thus, many widely grown varieties of strawberries, raspberries and potatoes are those that tolerate infection with viruses that are damaging to other varieties. After being in cultivation for some years such clonal varieties are usually largely infected, for viruses spread unhindered in them, and they can then become dangerous sources of infection for less tolerant varieties and, should the virus have a wide host range, for other crops also. Thus, the growing of tolerant varieties makes it increasingly difficult to grow intolerant ones, however desirable they may be for other reasons. Tolerance is the feature of many varieties of crops bred to resist virus diseases, but it is less satifactory than resistance to infection or hypersensitivity, for it carries intrinsic dangers. Since beets tolerant to curly top were introduced into the United States of America, it is noticeable that the virus has been increasingly recorded as causing damage to other crops. The reasons for this cannot be known with certainty, but the tolerant varieties obviously provided the virus with many host plants in which it could multiply and maintain large populations over several months, which not only directly increased the sources of infection for other crops but also provided increased chances of producing mutants able to infect other hosts. It is well to appreciate that the growing of tolerant varieties may solve a disease problem in one crop only to raise one in another.

Hypersensitivity and resistance to infection are preferable to tolerance, for their use carries no risk to other varieties or other species. It is surprising that genes for these characters have been little sought in most plants, especially as their value has been fully demonstrated by work with potato, tobacco and tomato. Thus, commercial potato varieties differ greatly in the rate at which they contract aphid-transmitted viruses when exposed equally to chances of infection, and some remain vigorous for years where others become too extensively infected in one year to be suitable for use as "seed" (Schultz *et al*, 1937; Stevenson, Folsom and Dykstra, 1943; Cockerham, 1943a; Larson, 1945; Bald, Norris and Helson, 1946). Resistance to infection by one virus is usually independent of resistance against another, and behaviour in field crops agrees closely with results obtained in glasshouse tests when the varieties are colonised with equal numbers of infective aphids (Bawden and Kassanis, 1946). Similarly, hybrids between commercial tomato varieties and the Chilean tomato, *Lycopersicum chilense*, contract tobacco mosaic virus less readily than most cultivated tomatoes (Holmes, 1943), and by combining minor and major genes for resistance, lines of tobacco have been produced that are not only extremely difficult to infect with tobacco mosaic virus but also resist infection by several other viruses (Holmes, 1960; 1961).

The genes responsible for the hypersensitive reaction of *Nicotiana glutinosa* to tobacco mosaic virus have also been transferred to *Nicotiana tabacum* (Holmes, 1938), but unfortunately they seem to be linked with genes that diminish yield (Gerstel, 1948); nevertheless, commercially acceptable lines seem to have been produced (Valleau, 1946) more readily with this type of resistance than with the type possessed by the Ambalena and similar varieties, which seems to depend on some degree of tolerance combined with ability to restrict virus multiplication and movement (Nolla and Roque, 1933; McKinney, 1939). Hypersensitivity also plays a large part in keeping some potato varieties free from viruses that spread readily in tolerant varieties; there are genes that make potato plants hypersensitive to most potato viruses and commercial varieties have been produced that are hypersensitive to four (Black, 1939; Schultz *et al*, 1940; Cockerham, 1943b; 1958; Hutton and Bald, 1945; Hutton, 1945).

There are clearly many opportunities to breed varieties that will suffer less from virus diseases than those now currently grown, but it would be vain to hope that plant breeding will provide all the answers. Viruses are extremely variable things and varieties bred in one place as resistant may not be resistant elsewhere, or continue to be resistant indefinitely where they first proved resistant. There are already examples of strains able to infect varieties introduced as resistant. For example, the varieties of sugar beet first grown in the U.S.A. as resistant to curly top later became susceptible (Giddings, 1946); the tomato variety Pearl Harbor resisted tomato spotted wilt in Hawaii but not in north America (Holmes, 1948b), and potato seedlings hypersensitive to strains of virus Y in Australia were not hypersensitive to some strains in the United Kingdom (Hutton, 1948). It is always uncertain for how long and in what conditions varieties bred for some form of resistance to virus diseases will retain this during cultivation. Frequency of virus mutation is likely to be correlated with the size of the virus population and more mutations can be expected when the widely grown varieties are susceptible to infection but tolerant, than when they resist infection or are hypersensitive. The success of the plant breeder in producing varieties likely to last resistant will be increased when their use is accompanied by other measures for lessening the number of infected plants, something that is impossible while breeders continue to introduce tolerant varieties in which infection is not readily recognised.

Therapy. The value of preventive measures such as planting on uninfested land and as far as possible from sources of infection will be self-evident and need no further comment. The use of uninfected seed or other planting material is equally self-evident, but does need discussion, for achieving this end often calls for special practices. Most virus diseases are not seed-borne, but some are and the first step towards the control of these, for example, lettuce mosaic, is to ensure that the seed sown came from uninfected parents.

The need for special practices in ensuring uninfected planting material arises mainly with clonal varieties. Bulbs, tubers, corms and cuttings taken during periods when plants are not growing rarely show clear symptoms and it is always dangerous to propagate by these methods except from parent plants whose health is known. To help ensure healthy material for planting many countries now operate certification schemes for various kinds of vegetatively propagated crops, and certified stocks are usually grown separately from the crops grown for their ultimate purpose. In the United Kingdom, for example, potato "seed" tubers are mostly grown in the north and west where aphid-transmitted viruses spread less and later than in the south and east, where most of the potatoes for eating are grown; the seed crops are examined while growing, rogued when necessary, and given certificates that define their state of health. Not all virus infections are readily identified by field inspections and to ensure freedom from those that are not, stocks have been propagated from single virus-free plants, and these stocks are regularly tested to ensure they are still virus-free, either by inoculations from them to suitable indicator plants or serologically with virus antiserum.

Until recently the development of such virus-free lines depended on finding an uninfected plant to initiate the stock, which with some clonal varieties entailed long searching and with some did not succeed. Fortunately, such tedious searches are now less necessary, because methods have been developed whereby many kinds of plants can be freed from all or most of the viruses that infect them. The time has not yet been reached when it can be said that every clonal variety can be made virus-free, but this may not be far off. The method that has found widest application is heat therapy, and it is extraordinary that its potentialities remained so little appreciated during the twenty or more years after high temperatures had been shown to cure some plants from virus diseases. The possibilities were first indicated by work with two suspected virus diseases of sugar cane, sereh and chlorotic streak, by the demonstration that cuttings from diseased canes produced healthy plants when they were immersed for periods up to an hour in water at 50° before they were planted (Wilbrink, 1923; Houtman, 1925; Martin, 1930; Bell, 1933). Kunkel (1935, 1936a, 1936b) extended the therapy to some diseases of peach trees and showed that, in addition to curing dormant trees and bud stocks by immersing them for appropriate periods in hot water, growing trees could be cured by keeping them continuously for two weeks or more at 35°. He (Kunkel, 1941, 1943, 1945) also showed that *Vinca rosea* and *Nicotiana rustica* could be freed from aster yellows and some other yellows-type viruses by heat, work that was followed by Kassanis (1949) freeing potato tubers from leaf roll virus by keeping them at 37° in a moist atmosphere for 10 to 20 days.

None of these early successes was with a virus whose properties *in vitro* were known, and it seemed to be generally assumed the method was applicable only to viruses exceptionally susceptible to inactivation by heat. However, Kassanis (1952, 1954, 1957a) showed this was not so, for he found that many viruses with high thermal inactivation points *in vitro* were inactivated *in vivo* when infected plants were kept continuously at temperatures around 37°, and the potentialities of heat therapy then became apparent. The lack of correlation between thermal inactivation point *in vitro* and the applicability of heat therapy is clearly shown by the fact that tomato spotted wilt virus, which has the smallest known inactivation point *in vitro*, will multiply in plants kept at 36° whereas tomato bushy stunt virus, which has one of the largest, inactivates in plants at 30°. Whether heat therapy is likely to be applicable to any virus that is readily transmitted mechanically can be gauged by inoculating healthy plants and putting them at 36°. If the virus infects readily, then high temperature is unlikely to eliminate it from systemically infected plants, but if it fails to infect, heat therapy is likely to succeed.

In general, heat therapy seems to work against viruses that have near spherical particles, but not against those that have rod-shaped or thread-like particles. However, there are exceptions because not all spherical viruses have proved susceptible and whereas heat therapy has succeeded with plants infected with some strains of cucumber mosaic and tobacco ringspot virus, other strains survived heat treatments (Hitchborn, 1956, 1957). From a review of the success achieved in clonal varieties of fruit, potatoes and ornamental plants, Kassanis and Posnette (1961) concluded that about half the viruses commonly occurring in horticultural crops can be eliminated by appropriate heat treatment. Success, of course, depends on the host plant being better able than the infecting virus to survive high temperature. Many plants are wholly freed from some viruses after two weeks continuously at about 36°, but to establish a virus-free clone does not necessarily demand eliminating the virus completely. After some days at 36°, some parts of plants may be virus-free while others are still infected (any new shoots produced during the treatment are especially likely to be virus-free), so when many cuttings are taken from the treated plants and rooted, one or more may grow into an uninfected plant. The ability of plants to survive in incubators at high temperatures is often enhanced by pruning their shoots, by acclimatising them to gradually higher temperatures rather than moving them from 20° to over 36°, and by giving supplementary light when days are short or daylight is dim.

Heat therapy has found its widest use in producing from infected clones a virus-free plant to act as a start in building a healthy stock for propagation. However, with sugar cane it is used as a regular routine in many countries, primarily to control ratoon stunting but also to eliminate other viruses. Cuttings for planting, a ton or more at a time, are placed in baskets that are then immersed for 2 to 3 hours in a tank of water at 50° (Hughes and Steindl, 1955). In the plains of India it seems likely that routine but unappreciated heat therapy may long have been controlling leaf roll in some potato varieties; plants become infected while growing during winter but storing the small tubers through the hot summers frees them from the virus.

With clonal varieties that cannot be freed from their viruses by heat treatments, virus-free plants can sometimes be gained by propagating from stem apices. Many viruses seem unable to enter apical meristems and the ability of different viruses to approach this region of actively dividing cells differs. Holmes (1948a) obtained healthy dahlia plants by simply propagating shoots newly emerging from tubers infected with tomato spotted wilt virus, and shoots from potato tubers infected with virus Y are also sometimes initially uninfected. However, more often it is only the apical meristem and immediately adjacent cells that are uninfected and to get these to grow requires culturing them aseptically on nutrient medium (Morel and Martin, 1952, 1955). When too small, the tissue fails to differentiate, and the problem is to excise a piece that is both virus-free and large enough to develop into a plant. A major success of the method has been to produce a virus-free line of the widely grown potato variety King Edward VII. This variety has long been known to be fully infected with paracrinkle virus, which was generally assumed to be tolerated without harming the plants. However, by propagating from the initial virus-free plantlet shown in Fig. 15–1 (Kassanis, 1957b), a large stock now exists that in field trials has consistently yielded 10% more tuber weight than other stocks.

When meristem culture alone fails to produce a virus-free line, it sometimes succeeds when combined with heat treatment, and the plant from which the meristems were excised first has its virus content diminished by keeping it for a time at around 36° (Thomson, 1956; Quak, 1957). There are, too, obvious possibilities for applying meristem culture to plants whose virus contents have first been diminished by treatment with such analogues of purines and pyrimidines as thiouracil and azaguanine. There is no report yet of these treatments on their own freeing systemically infected plants from viruses, but callus tissues growing in culture were freed from potato virus Y by thiouracil (Kassanis and Tinsley, 1958).

The only claim for successful chemotherapy is by Stoddard (1942), who stated that bud-wood from peach trees with X-disease was cured by soaking in water solutions of quinhydrone, urea and sodium thiosulphate, but his claim has yet to be confirmed. The value of chemotherapy for producing virus-free clones is too obvious to need comment, but even more urgently chemotherapy is needed to combat virus diseases of trees. Now all that can be done to control these diseases is to fell infected ones in the hope of checking the rate at which the disease spreads, and considerable success has been achieved in this way in controlling swollen shoot of cocoa in West Africa (Thresh, 1958). Although costly, this may remain the most economic measure with small trees that grow quickly and have only a small capital value, but to cure established trees that grow slowly and have a large capital value chemotherapy would be a practical proposition. To save a row of fine elms from phloem necrosis, or large fruit trees in their prime of bearing, would repay a costly treatment, and it would be of no great concern if the treatment temporarily damaged the trees, provided it later returned them to full health and vigour. Considering the need of such a treatment,

Fig. 15–1. Virus-free plantlet of the potato variety King Edward growing from an excised apical meristem on nutrient agar. (B. Kassanis, 1957, Ann. appl. Biol. 45: 422).

it is surprising that no attempt seems to have been made to free trees from their viruses by treating them with such analogues of purines and pyrimidines as have been shown to diminish the concentration of some viruses in herbaceous plants.

The use of insecticides. Many important virus diseases are spread by insects, and there are now insecticides that deal effectively with most kinds of insect pests, so insecticides might also be expected to control the virus diseases spread by these insects. It is true that persistent insecticides have proved very valuable in diminishing the losses caused by some diseases, but they are far from being a general panacea. Unfortunately, the control of insects as vectors of viruses is a different and more difficult problem from their control as pests. For example, to control aphids as pests requires only bringing the population below the numbers at which their feeding directly harms a crop. This means mainly preventing the wingless individuals that are born in a crop from reaching a damaging infestation, but these wingless individuals seem rarely important in spreading viruses. To be a vector, an aphid must first feed on an infected plant and then move to a healthy one, and wingless ones do this less often than winged ones. The most that wingless ones are likely to do is to spread viruses between nearby plants within a crop, but they do even this less efficiently than winged ones (Broadbent and Martini, 1959). The problem of preventing the spread of aphid-transmitted viruses, therefore, is mainly one of controlling the winged migrants, a small minority of the total population.

Winged insects spread viruses in two ways: (1) by bringing viruses into a crop from outside sources and (2) by spread from infected to healthy plants within the crop. In annual crops like sugar beet, which are raised from seed, spread is first by method (1) and later by method (2). Contact, non-persistent insecticides are rarely of value in controlling aphid-transmitted viruses, although Watson (1937), who seems to have been the first to test an insecticide in a field crop, found that weekly spraying of *Hyoscyamus niger* with nicotine increased yield enough to justify the cost. However, with other crops, although such insecticides have often been reported as effective in preventing aphid infestations, they either had no effect on virus spread or sometimes increased it. The increases can happen either because the treatment makes some wingless individuals move when otherwise they would have remained static, or because it prolongs the life of the sprayed crops and makes them liable to late infestation from nearby untreated crops. These increases need not concern us further, but the point that needs making is that non-persistent insecticides can kill only aphids that are on plants at the time of the spraying; the treatments are useful only when an infestation has begun to develop and winged migrants have stopped coming into the crop, by when viruses may already have spread extensively.

To deal with the winged migrants, which are the important vectors, the plants must be continually toxic to aphids during the period while the migration is happening. This can be achieved with some of the persistent insecticides, especially the systemic types, which can be applied either as sprays to the crop as soon as it emerges above ground or applied to the soil at planting time (Gates, 1958; Burt, Broadbent and Heathcote, 1960). These insecticides do not wholly prevent virus diseases in treated crops because none kills the incoming aphids rapidly enough to prevent them from feeding on the first plants on which they alight. Although spread by method (1) will not be wholly prevented it may be diminished, but the extent will differ with different viruses, depending on the manner in which they are transmitted by their vectors. The many kinds of behaviour are described in Chapter 6 and here there is need only to repeat that whereas some viruses are immediately transmissible by aphids that feed only briefly on infected plants and their vectors soon lose the ability to transmit, others take longer to become transmissible but their vectors may remain infective for some days. Insecticides will have little effect on the introduction into a crop of viruses of the first type, for the aphids will have stopped being infective before they are killed, but they may lessen the number of plants that become infected by the second type of virus because, although aphids may infect the first plants on which they feed, they will be killed before they have lost their infectivity.

Similarly, the extent to which insecticides will diminish spread within the crop depends on virus-vector behaviour. They can largely prevent the spread of viruses whose vectors do not become infective until some time after they start to feed on infected plants, but will have less effect on the spread of those whose vectors become immediately infective. Potato leaf roll is a virus of the first type and virus Y, the cause of rugose mosaic, one of the second type. Although both are transmitted by *Myzus persicae*, Fig. 15–2 shows that spraying potato crops diminished the spread of leaf roll much more than of rugose mosaic. The total effects, however, are large enough to allow potato stocks to be maintained in a state suitable for use as "seed" for several years in parts of the United Kingdom where otherwise a new stock would have to be obtained at least every other year from the recognised "seed"-growing areas (Broadbent, Heathcote and Burt, 1960).

Spraying is probably practised more extensively against sugar beet yellows than any other virus disease and spray-warning schemes are operated in several countries of western Europe, by which growers are told that there is need to spray because aphids are becoming active in their district (Hull, 1961). Yellows is a virus that somewhat resembles potato leaf roll, but it spreads much more readily. Although beet crops start initially virus-free, in years when aphids are plentiful and active early, crops may be almost wholly infected by August. Spraying when aphids begin to arrive in the crops does not prevent the disease, but can so slow the rate of spread that it can have very large effects on yield, and a timely spray can repay its cost in increased price of crop by factors of more than twenty.

Although so useful against beet yellows, insecticides did not control lettuce mosaic or the viruses that commonly infect cruciferous

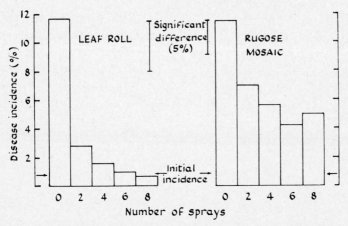

Fig. 15–2. The greater effect of spraying with DDT in checking the spread of potato leaf roll than of rugose (severe) mosaic, caused by potato virus Y. The disease incidence was measured in crops grown from tubers taken from the crop sprayed the stated number of times during the previous year.

crops, all of which are transmitted by aphids in much the same way as potato virus Y. Surrounding seed beds of cauliflower with strips of cereals, or other kind of barrier to incoming aphids, proved much more beneficial than insecticidal treatments (Broadbent, 1957). Similarly, seed beds of sugar beet to provide plants for the seed crop are largely protected against yellows in their early life when sown under barley or other cereal, and spraying with systemic insecticides will protect them after the cereal is harvested (Hull, 1961).

In summary, then, current insecticides can be expected to lessen the incidence of viruses whose spread is mainly from infected to healthy plants within the treated crop, especially of those viruses whose vectors do not become immediately infective after feeding briefly on infected plants, but they will be much less effective against viruses that are mostly brought in from outside or are immediately transmissible by aphids after a brief feed on an infected plant.

Soil-borne viruses. The description in Chapter 4 of what is known about the behaviour of soil-borne viruses makes it obvious that they are too varied for all to be controlled by the same practices, except by the one of not growing susceptible crops on infested land. Even this is not always easily applied, for past cropping may be little guide to likelihood of infestation. Land that has long been out of cultivation, or that has never been cropped, may be infested with nematode-transmitted viruses, for these have an extensive host range in weeds and wild trees and bushes. Indeed, Harrison and Winslow (1961) suggest that *Xiphinema diversicaudatum* and arabis mosaic virus, which is so damaging to many fruit and vegetable crops, were prevalent in natural woodlands and have probably diminished under cultivation. Before putting new land down to potentially susceptible crops, therefore, particularly before making raspberry plantations, vineyards or orchards, it is well either to grow a susceptible annual crop that will act as an indicator or to sample the land to see whether it contains the nematode.

The extent to which partial sterilisation of the soil by steam or chemicals will be used to eliminate either the viruses or their vectors will depend on the ratio between the cost of the treatment and the increased value of the crop. Obviously, it is unlikely to be applied to the vast areas of land that are infested with cereal mosaic viruses, though various chemicals are effective (McKinney, Paden and Koehler, 1957), but fortunately this is not necessary for there are cereal varieties that can be grown on infested land without being greatly harmed (McKinney, 1948); also, a period of a few years without cereals greatly decreases the incidence of the disease in subsequent susceptible varieties (McKinney, 1923). Changing the sequence of crops, however, is unlikely to be effective in decreasing the incidence of viruses such as arabis mosaic virus which can infect most common weeds of arable land and many different kinds of crop. Against such viruses, only nematicides seem likely to be of avail; these have already proved to be effective (Vuittenez, 1957; Cadman and Harrison, 1960) and could well be economic with crops as valuable as are strawberries or other fruit. Similarly, the viruses for which fungi have recently been discovered to be vectors will presumably be controllable by treating with suitable fungicides, but whether this will be practised will depend on the value of the crop.

New knowledge about the ways soil-borne viruses are transmitted makes it probable that they have till now probably been widely distributed as contaminants of soil adhering to bulbs, tubers or the roots of plants being transplanted, and precautions against this are obviously needed to prevent such further spread to land currently free from the nematodes.

Whether tobacco mosaic virus does any more than survive in contaminated soil and infect plants mechanically when either their roots, lower leaves or stems become damaged, is uncertain, but it seems not to survive in soil for very long (Johnson and Ogden, 1929). However, contaminated soil is a common source of infection, but usually leads only to a few plants becoming infected, after which the virus spreads from these above ground, either to plants whose leaves rub against them or by workers who get their hands, clothes or implements contaminated when moving in the crop. As shown in Chapter 4, there are many substances known to inhibit infection when present in inocula of such mechanically transmissible viruses as tobacco mosaic. Such inhibitors can also prevent infection when sprayed over the leaves of plants before the leaves are rubbed with viruses, and spraying crops with them seems a possible method of lessening the spread. A few critical tests have been made, mostly by spraying tomato crops with milk, which contains some powerful inhibitors of infection, and these have given conflicting results, but the claims that spread was diminished (Hare and Lucas, 1959, 1960; Hein, 1960) suggest the idea merits further testing.

Viruses were discovered by work on tobacco mosaic and there is no other virus about which so much is known. It is therefore ironical that in some countries where such viruses as potato leaf roll, whose nature and composition are unknown, have been almost eliminated, tobacco mosaic virus is still widespread, particularly in tomato crops. The use of resistant varieties and strict hygienic precautions by growers have greatly lessened its prevalence in the tobacco crops of some regions, but for tomato crops it is still impossible to make recommendations with the confident expectation that, if adopted, mosaic will be avoided. The stability of tobacco mosaic virus, the large concentration it reaches and its extensive host range, obviously favour its survival and chances of infecting susceptible plants, but while research has been so concerned with such problems as its morphology, composition, multiplication and genetic variability, some practically important feature in its ecology may well have been overlooked.

There are, of course, many other virus diseases for which there are as yet no adequate control measures, but these are mostly those that have been little studied. The fact that many that used to cause great losses can now be controlled means that others will also be brought into the controllable category when there is more known about them. Information about soil-borne and other viruses now accrues at an unprecedented speed and, although it is unfortunate that fewer people seem to be attracted to study control measures than to some of the other problems raised by viruses, there is little doubt that progress in control will continue to be rapid. It is vain to try and forecast these developments, except to say that the epidemiology of each disease will need to be studied in detail, to know where the virus comes from, when it mainly spreads, what spreads it and the behaviour of the vector when transmitting. Given this knowledge, some method has usually been found to ameliorate losses, but experience with tobacco mosaic virus shows that finding control measures can be difficult.

REFERENCES

BALD, J., D. O. NORRIS, and G. A. H. HELSON. 1946. Bull. Coun. Sci. industr. Res. Aust. 196.
BAWDEN, F. C., and B. KASSANIS. 1946. Ann. appl. Biol. 33: 46.
BELL, A. F. 1933. Qd. agric. J. 40: 460.
BLACK, W. 1939. Rep. Scot. Soc. Res. Pl. Breed. 5.
BROADBENT, L. 1957. Rep. agric. Res. Coun. 14.
——, and CH. MARTINI. 1959. Advanc. Virus Res. 6: 93.
——, G. D. HEATHCOTE, and P. E. BURT. 1960. Eur. Potato J. 3: 251.
BURT, P. E., L. BROADBENT, and G. D. HEATHCOTE. 1960. Ann. appl. Biol. 48: 580.
CADMAN, C. H. 1961. Hort. Res. 1: 47.
——, and J. CHAMBERS. 1960. Ann. appl. Biol. 48: 729.
——, and B. D. HARRISON. 1960. Virology 10: 1.
COCKERHAM, G. 1943a. Ann. appl. Biol. 30: 80.
——. 1943b. Ibid. 30: 338.
——. 1958. Proc. 3rd Conf. Potato Virus Diseases, Wageningen-Lisse, 1957, p. 199.
DONCASTER, J. P., and P. H. GREGORY. 1948. Rep. agric. Res. Coun., 7.
EDMUNDSON, W. C. 1940. Bull. U.S. Dep. Agric., 1843.
EVANS, A. C. 1954. Ann. appl. Biol. 41: 189.
GATES, L. F. 1958. Ibid. 47: 492.
GERSTEL, D. U. 1948. J. agric. Res. 76: 219.
GIDDINGS, N. J. 1946. Proc. 4th Gen. Meeting Amer. Soc. Sug. Beet Tech., p. 405.
HARE, W., and G. B. LUCAS. 1959. Phytopathology 49: 544.
——, and ——. 1960. Ibid. 50: 638.
HARRISON, B. D., and R. D. WINSLOW. 1961. Ann. appl. Biol. 49: 621.
HEIN, A. 1960. Phytopath. Z. 42: 263.
HITCHBORN, J. H. 1956. Ann. appl. Biol. 44: 590.
——. 1957. Virology 3: 243.
HOLMES, F. O. 1938. Phytopathology 28: 553.
——. 1943. Ibid. 33: 691.
——. 1948a. Ibid. 38: 314.
——. 1948b. Ibid. 38: 467.
——. 1960. Virology 12: 59.
——. 1961. Ibid. 13: 409.
HOUTMAN, P. W. 1925. Arch. Suikerind. Ned. Ind. 33: 631.
HUGHES, C. G., and D. R. L. STEINDL. 1955. Tech. Commun. Bur. Sug. Exp. Stas. Qd. 2,

HULL, R. 1961. J. R. agric. Soc. 122: 101.
HUTTON, E. M. 1945. J. Coun. sci. industr. Res. Aust. 18: 219.
———. 1948. Aust. J. sci. Res. B. 1: 416.
———, and J. BALD. 1945. J. Coun. sci. industr. Res. Aust. 18: 48.
JOHNSON, J., and W. B. OGDEN. 1929. Bull. Wisc. agric. Exp. Sta. 95.
KASSANIS, B. 1949. Nature, Lond. 164: 881.
———. 1952. Ann. appl. Biol. 39: 358.
———. 1954. Ibid. 41: 470.
———. 1957a. Advanc. Virus Res. 4: 221.
———. 1957b. Ann. appl. Biol. 45: 422.
———, and A. F. POSNETTE. 1961. In Recent Advances in Botany. University Press, Toronto.
———, and T. W. TINSLEY. 1958. Proc. 3rd Conf. Potato Virus Diseases, Wageningen-Lisse, 1957, p. 153.
KUNKEL, L. O. 1935. Phytopathology 25: 24.
———. 1936a. Ibid. 26: 809.
———. 1936b. Amer. J. Bot. 23: 683.
———. 1941. Ibid. 28: 761.
———. 1943. Proc. Amer. phil. Soc. 86: 470.
———. 1945. Phytopathology 36: 805.
LARSON, R. H. 1945. J. agric. Res. 71: 441.
MCKINNEY, H. H. 1923. J. agric. Res. 23: 771.
———. 1939. Phytopathology 29: 16.
———. 1948. Ibid. 38: 1003.
———, W. R. PADEN, and B. KOEHLER. 1957. Plant Dis. Reptr. 41: 256.
MARTIN, J. P. 1930. Hawaii. Plant. Rec. 34: 375.
MOREL, G., and C. MARTIN. 1952. C. R. Acad. Sci., Paris, 235: 1324.
———, and ———. 1955. C. R. Acad. Agric. Fr. 41: 472.
MURPHY, A. M. 1946. Proc. 4th Gen. Meeting Amer. Soc. Sug. Beet Tech., p. 408.
NOLLA, J. A. B., and A. ROQUE. 1933. J. Dep. Agric. P. R. 19: 301.
PLANK, J. E. VAN DER. 1946. Trans roy. Soc. S. Afr. 31: 269.
———. 1947. Ann. appl. Biol. 34: 376.
———. 1948. Ibid. 35: 45.
———, and E. E. ANDERSSEN. 1945. Sci. Bull. Dep. Agric. S. Afr. 240.
QUAK, F. 1957. Tijdschr. PlZiekt. 63: 13.
SCHULTZ, E. S., C. F. CLARK, and F. J. STEVENSON. 1940. Phytopathology 30: 944.
———, C. F. CLARK, W. P. RALEIGH, F. J. STEVENSON, R. BONDE, and J. H. BEAUMONT. 1937. Phytopathology 27: 109.
STEVENSON, F. J., D. FOLSOM, and T. P. DYKSTRA. 1943. Amer. Potato J. 20: 1.
STODDARD, E. M. 1942. Phytopathology 32: 17.
STOREY, H. H. 1935. E. Afr. agric. J. 1: 206.
SUMMERS, E. M., E. W. BRANDES, and W. D. RANDS. 1948. Tech. Bull. U.S. Dep. Agric. 955.
THOMSON, A. D. 1956. Nature, Lond. 177: 709.
THRESH, J. M. 1958. Tech. Bull. W. Afr. Cacao Res. Inst. 5.
VALLEAU, W. D. 1946. Phytopathology 36: 412.
VUITTENEZ, A. 1957. C. R. Acad. Agric. Fr. 43: 185.
WALLACE, J. M., and A. M. MURPHY. 1938. Tech. Bull. U.S. Dep. Agric. 624.
WATSON, M. A. 1937. Ann. appl. Biol. 24: 557.
———. 1942. Ibid. 29: 358.
———, D. J. WATSON, and R. HULL. 1946. J. agric. Sci. 36: 151.
WHITEHEAD, T. 1927. Welsh J. Agric. 3: 169.
WILBRINK, G. 1923. Arch. Suikerind. Ned. Ind. 31: 1.

Author Index

347

Subject Index